DEAD BY DESIGN

Behind the Dumpster, a woman was lying on her side. She wasn't moving. Her blond hair was damp and oozing big clots of something that looked black. Oil? Who would smear oil in her hair? As I got closer, I saw her hair was thick with blood. Her nose and cheekbone were strangely flattened. Blond hair and black blood were smeared across her eyes. A gold button winked in a puddle near her shoulder, and dirty gold braid trailed from one bloody wrist.

I didn't recognize the face—not in its current condition—but I'd know that outfit anywhere. It was Sydney, very dead in her designer leather. . . .

Books by Elaine Viets

Backstab
How to Commit Monogamy
Rubout

RUBOUT

A Francesca Vierling Mystery

ELAINE VIETS

A DELL BOOK

Published by
Dell Publishing
a division of
Bantam Doubleday Dell Publishing Group, Inc.
1540 Broadway
New York, New York 10036

The trademark Dell® is registered in the U.S. Patent and Trademark Office.

ISBN: 0-440-22444-6

Printed in the United States of America

Published simultaneously in Canada

June 1998

10 9 8 7 6 5 4 3 2 1
WCD

To my agent, David Hendin,
and my editor, Jacquie Miller

Many thanks to the people who helped me with this book, from Ladue to South St. Louis and across the U.S.A.

They include Pat and Roseann Brannon of the St. Louis Casa Loma Ballroom, Richard Buthod, Susan Carlson, Dean Engledow of Iron Horse Taming, Tom Finan, Jinny Gender, Gerald Greiman, Jane Gilbert, Kay Gordy, Karen Grace, Esley Hamilton, Debbie Henson, the Kirkwood HOGs, Marilyn Koehr, Cindy Lane, Robert Levine, Betty and Paul Mattli, Sharon Morgan, Donna O'Toole, Dick Richmond, St. Louis Police Officer Barry Lalumandier, the staff of the St. Louis Public Library, Janet Smith, Ron and Pat Steger, and Anne Watts, who has an amazing mind for murder.

Finally, thanks to all those folks who must remain anonymous, including several divorced women and my favorite pathologist.

1

"**S**o, do you think the boots are too much?"

Lyle, the man I semi live in sin with, looked at the black Italian suede boots that went almost to my thighs. Where they stopped, a pair of skintight black leather pants took over. I'm six feet tall, so I was covered by a lot of cow. The outfit was finished off by a silver chain belt and a black blouse. Lyle's expression was somewhere between lust and disgust.

"Is that a joke?" the professorial Lyle asked.

We certainly didn't go together. In fact, that was the problem tonight. We weren't going together. He was wearing a wheat-colored lamb's wool sweater, khaki pants, and some fancy German walking shoes, although he wasn't walking. His feet were propped on a leather hassock in front of the gray slate fireplace in his West End town house. A pale shot of single-malt scotch in a crystal rocks glass complemented the ensemble. On his lap was the latest *New*

Yorker. He had settled in for the evening, and he was going to spend it without me. I thought I'd zing him a little.

"Where I'm going," I said, subtly reminding him I'd be parading around in this outrageous outfit alone, while he sat home, "this is as conservative as a white satin formal and twelve-button gloves."

I was heading for the Leather and Lace Bikers' Society Ball, the most exclusive social event in St. Louis—if you're a biker. I'd finagled a ticket, and it wasn't easy, even for a columnist at the *St. Louis City Gazette.* Tickets are restricted to keep out sightseers and RUBs—rich urban bikers—and keep the dance for the real Harley riders. I've always had a thing about Harleys, but then again, I like anything fast. That's why I drive a blue Jaguar X-JS. It shocks the heck out of my colleagues at the *City Gazette.* They think female newspaper reporters should dress like rumpled nuns, male reporters should drink like Mike Royko, and both sexes should drone on in news stories like they're writing a doctoral thesis. Oops. I didn't mean to knock all professors. Just one. I was peeved at Lyle, and I guess it showed. I wanted him to go with me to the biker ball, and he refused.

"It's not really my scene, Francesca," he said. "Never play another man's game."

Lately Lyle didn't seem to be playing any games at all. I didn't want to go to the ball alone. This outfit should have raised the dead, but it couldn't even get Lyle up off his chair. Well, I was too proud to beg. But I'd been going to too many events by myself recently because Lyle didn't want to bestir himself. I'd begun to wonder if maybe I'd be better off alone, without Lyle.

"I'm leaving," I said. "Good night."

"Have a good time," he said absently, already deep in his magazine.

"I'll make sure," I promised, and slammed the door. The damp rainy night stuck cold fingers down my collar the minute I stepped out the door. I shivered as I unlocked Ralph, my blue Jag, and waited for his engine to purr. The sleek car was named for my favorite old-time sitcom character, Ralph Kramden, of *The Honeymooners*. Neither Ralph seemed to mind. Lyle's neighborhood, the Central West End, was supposed to be the most beautiful part of St. Louis. Maybe it had the grandest houses. But I was headed for South St. Louis, where I felt most at home. There, the air smelled of city smog and beer, and the houses had more recliners than a Sears showroom. It looked especially romantic on a rainy November Saturday night. I passed rows of redbrick flats, silvered by the streetlights and glistening in the rain. The windows were warm with light. Evidently, even my section of the city agreed with Lyle—it was a good night to stay in.

Until I got to Iowa Street. That's when I saw the traffic for the biker ball: a line of shiny pickups, sedans, and stretch limos letting off passengers in front of the Casa Loma Ballroom. There were even a couple dozen bikes at this biker ball. It wasn't a good night to ride, especially if you planned to drink and party. As the bikers hurried inside, wrapped in coats and rain gear, I caught interesting glimpses of black leather, chains, stretch lace, and skin. By the time I pulled into the Casa Loma parking lot, I'd quit brooding on my lagging love life. There was too much happening here.

The Casa Loma was a city success story. The seventy-year-old ballroom used to host the best of the big bands. Artie Shaw, Glenn Miller, and Benny Goodman played there. A young and skinny Frank Sinatra sang there, and so did Bill Haley and the Comets. You'd never guess that by looking at the outside. It was one more slightly dingy brick building. What made it spectacular was the ballroom on the second floor. The dance floor was five thousand square feet of mellow, polished wood cushioned by rubber. A floor like that turned every couple into a light-footed Fred and Ginger. The balconied ballroom, with its clean, sweeping lines, looked like an ocean liner in an old movie. The Casa Loma had been slated for destruction in 1990. But it was saved by those who loved it. Two ballroom dancers, Pat and Roseann Brannon, took it over. Now the Brannons had ballroom dancing on Friday nights. Some Casa Loma couples had had the same table for forty years. They brought their dance shoes in bags, for real ballroom dancers' shoes never touched a sidewalk. Saturday night dances were usually devoted to rock, Latin, or Mexican music. St. Louis has a large, loyal Hispanic population, and whole families, from grandparents to little kids, would go to the Casa Loma in their best dancing clothes. Other nights there were proms or private parties. And one night a year there was the Leather and Lace Ball.

As I walked in the door, I was hit with a blast of sound from the band, the King of Hearts. It was a

solid wall of rock. I saw four guys in leather wres-
tling a seven-hundred-pound black-and-chrome Harley up the ballroom steps. "Easy, now, easy. Almost
there," said a Harley wrestler in a leather biker cap
with a chain headband, leather vest, and barrel
chest. That was Sonny, head honcho of the South
Side HOGs. HOG is short for Harley Owners Group.
I waved and headed up to see him. Sonny got me
into the ball, and I owed him a thank you. The Harley was now resting at the top of the stairs. So was
Sonny. He was drinking Busch from the bottle. "Nice
outfit," he said, taking a swig from his beer.

"Nice Harley," I returned politely.

"It's the centerpiece for the ball," he said.

"Sure beats flowers and balloons for decorations,"
I said.

I'd seen plenty of those. In fact, I'd been to so-
called charity balls where most of the money was
spent on decorations. The bikers raised more money
at their events than some charity balls that got kid-
glove treatment in the paper. I'd had to cover my
share of society events as a young *CG* reporter, and I
hated them. The two worst, at least for me, were the
Veiled Prophet and the Fleur de Lis balls, where St.
Louis society made their debuts. The Fleur de Lis
was the Catholic coming-out ball, and when I covered it fifteen years ago, rumor had it that the rich
doctors and car dealers paid twenty thousand bucks
for their daughters to bow before the cardinal. I was
raised Catholic, but I lost what few shreds of religion
I had when I heard the old gray cardinal tell the ballroom, "You are the backbone of the church." I
thought of my grandmother and her friends, working

the St. Philomena's bake sales until their feet hurt, to make two hundred dollars for the church. The cardinal had just wiped out their hard labor in favor of some guys who uncapped a pen. The cardinal must have forgotten that part in the Gospel about the widow's mite.

The Veiled Prophet Ball was even weirder. This was supposed to be for the richest and most powerful families in the city. The Veiled Prophet was always an old white corporate guy who wore robes and covered his noggin with a funny-looking crowned veil. But nobody laughed at this getup. Young society women in white dresses actually had to bow down before him. Not just bow—prostrate themselves on the floor. Would you let your daughter do that? You didn't have to be Sigmund Freud to see the symbolism. Especially when the sons didn't bow. To me, it looked like the rich families were saying they were willing to sacrifice their daughters to money and power. I thought being rich meant you didn't bow down to anyone, but Lyle, who had family money, said I missed the point. He didn't go to either ball, by the way.

The Veiled Prophet was weird from a news standpoint too. The *Gazette* never printed the name of the Veiled Prophet. Anyone who was anyone claimed to know who the veiled bigwig was, and Babe, our gossip columnist, always came back from the ball and told his friends. The VP's name was supposed to be a secret from us little people. To know his name was a sign you belonged to the city's ruling class. At a features meeting, I told our then managing editor, Hadley Harris III, we should print the Veiled Prophet's name. He was as shocked as if I'd wanted to run nude photos of the Prophet's Queen of Love and Beauty.

"We have a city tradition to maintain," Hadley said firmly, "and we will uphold it."

I thought it wasn't a tradition. It was a promise in writing that the *Gazette* wouldn't name the Veiled Prophet—and would extend the same courtesy to the area's white ruling class. The old boys could make their backroom deals without accountability. The paper's first loyalty was to the city establishment. The top editors all went to the Veiled Prophet Ball. Even the publisher, who lived most of the time in Boston, flew in to attend the silly thing.

The only ball I wanted to go to was the biker's society ball, and it was much harder to get in to. In biker circles, it didn't matter how important your dead relatives were. Money wouldn't help either. In fact, it might hurt. This society was based on skill. If you could handle a bike, you were admired. Tickets to the Leather and Lace Ball were twelve dollars. But you could buy them only at a HOG chapter meeting or a Harley dealer, and you had to act quickly. The thousand tickets were gone in two days. After that, Sonny had been offered a hundred dollars for a ticket to the ball. He always said no.

A big hot Harley was not just the perfect centerpiece for this ball, it was the only centerpiece. The only other thing on the tables were bottles of beer. Anything else would have been a distraction. At the Leather and Lace Ball, the dancers were the decoration. Each new arrival was more incredible. Behind Sonny, I could see a tall blonde with long straight hair, wearing a lace body stocking and a fringed miniskirt loosely laced up the sides. Her guy wore the biker's formal wear: a black Harley T-shirt, black jeans, and a panther tattoo. His black beard was braided, biker style, to keep it from blowing in his face while he rode. I had an almost overpowering urge to yank it. Most guys wore some variation on this costume. But there were notable exceptions. A big tawny-haired man in fringed buckskin looked like he'd stepped off the set of a Western. A broad-shouldered man dressed like a riverboat gambler in a black frock coat and ruffled shirt looked like he was still on the set. Verrrry nice. He was talking to a tiny brunette wearing a black lace blouse over a white lace bra, a scrap of skirt, and thigh-high boots with white bows up the back. Her friend had hair the color of cold beer, a black body stocking, red bra, and jeans with heart cutouts down the legs. I bet there wasn't an unbought body stocking in a fifty-mile radius.

I loved it. This was the only society ball where there wasn't a tummy tuck or a face-lift in the whole room. Real biker women weren't afraid of a few sags, lines, or saddlebag thighs. I saw a red-haired woman with her love handles boldly outlined by black lace. Her man, who sported a matching gut, couldn't keep his hands off her overhangs. It gave me hope for when I turned forty, only three years from now. I was thirty-seven and holding, but my grip wasn't as good as his.

"Looks like your anti-RUB measures succeeded," I told Sonny. "This isn't the Malcolm Forbes crowd."

He smiled his crooked smile. "We tried to discour-

age the yups," he said proudly. "Most of these bikers
aren't your ZIP-code riders."

He saw the puzzled look on my face.

"Those are guys living in your desirable ZIP codes,
rich guys who buy Harleys for status and take them
out three weekends a year. The people here are
mostly your big-mileage riders. They'll put ten,
twenty, thirty thousand miles a year on their bikes.
They're not afraid to get a few bugs in their teeth."

As Sonny bragged, in walked the biggest, gaudiest
RUB I'd ever seen. She entered the same way a roach
strolls across your kitchen floor when you're trying
to convince a stuffy relative that you keep a clean
house. This particular bug was an exotic breed. Her
blond hair had been artfully tossed for about eighty
bucks, and she wore at least three thousand dollars
of designer leather. I recognized the outfit. I'd seen it
in *Vogue.* It was by Escada, or Versace, or one of
those designers who use lots of gold buttons and
gold braid. She was wearing leather to the Leather
and Lace Ball, but it was the wrong kind. Her outfit
was soft designer leather. Real biker leather is hard
because it acts as armor when you fall off the bike.
Her outfit would have been stunning in her circles.
But here she looked ridiculous, the way Marie Antoi-
nette dressed as a shepherdess must have looked to a
real sheepherder.

As she walked closer, I recognized not just her outfit but her face. Holy cowhide! This was Sydney Vander Venter. She really was a socialite, a former maid
of honor in the Veiled Prophet court, and cochair of
a half-dozen major galas and parties. Her picture
was always in Babe's column, but I bet she wasn't

too pleased with his last mention. Babe ran an item about her upcoming ugly divorce. Babe called Sydney "the bitter half" and said she was the estranged wife of local venture capitalist Hudson Vander Venter. Sydney and Hudson lived in Ladue, the richest suburb of St. Louis—at least they had when Babe announced the breakup. She had the underfed look favored by fashionable types. Sydney was fortyish, face-lifted, dyed, and dieted almost to starvation. What was this woman doing at a biker ball in low-rent South St. Louis?

"How'd she get in?" I asked Sonny.

"She doesn't count." He shrugged.

"She does if you read Babe," I said.

"Gimme a break," said Sonny. "Do I look like I read Babe? She goes out with a guy in our HOG chapter—Jack."

This was more incredible. Jack lived in my neighborhood. He wasn't quite what Sonny called a one-percenter, but he was somewhere between an angel and a Hell's Angel. Bikers have a dirty little secret: Even the hardest riding, toughest-looking were mostly family men and women who held responsible jobs, had nice kids, and went to church. They just liked to ride hard and look bad. The one-percenters—the rare ones involved in drugs, prostitution, mayhem, and murder—around on the edges added some glamour. Personally, if I was going to take up with a bad biker, I could find one hand-somer—and less hairy—than Jack.

"I can't believe Sydney Vander Venter hangs around a guy who wears a helmet that says 'Helmet Laws Suck,'" I told Sonny.

He took a thoughtful sip of beer and said, "Hey, she spent most of her life with prissy guys in suits. Now she wants to experience real life. Jack wants to experience real money. You can't blame either one. If she . . ."

I didn't hear the rest. My attention went elsewhere. A couple strolled by in a jaw-dropping getup. She was wearing nothing but black leather boots and a black lace body stocking. It was obvious—in that outfit—that she was a natural blonde. It was also obvious she had serious muscles.

"Who's that?" I said, awed by the raw display.

"That's Stephanie, Ms. Gypsy Tour," he said. "She's the woman who handled her bike best at the trials. She comes by her skills naturally. She's an over-the-road trucker."

"That's quite a pair," I said.

"She *is* built like a brick shithouse," Sonny said, and his crooked grin slipped into a leer.

"I meant Stephanie and her escort make quite a pair," I said.

"Oh, him. That's her boyfriend, Crazy Jerry," he said, and shrugged. Crazy Jerry was nobody I'd shrug away. He had almost as many muscles as she did, plus a flawless tan. I could tell because he was wearing only a black vest, black leather chaps, and a black Harley G-string. I looked, then quickly looked away. Almost every woman in the room did the same thing. It wouldn't be good for our health to stare too much at Jerry's stuffed G-string. Stephanie looked like she'd decked more than one man and wouldn't hesitate to hit a defenseless woman.

I noticed Sydney couldn't keep her eyes off the

guy's crotch, and she was pretty obvious. If she didn't stop staring, Stephanie would boot her designer derriere all the way back to Ladue. Sydney had a flush on her face that didn't come from her Chanel blusher. Judging by the drink in her hand, Sydney was chugging a biker favorite—Jack and Coke—a lethal combination if you're not used to it. The sweet, strong Jack Daniel's sipping whisky is hidden in the sweeter Coke. It tastes harmless going down. Then you try to stand up and realize you're blitzed. Sydney must have been really drunk to stare at another woman's man that way.

Fortunately, Stephanie was distracted by her duties. She was raising money for the night's charity, the Troubled Children's Foundation, by letting bikers stuff bills in her already bulging cleavage. I counted several hundred dollars sticking out of the gaps in the lace when she strolled by, and Sonny tucked another ten in there. "I like a gal who's up front about her money," he said, and this time he was definitely leering. Stephanie leered back. But when she turned to the dance floor, she tensed. What she saw wiped the smiles off everyone's face.

Sydney the society lady had asked Jerry to dance, and Jerry had lived up to his name by being crazy enough to say yes. They were slow-dancing to some tune with a lot of sax. You'd need a crowbar to pry their pelvises apart. Sydney had her arms around Jerry's waist, and she was grasping his cheeks—and I don't mean on his face. Sydney must have a death wish.

Stephanie stalked over, grabbed Sydney by her artfully tossed hair, and pulled it back so hard I saw the dye line on her roots. It must have been a sobering experience. Sydney looked terrified.

"Get your hands off him, bitch," Stephanie said in a low hiss, like a deadly snake. "Or I'll kill you."

I thought she meant it. So did Sydney. She was too scared to say a word. She didn't even straighten out her hair, which stuck out at a stupid angle when Stephanie let go. Sydney looked around to see if anyone would help her, but we all pretended to be interested in the dancing or the drinks. Her date, Jack, was nowhere in sight, and nobody went looking for him. Sydney got herself into this, and she could get herself out. She worked her way toward the edge of the dance floor and then slunk up the steps toward the ladies' room. Good. Let her hide out there for a while until she sobered up and Stephanie cooled off. Jerry had a sheepish grin on his face and looked rather pleased with himself, but I didn't see him dance with anyone else. Stephanie went back to collecting money, and the bills the guys stuffed down her front were bigger than ever. I guess they were afraid not to contribute. I lost sight of Stephanie, Jerry, and Sydney, while I danced with two different guys. One worked at a furniture factory and the other wore the most gorgeous turquoise jewelry. He designed it himself. He was fun to talk to, but I wished Lyle had been there, and I was mad at myself for missing him. This was one night when I didn't have to work. I was there as a guest, not a columnist. I wouldn't have to stay up late to write afterward. We could have had fun.

Then Sonny tapped me on the shoulder for a dance, and I didn't waste any more time thinking about Lyle. When I looked at my watch next it was almost midnight. I was dancing with a skinny biker named Mitch. He'd had enough beer to loosen up into a first-rate dancer. Sonny was dancing nearby with his cute blond wife, Debbie. When the music stopped suddenly, I heard Sonny tell her, "Oh, shit. Sydney's started another commotion. Stay here while I see what it is."

I couldn't see or hear anything wrong, but I followed Sonny as he pushed through the crowd. Near the bar, I saw Gilly, a big ugly biker with a beer gut. He had his arms wrapped around Sydney in a bear hug. He was crushing her up against his chest and saying loudly "I thought you was looking for a big man, honey. I'm bigger than that Crazy Jerry and I can prove it."

Sydney was struggling to get free, but she couldn't. Gilly weighed three hundred pounds, and there was a lot of muscle embedded in that beer fat. Sonny walked up to Gilly. He was at least a hundred pounds lighter and a foot shorter, but he stared at the giant and tapped him on the arm. That's all. Just tapped him. Gilly let go of Sydney like she might scald him. I wish I had that kind of power.

It looked like this encounter was going to end quietly. But then Jack, Sydney's biker boyfriend, walked up out of nowhere and punched Gilly in the mouth, which hurt Jack's hand pretty bad. Sonny and two of the other Harley wrestlers pulled them apart. It wasn't much of a fight. Jack wasn't really mad at Gilly. He just felt he had to do it. He saved his harsh words for Sydney. "You slut!" he screamed, while she cowered against the bar. "I'm not enough for you, huh? Huh? You gotta go after two guys in one night? Rich bitch gotta have everything and everyone. 'Oh, bring your bike, Jack,'" he said, doing a simpering imitation of a woman. "'I want to wrap myself around you and ride home with you in the rain.' You're so good at gettin' guys, you can get another one to take you home." Jack left her there and stormed down the stairs. Gilly seemed to be gone too, although I don't know when he took off. Probably sometime during Jack's speech.

We stared at Sydney. Her lip trembled and she started to cry silently. Dark streaks of eyeliner ran down her face. Some braid trim had pulled loose on her sleeve and a button was missing. She stumbled a little on her high heels, picked the gold button off the floor, and looked around for her little gold purse. Holding the handrail, she started unsteadily down the stairs. Everyone looked relieved.

"Shouldn't someone go with her?" I asked. "She looks drunk."

"She can call a cab from the lower lobby," said Sonny. "There are guards out front. Let her alone. She's caused enough trouble tonight."

She wasn't through causing trouble. But we didn't know that.

"This is why we don't want RUBs at the ball," Sonny said. "They don't know how to act."

The bikers watching nodded, and I could feel the mood turning sour. Then the band broke into the official bikers' anthem, "Born to Be Wild." The King of Hearts wailed this song of freedom almost as well as Steppenwolf. Sonny revved up his black Harley and rode the centerpiece around the outside of the dance floor. It rumbled over the music and vibrated the floor. I danced with Panhead, lost in the wild, roaring sound. After the song, I heard the band paging Crazy Jerry. They must have paged him on and off for half an hour. Finally Sonny came up to me, looking worried. "Francesca, we need you to be a judge for the Leather and Lace contests," he said. "We can't find Jerry, and he's one of our judges. I don't want to stir up any more trouble looking for him."

You never know when a woman is going to have to represent her sex. I knew I shouldn't have said yes. But it was after midnight, he was cute, and I was weak. So I agreed to be the only female judge at the Leather and Lace Ball. There were three other judges. Parker had gray hair, a broad, calm face, and a vest with the Viet Nam Veterans colors. Will was a lean guy in a black T-shirt. Streak was named for the speed he rode and the iron-gray streak in his black hair. I also heard he got his name for riding bareassed through the downtown police lot on a dare. Streak just grinned when you asked where he got his name. He smoked incessantly.

Sonny explained our duties. "You gotta judge the Best in Leather—Female, the Best in Leather—Male, and the Best in Lace. Ladies' leather competition first."

"What are the criteria?" I asked.

"Just pick the best," Sonny said, and shrugged. I could tell this wasn't going to be the Pillsbury Bake-Off.

Eight women lined up in front of the bandstand. The first Best in Leather wore a lace body stocking and leather chaps. The second entry wore almost the same outfit, but dropped her leather chaps and wiggled her butt. The men in the crowd cheered.

"Yeah!" cried three of the four judges.

The third contestant looked like a leather cheerleader. She wore a white leather skirt that was short and flippy, lace-trimmed white leather boots that were short and frilly, and a look of innocence that charmed the men and didn't fool the women. The next woman had a leather vest and the cheeks cut out of her jeans. She wiggled her rear, to the delight of every judge but me. After that, bottoms started jiggling like Jell-O in an earthquake. "We need to look again," cried Will, so the contestants wiggled some more, but the sight didn't inspire me.

"Who are you picking?" asked Streak, wrapped in a cloud of cigarette smoke.

"I'm not voting this round," I said.

"Hey, yes, you are," Parker said gravely. "We need a woman's view."

I thought there were plenty of women's views, but I peeked at the other scorecards. The judges had given the leather cheerleader high marks. I could go along with that. "Number Three," I said.

"Good choice," Streak said, letting out an approving puff of smoke. I was one of the guys.

Sonny presented the winner with the brass plaque to huge applause. I wondered where you hung an award like that.

"Best in Leather, Men's Division," Sonny announced, and a string of leather-clad guys stumbled to the front.

All three male judges said simultaneously, "I'm not judging men."

"Yes, you are," I said. "If I had to judge the women, you have to judge the men."

"Fair is fair," said Streak, and the other judges nodded and went to work.

Contestant Number One was just Busched enough that he switched his rear saucily when he paraded in his black leather chaps. "Hey!" a woman in the audience cried. "We saw the women's butts, now what about the men's?"

He ignored this request. So did Number Two. But contestant Number Three unbuckled his chaps, dropped his trou, and showed a really nice set of buns. They were fat free and tanned to a golden brown. There were no unsightly dimples or pimples. The women in the audience cheered his courageous move. The Catholic schoolgirl buried inside of me came out and disapproved. She knew I was going to hell for watching bikers drop their pants. The rest of me thought it was pretty funny.

Contestant Number Four was an impressive sight. He had a strong jaw, stronger shoulders, narrow hips, and sexy sun wrinkles around his blue eyes. He wore a brilliant blue jacket made of zillions of leather scales, blue jeans, and blue lizard boots. "That's a really bad-ass jacket," Parker said respectfully. Streak and Will agreed. In a fairer world, Number Four would have the plaque. But sex wins every time.

The women in the audience were screaming "Number Three! Number Three!" I explained the facts of life to the judges. "If you don't vote for Number Three, you're dead meat." They looked out at the beer-bottle waving audience. The people had spoken, and they were pretty drunk. Number Three won.

"Now it's time for our Ladies in Lace!" said Sonny. This was clearly the climax of the contest. Contestant Number One was a repeat from Ladies' Leather, the bottom-waver in chaps and a lace body stocking. The judges waved her on. Next was a woman with rippling blond hair and a ruffly sheer red gown cut to reveal red lace panties. "Yeah!" three of the judges said. They barely had time to wipe off the drool before an even more astonishing outfit paraded by—a Spandex suit cut into a spiderweb of strange and wonderful holes. She waggled her rear and the men did everything but sit up and beg.

The Spandex Wonder was followed by a woman wearing only a black-lace body suit, cut high on the thigh. It was an awesome display of smooth skin from hip to heel. "That's the best wax job I've ever seen," I said. "That woman deserves to win for the pain endurance alone. I'd need a full anesthetic to be that hairless." The guys didn't get it, but the women sitting near me applauded her.

Another contestant wore an animal-print outfit that was two strips of cloth over her bosom and one on the bottom. The three male judges looked dizzy, but Judge Will brought them back to duty. "Impressive," he said, "but this is not the *Leopard* and Lace Ball." They admired the view and crossed her off the winner's list.

The next woman belonged on a New York fashion runway. She was tall, bone thin, and bore up an intricate arrangement of leather and lace strips that moved every time she did. I couldn't figure out how she kept the strategic parts covered. I had more leather on my keychain.

The final contestant wore a body stocking made of black Harley lace. Her body was covered with lacy Harley cycles. She had the generous womanly proportions that painters in another age loved.

The male judges were having a tough time deciding on a winner, and I wasn't any help. "Let's see them again," they said. All the women paraded past and some waggled their rear ends, which thrilled three of the judges.

And, then to my delight, the male judges chose the handsome and generously proportioned woman. She was rejected by fashion, but these male bikers saw lightning in those thunder thighs.

"Gentlemen, I'm proud to confirm your decision," I said.

The loser in the lace and leather chaps was not. She snarled, "You are *all* on my shit list."

"I'm dead anyway," Parker said, with resignation. "You eliminated the woman I'm sleeping with."

"Correction. Used to sleep with," Streak said. Everyone laughed but Parker.

Speaking of sleeping, it was almost two A.M. I was tired. I told Sonny and his wife Debbie good night, waved good-bye to the judges, found my purse and walked down the staircase. The night was still cold, but now, after the heat and cigarette smoke at the ball, it felt good. There was a light drizzle, and mist rose up from the rain-slicked streets.

Just outside the Casa Loma, I saw a buxom young woman, with pale hair like a spring dandelion. I

watched Dandelion slug a young man right in the
jaw with surprising strength. Young women certainly
have improved their upper body strength since I was
growing up. The young man rubbed his jaw and
shouted, "I said I was sorry. What else am I supposed
to do?"

Dandelion didn't answer. Head high, she walked
past him to the end of the building and turned down
the alley. The off-duty cop guarding the Casa Loma
door shrugged but didn't follow her. The wide alley
was lit so we could see her progress. Dandelion
walked past an old garage with gray wooden doors
and an abandoned plaid couch. Why are couches in
alleys always plaid? The young man went to the alley
and stood there. "I said," he shouted at Dandelion,
"what else do you want from me?"

Silence. Dandelion had almost reached a big
Dumpster, tall as an upended van.

"Answer me," he pleaded.

She screamed. It wasn't a scream of rage. This was
sheer fright mixed with horror, as if she'd seen some
hellish sight. She backed away from the Dumpster,
still shrieking, ran straight to the young man, stumbled and buried her pale face in his chest. She began
rocking back and forth and crying "No! No! No!" He
looked bewildered. The off-duty cop knew what her
behavior meant: She had seen something so horrible,
she didn't want to believe it. The cop ran down the
alley toward the Dumpster, and I ran after him.

Behind the Dumpster, a woman was lying on her
side. She wasn't moving. Her blond hair was damp
and oozing big clots of something that looked black.
Oil? Who would smear oil in her hair? As I got

closer, I saw her hair was thick with blood, not oil. It covered her face like some exotic native mask. Her nose and cheekbone were strangely flattened. Blond hair and black blood were smeared across her eyes. Her lips looked mashed. A gold button winked in a puddle near her shoulder, and dirty gold braid trailed from one bloody wrist.

I didn't recognize the face—not in its current condition—but I'd know that outfit anywhere. It was Sydney, very dead in her designer leather.

2

Red police lights pulsed on the Casa Loma's walls and mist rose from the alley potholes, turning the murder scene into a hell's parody of the biker ball. For music, we had the shriek and wail of sirens. Yellow police-line tape festooned everything like some failed festive decoration. The T-shaped alley behind the Casa Loma was blocked at all three entrances, by what seemed to be every police car, marked and unmarked, in St. Louis. There was even a hook and ladder truck. The Evidence Technician Unit arrived, and police searched the alley carefully with flashlights to make sure they didn't miss anything before they brought in the bulky vehicle. The ETU pulled up near the murder scene. Harsh lights on the roof illuminated the alley. An evidence technician snapped Sydney's photo from every angle, and they were all bad. Sydney had been beaten until the fragile bones in her face cracked and collapsed. I could see some of the brutal damage

even through the thick blood. I saw her small, blood-
smeared hands, still trying to protect her face. Two
nails were broken, but her hands were still beautiful,
well tended, and useless. Like Sydney.

She'd been beaten with what looked like a motorcycle drive chain. It was artlessly draped near the
shoulder of her leather jacket, as if the designer put
it there for a prop. I'd just about convinced myself
that the gobs of dark stuff on the chain were grease.
Then I saw the clump of pretty silky blond hair, the
size of a skein of embroidery thread, clinging to the
drive chain. One end had a saucy curl. The other had
a bloody bit of scalp.

I made it to the back of the old garage before I was
sick. I managed to miss my suede boots, which were
already sodden from the pothole puddles. I squatted
by the garage for a bit, woozy and shaking. Actually,
it was a good spot to observe things without being in
the way. I could hear the crackle of police radios, see
uniformed officers interviewing people in the alley,
watch the brass standing around looking important
and posing for the TV crews. Four unlucky cops were
taking the Dumpster apart. Others had a dangerous
assignment inside the Casa Loma. They had to close
the bar in a roomful of one thousand bikers and then
start interviewing people.

In the alley, several officers seemed awfully interested in a scrawny biker I'd danced with earlier. I
thought his name was Mitch. I caught snippets of
questions aimed at him: "Can you describe the person? How tall was the person?" I wanted to hear
more, but then I was sick again.

When I stood up, sour-mouthed and shivering, a

man handed me his white silk handkerchief. Terrific. Homicide Detective Mark Mayhew had been watching me barf my guts out.

"Francesca, are you okay?" he asked, and he sounded like he meant it.

"I'm fine," I lied.

"Do you want to go inside and sit down? Can I get you a drink? Have someone drive you home?"

I answered no to all his well-meant suggestions. Every time I met him, I had to remind myself that he was married. Mark was the nicest fashion plate I'd ever met. Even at 2:00 A.M. the man was beautifully dressed. He took off his trench coat and put it around my shaking shoulders. It felt warm and smelled faintly of some spicy, manly scent. He was wearing a blue-striped silk shirt like the Perry Ellis I gave Lyle for his birthday and a gray suit so well cut it almost hid his shoulder holster.

"Nice outfit for hanging around alleys," I said.

"So is yours," he said. Suddenly I was very aware of my long black boots, leather pants, and dark hair, wild in the damp night. This wasn't the way I usually dressed when I saw Mark. This was a nice outfit for an alley. It was an even better outfit for the nearby Cherokee Street Stroll, where the prostitutes paraded. He didn't ask why I was dressed like a hooker, but I gave him an explanation anyway.

"I was at the biker ball," I said. "As a guest. For once I didn't have to do a column." But now I did. I was within throwing-up distance of a major story. I should be covering it for the *Gazette*. I slipped into my reporter role. I wore it like armor. If I worked hard enough, I wouldn't think about the other murder I saw, years ago. I still had nightmares about the dripping blood. I knew this would be one of the bad nights with bad dreams. But I could fight them off for a while if I played reporter.

"Sydney was beaten with a bike chain, wasn't she?" I said. I wanted Mark to confirm it. He wouldn't.

"The autopsy will tell us for sure," he said, a non-committal answer.

I tried again. "Why were the uniformed officers asking Mitch to describe someone? He seemed pretty drunk. Is he a suspect?"

This time Mayhew laughed. "Mitch a suspect? No, he was upstairs in the men's room—he pointed overhead at a square, lit window that looked out on the alley—"about twelve-ten or so, which is about ten or fifteen minutes after Sydney left the building. He says he stuck his head out for some fresh air and saw a little old lady—his words—hurrying down the alley toward Utah Street."

"That information must be a big help," I said sarcastically. Older women were as common as dandelions in this aging neighborhood.

"Did he get a description?"

"Yeah," Mark said. "Mitch told us that she was 'not too fat' and wore what he calls 'an old lady coat.' He says it was maybe dark blue or black. The woman had a dark hat pulled over her hair, which was maybe gray. Or maybe white. She also carried a 'big black old lady purse.'"

"That only describes every third older woman in South St. Louis," I said.

"I know. But we'll look for her anyway. Maybe the woman—if she exists—saw something in the alley and got spooked. But I'm not sure how reliable his description is. The condition Mitch is in, I'm surprised he didn't see two old ladies walking a pink elephant."

"If he saw any alcohol-induced animal, it would be a Clydesdale. Mitch was doing his best tonight to keep the Busch family in the style to which they're accustomed." The massive Clydesdale horses pulled the beer wagons in parades and commercials for the nearby Anheuser-Busch brewery.

Mark took a formal statement from me. He started with the questions he already knew the answer to: where I worked and what my address and phone number were. Then he asked what was my business in the alley.

"I wasn't doing any business in the alley," I said. "I just look like I was."

"This is serious, Francesca. I need to know why you were in the alley." So I told him about Dandelion and the fight with her boyfriend, and how she found Sydney in the alley.

"What was Sydney doing in the alley, anyway?" I asked Mayhew. "She had a fight with her boyfriend, Jack, and he refused to take her home on his bike. We figured she'd call a cab from the lobby. But the cab would have stopped by the front door."

"She was probably going to drive herself home," Mayhew said. "That's her Jeep there."

He pointed to a black Grand Cherokee parked nearby on a muddy lot at the top of the alley's T. There was room for about eight cars, but only Sydney was naive enough to use that lot and walk alone to the building. Sydney died about fifteen feet from the vehicle, and I didn't have to ask if it was hers. Few bikers send their sons to prep school, and the Grand Cherokee had a John Burroughs sticker on the back window.

I felt my stomach lurch again. Maybe if one of us— no, I was standing right there—maybe if *I'd* insisted she call a cab, Sydney would be alive now. She certainly wouldn't have walked into a deserted alley. But I didn't know she drove to the ball.

"I was right there, Mark. I heard Jack say she asked him to bring his bike in the rain so she could ride home with him. Why did she drive to the ball?"

"That's one of the questions we'd like to ask Jack," he said. "But right now we can't seem to locate him. We can't find her husband or her son, either. No one was home at the Vander Venter house in Ladue at two in the morning.

"We heard Sydney was a busy lady tonight at the Leather and Lace Ball, making a big impression wherever she went: She had one death threat, one attempted rape, one fistfight, and one irate boyfriend in one short evening. We also heard she gave new meaning to 'dancing cheek to cheek.' And Crazy Jerry was missing for more than half an hour during the time she was probably murdered."

"I have no idea where Jerry was," I told Mark, "but from what I saw, all he'd do is love her to death."

"I've seen that, too," said Mark. "You got one drunk guy who can't get it up and one drunk woman who says the wrong thing, and the next thing you know, he beats her to death for laughing at him."

Sydney's bloody, broken face flashed in front of me again. Whoever killed her had wiped her smile off, along with most of her face. The killer could have been anyone at the ball tonight. A hundred people saw her leave. She was plainly drunk. So drunk she staggered down the steps. So drunk she walked alone into a dark alley.

"Why didn't the off-duty officer escort her to her car?"

"He says he didn't see Sydney leave. He was walking a couple of women to their cars in the far lot about that time."

I wanted to get away from there. The cold, clammy air felt like it came from an open grave. The flashing lights and the mindless noise made it hard to concentrate. I handed Mark back his coat. "Thanks for your help," I said. "I need to call the *Gazette* and then go."

"You can use my cell phone," he said, and handed it to me. Just briefly our hands touched, and there was a little electric shock that I don't think came from the phone. We smiled stupidly at each other, like we'd been hit on the head with beer bottles. Then I heard the voice of the last person I wanted to witness this thrilling little scene. "Babe, you can use my cell phone, too."

Damnation. It was Babe, the *City Gazette* gossip columnist. Mayhew took one look at Babe and simply dematerialized. Babe earned his nickname because he called everyone, male and female, Babe. Babe had a face like a cod and an unhealthy body. He was thin and pale and looked like he left his coffin at sundown. He even wore a tux, like a B-movie vampire. He really did come alive after dark. Babe loved to cover society parties, and he would go to five or six a night. He worshiped the rich and powerful. "We're having a wonderful time" was a bon mot for Babe when it came from blue-blooded lips. His excessive enthusiasm could be quite funny. Babe once wrote this gushy lead to a Veiled Prophet story: "There are balls and there are balls, but there are no balls like the Veiled Prophet's balls."

Babe had another valuable function besides his entertainment value. He was a company spy. He was uncanny at sensing power shifts at the paper, and he immediately became the rising stars' new best friend, feeding them choice tidbits of gossip and shameless servings of flattery. The *Gazette* had gone through some dreadful upheavals recently, but Babe had managed to sniff which way the winds blew and stay on top. God knows what tale he'd take back to the new *Gazette* managing editor. I saw him sizing up my leather outfit. He'd probably report that I was into bondage. I tried to head him off, without actually seeming to give him a reason why I was hanging around an alley in leather.

"Nice tux, Babe," I said. "Armani?"

"Yes," he said. "That idiot on the copy desk asked me why it was so baggy. He didn't understand drape."

"Probably thinks drape is something you hang in a window. I can tell you've been somewhere important."

He preened. "What a night," he said. "The art museum had an opening for the Monet show, and the publisher flew in for it. Then the symphony gala. And the charity cigar dinner at the Progress Club."

"I've been to a charity ball, too," I said brightly.

"The Leather and Lace Ball. Are you covering it, too?"

He screwed up his face like I'd just offered him a cod liver oil cocktail. "No," he said. "Those aren't my sort of people. The *Gazette* beeped me because they heard the commotion on the scanner. The night city editor deduced that a prominent person had met with an accident and asked me to check it out. I didn't know you'd be here."

He seemed to feel I'd crashed his news event. The *Gazette*'s promise of "24 Hours of News You Can Use" got a little thin in the wee hours. Our ads showed a bustling newsroom, but those pictures were taken during the hyperbusy late afternoon. Between about 1:00 and 6:00 A.M. the tight-fisted *Gazette* didn't even have a skeleton staff. It had a single bone. Maybe that's bonehead. The paper used one editor to cover the entire city, usually an exile who worked the graveyard shift because he or she had screwed up big time. The night city editor's miserable—and impossible—task was to monitor the scanner for major police and fire calls and watch the news wires. If something big happened, the night city editor would call the staff at home and try to make us feel guilty enough to come into work. Most of us monitored our answering machines and wouldn't pick up, no matter how much the editor groveled. Some staffers saved these pathetic phone pleas and cruelly played them for the newsroom.

But this night city editor seemed destined to see daylight soon. He'd figured out that a night owl like Babe would prowl until almost dawn, and if he used the magic words "prominent person" he could get

Babe to cover the story without putting in for overtime.

"Who is the deceased?" Babe asked. For one instant, his eyes grew brighter and I swear he licked his lips.

"It's Sydney Vander Venter," I said.

"That bitch." He spat. "Couldn't happen to a nicer person. The way she treated her poor husband. She called me up after I mentioned her upcoming divorce and whined that Hudson had left her for another woman. She wanted me to print that! I told her that she drove him to it. I heard she was a dyke."

"I'm sure the word you heard was bike," I said. "Sydney was dating a biker, as in Harley, and they were both definitely straight."

Babe was behind the times. He called everyone he didn't like gay and thought that was an insult. St. Louis is a peculiar city. Its arts and education circles were surprisingly liberal. So were its middle classes. But the city was saddled with too many so-called civic leaders who were sexist, racist, and homophobic. Many men who were Babe's age—fifty and up—still weren't out of the closet because it could hurt them at their brokerage firm, law firm, or other old-line St. Louis institution. Most of these in-the-closet types were married with children. They played around on their wives with pretty boys.

I found this out the strangest way. Richard, a gay friend who worked at a society hair salon, came to me with a peculiar problem. He'd fallen in love with a beautiful male prostitute. At least, my friend Richard thought the boy was beautiful. To me, he looked like a pouty kid with a good body and a bad attitude.

Anyway, the beautiful boy lived in my South Side neighborhood and used to hold Wednesday night parties. He invited his other working friends, their clients, and Richard. "I went to a few," Richard said, "and I saw some of the biggest names in St. Louis cruising. Prominent men with prep school accents standing around this dingy South Side flat, eating Kas potato chips and drinking Busch beer. They were so well bred they always showed up at the door with a bottle of wine. Imagine bringing a hostess gift to an orgy. But what really bothered me was that several were the husbands of my clients. I'm sure these women hadn't a clue their husbands were gay. After all, they had children. It made me angry. My innocent customers could get AIDS because their husbands were too cowardly to come out. So now I'm asking you: Should I tell my women customers their husbands see gay prostitutes?"

I didn't know how to answer that, although my instincts were to keep quiet. I was glad this wasn't my decision. Richard agonized for weeks and finally decided to say nothing. He figured his clients would rather die than have someone else know their husbands were cheating on them with other men. One Wednesday night I went by the pretty boy's flat and noticed the black Lexuses and BMWs parked nearby. Just for the heck of it, I wrote down the license plate numbers and ran them on the state drivers license program on the paper's computer. The list read like the *Social Register*.

Babe wasn't through assassinating the good name of the Vander Venter family. "Well, if that bitch Sydney isn't gay, her son is. I heard he was kicked out of college for drugs. Now he's living with another boy. Kid's a fagola. But what can you expect with a mother like that?"

"It takes two to make a child, Babe," I reminded him. "Her husband contributed half."

"Hudson contributed more than his share," Babe said piously, and I knew who had the major money in that family. I wondered why I was defending Sydney. The only time I saw the woman was tonight, and she acted like a jerk. Of course, if jerky behavior got you the death penalty, we'd all be dead.

Enough of this. I grabbed Babe's cell phone and called the special city desk number, the one not hooked up to the answering machine that protects us from bothersome readers. I told the night city editor where I was and what I'd seen. "Just tell Babe, Francesca," he said. "He knows these people. He can handle this story. You go home and rest."

This was a bright boy indeed. Smart enough to know I was currently out of favor with the management at the *Gazette*. This night city editor definitely would see sunlight soon. So would I, for that matter. It was after 3:00 A.M. I was so cold and tired, I couldn't stop shivering, even with the heat turned up full blast. I drove home, fuming at the idiocy of editors and the loss of my story. I'd find a way to write it yet.

When I got home, my thin suede boots were soaked through and probably ruined. I unzipped them and wiggled my toes to see if they still moved. My toes were dyed black from the wet boots. Lovely. I picked up a big stack of *Gazette*s from the floor and crumpled them to pack in my boots. I picked up one wet boot and began to stuff it. Stuff it. That's how I felt about the *Gazette* tonight. And Lyle, too. So there.

■

Sunday I slept in late. It was a sad and restless sleep. The bloody face of Sydney alternated with that other death scene, then awful scenes I can't remember. I woke up feeling like I'd slept on a park bench. The thick gray clouds looked like dirty cotton and there was a cold mist. No reason to go out in that. I was too tired to do anything but putter around my apartment in my bathrobe. For lunch I ate tuna out of the can and a mushy out-of-season peach over the kitchen sink. This is the kind of disgusting behavior I can indulge in only when there's no man around. Then I cleaned my apartment. Some of the women at the *Gazette* laugh at me because I like to do housework. They think being a slob is a sign of female intelligence. I heard one assistant city editor brag that a visitor unearthed a stale jelly doughnut from under her couch cushion. People never wore black to her house because it would be covered in dust and dog hair. Since she and her executive husband pulled down a total of two hundred thou a year, I figured they could afford to hire a cleaning service.

Thanks to my grandmother, I found cleaning therapeutic. Grandma's family motto was "We were never so poor we couldn't afford soap." To her, a clean house was a sign you were part of the social fabric. She really believed you could wash your troubles away—as well as dust, vacuum, polish, and scrub them out. She lived in South St. Louis when it was still the German section of town, and she was house proud. She starched and ironed her kitchen curtains weekly and scrubbed floors on her hands and knees. Compared to her, I'm a slacker.

Grandma and Grandpa ran a confectionery, which is what St. Louisans called an early type of convenience store. Neighborhood people would run in and buy cold cuts, cans of soup, Pampers, and milk. My grandparents made just enough to live on and send me to school. They worked six days a week, twelve hours a day. I admired their toughness. I miss them. I guess that's why I still lived in my grandparents' apartment and didn't change a thing after they died twelve years ago. Well, I did rent their confectionery on the first floor to Mrs. Indelicato. But she ran it the same way they did. Upstairs, their apartment was a South Side classic, from the beige recliner and my grandfather's bowling trophies, to the slipcovers on the sofa and the plastic runners on the wall-to-wall carpet. In the kitchen, the Sunbeam toaster sat under Aunt Jemima's skirt. The bathroom had plaster fish blowing gold bubbles. The dining-room table had the same machine-lace tablecloth. The only change I made was to set up my computer on the table, but I put the pads down first, to protect the finish.

My apartment confused my friends. Some thought I was making a witty statement about kitsch. Some saw it as my own private South Side museum. Only Lyle understood that I kept it that way because I admired my grandparents' good, ordinary lives. If your parents were as screwed up as mine, you'd value something ordinary, too. But that's another story.

Anyway, my day at home alone was relaxing. I ended it by reading the *New York Times*—a paper I enjoy because I don't know anyone who works there. I fell asleep in the recliner, wrapped in my grandmother's yellow-and-brown afghan.

■

Monday morning I felt ready to face the world. And most of the world I was interested in went to Uncle Bob's Pancake House. It was the perfect hangout for a newspaper columnist. Readers knew I would be there most mornings and brought me story ideas. I overheard fascinating things, too. Uncle Bob's was the sort of place where people felt comfortable, and they would forget the booths only gave the feeling of privacy. The police ate there as well as local crime families, church people, lawyers, families with kids, senior citizens, and salespeople. It was open twenty-four hours a day, seven days a week. I used it as my office because I didn't like to make readers endure the rudeness of the *City Gazette*. The *Gazette*'s phone system was chaotic, and callers were transferred endlessly from one editor to another, and God help the callers if they were transferred to a reporter like Jasper, who rejoiced in his rudeness. I'd actually heard him snarl at a woman, "Listen, lady, you wouldn't know a story if it bit you in the ass. Don't bother me again." The editors seemed to find Jasper's loutish behavior amusing, the way some homeowners enjoy a nasty, barking dog. But I wasn't going to subject my readers to that treatment.

At a place like Uncle Bob's, you pick your usual with the same care you picked your spouse, because you would have it forever, for better or worse. A decade ago I declared that my usual breakfast was decaf coffee, one egg scrambled, and one piece of toast. Tom the cook grumbled. Marlene the waitress made fun of my meager meal, but it was my choice, and they honored it. Sometimes I got a little restless with my choice, the way any faithful person did, but I knew this was the only food for me. I no longer had to order it. By the time I parked my car and hung up my coat, it was waiting for me. I did, however, have to listen to Marlene do her usual riff on my boring breakfast. She was a generous woman that my grandparents would have called pleasingly plump. She considered my skimpy breakfast a personal insult to Uncle Bob's bounty.

"Your usual," she said, and plunked it down on the yellow placemat that also served as a menu. "Now, would you like to order some food?"

I was saved from trying to think of a snappy reply before eight o'clock. Detective Mark Mayhew came in the door and walked over to my table. I invited him to sit down. Marlene brought him his usual, which was a syrup-drenched Belgian waffle with a side of ham and hash browns, irrigated with gallons of black coffee. I wondered how long he would fit in that slim charcoal suit eating like that.

"Now, *this* is food," she said with satisfaction, as she put his grease-soaked plates on the table. "Study it, Francesca. I know you've never had food before, but many people eat it three times a day. You might like to try it."

"Nah, it would be a shock to my system," I said.

Marlene laughed, poured me more decaf coffee, and left us to talk about the murder.

"I see Babe wrote the *Gazette*'s front-page story on the Vander Venter murder," Mayhew said. "He got a little confused with his facts, but we don't want too much information out now, anyway."

"You won't have to worry with Babe on the story," I said. "He said Sydney was beaten with a bicycle chain." As soon as I said it, I felt guilty. What a bitchy way to talk about a colleague.

"Yeah, he heard somebody at the scene say she was beaten with a bike drive chain, and he decided that it was a bicycle," Mark said, polishing off a syrupy hunk of waffle piled with hash browns. "In the next paragraph he quoted an unnamed source who said the killer was definitely a motorcycle gang member, probably the Hell's Angels or the Saddle Tramps, and those folks don't usually ride Schwinns."

"Do you think it was a biker gang killing?" I asked.

"Are you going to write about this?" he asked.

"The *Gazette* took the story away from me and gave it to Babe." That wasn't a completely honest answer, but it satisfied Mark.

"She might have been killed by a biker, but I don't know," he said. "At this point, we have too many suspects. Most are bikers, but they don't belong to a gang. It was true that Mrs. Vander Venter was killed by a motorcycle drive chain, and the murderer left it near her body."

"A lot of people were mad at her," I said. "Did you ever find Jack?"

"Yeah. Located him about three in the morning. He says he left Mrs. Vander Venter at the ball and went driving around, but no one saw him from mid-night till three A.M."

"Don't forget Stephanie," I said. "She was mad enough and strong enough to kill Sydney."

"Yeah, Stephanie is in the running. So is Gilly, the guy with the gut who fought with Jack. He's got a little past history with us, and he's got an hour or so when no one saw him."

"What kind of past history?"

"Small-time stuff. Possession of stolen property. Receiving stolen property. Nickel-dime dope dealing. A weapons charge: known to carry without a license.

"I haven't finished my list," Mayhew said. "We can't forget Crazy Jerry, Stephanie's boyfriend."

"*You* can't forget the man," I said. I couldn't forget his fetching Harley G-string and lightly browned buns. "I keep telling you he's a lover, not a fighter."

"He was all too friendly with Mrs. Vander Venter," said Mark. "But we found his handprints on the emergency exit door to the alley, a few feet from the crime scene. There were a million other prints on the door, but Jerry's are flat on the upper panel, as if he leaned against the door. That's not enough evidence to arrest him, but we'd like to know what he was doing back there and why he disappeared for half an hour."

"What did he say?"

"Nothing. Says he didn't hear the page," Mark said.

"Find anything else interesting back there in the alley?" I asked.

Mark shrugged and pushed away his empty plate. "Nothing useful," he said. "No one saw anyone, ex-cept Mitch and his vision of a little old lady. Besides a ball with a thousand bikers, we have the usual family suspects. We always look at the husband when a wife gets killed, and if any husband had a reason to be relieved that his wife was dead, it was Hudson Vander Venter. Now that Mrs. Vander Venter is gone, Hudson doesn't have to worry about an expensive, embarrassing divorce. He is free to marry Brenda, the lawyer he's been dating. Not that we're hearing this from him. Hudson refused to talk to us without an attorney. When he and his lawyer did come down to the station, we learned almost nothing."

"Did he tell you where he was late Saturday night?"

"Yeah. The cigar smokers' dinner at the Progress Club, with two hundred other people who will vouch he was there until two A.M."

"Babe told me their son is a gay drug user."

Mayhew rolled his eyes. "I don't think the kid's gay. Hud Junior left home, the way kids do when they have a fight with their parents, and moved in with a friend who's going to St. Louis U. The friend has an apartment in Richmond Heights. The place looks like your basic college kids' pad: backpacks and Rollerblades in the hall, scrounged family furniture, bowls of old cereal, microwave popcorn bags, and pizza boxes all over, and absolutely the newest sound system. There were lots of attractive young women going in and out of there, and I don't think Hud wore the lace panties I stepped over in his bedroom."

"What about drugs?"

"I didn't see anything visible when I showed up for a surprise visit, but he could keep it well stashed. He

and his Ladue friends have a lot of money, and that
can mean a lot of drugs. I do know the kid had a
definite drug problem six months ago. He was using
cocaine, and when his mom found out and put him
in a rehab clinic, he dropped out of college, probably
to spite her. His father cut off his allowance until he
went back to school. Hud had no money except what
he made as a waiter. Now he'll get the income from a
trust fund that his maternal grandfather set up for
Mrs. Vander Venter. The income passes on to her
only child at her death. Two thousand a month isn't
much in Ladue, especially if you're doing coke. And I
suspect Hud needed money."

"So did he kill his mother for his trust fund?"

"I wouldn't rule it out. But the husband benefits
even more from her death."

I agreed with Mayhew. That was new. The last
time Mayhew and I talked about a murder, we had
very different ideas about who did it. This time we
agreed. We were agreeing about a lot of things lately.
In a strictly business way.

"So are you going to lay off the bikers?" I asked.

"Nope. There's always the possibility that the son
or husband hired one to murder Mrs. Vander Venter.
That's why I keep talking with your biker friends.
And their friends. And their bosses, wives, girlfriends, boyfriends, and drinking buddies. It's going
to cramp their style. I suspect they'll be pretty pissed
before this is over."

Mayhew's beeper went off and he left. It was time
for me to go to work, too. The newsroom was quiet
in the early morning. A few reporters were talking on
the phone. A meeting of editorial department heads

was just breaking up in the glass-windowed conference room. I saw Wendy the Whiner, our new Family section editor, shoving papers into a battered beige folder. I tried to slip by unnoticed but that's hard to do when you're as big as I am.

"Francesca, you're finally here. I didn't know where you were," she said. It sounded like an accusation.

"What do you mean I'm *finally* here? It's nine o'clock, and I'm in before most of the staff." The woman could put me on the defensive like no one else.

"You don't have to get angry at me," she said, giving me her most pathetic look. Wendy was a sad creature, a corporate nun who dedicated her life to serving the *Gazette*. She had a permanently martyred air and no life outside the newsroom. She even dressed like a nun, in shapeless, sexless suits and low heels. Today she had on a bunchy beige blouse and a sacklike beige suit trimmed with cat hair. Her sensible beige shoes were scuffed, and a run had popped out at the knee on her beige pantyhose. Even her hair was beige.

"You didn't tell me what your next column is about. I'm so busy and you just run around and do as you please," she said resentfully. Wendy whined constantly about how overworked she was, but I'd never seen her do anything but attend meetings.

"I sent you a memo with my column ideas two days ago," I said.

"I lost it," she said. "I can't keep track of everything. Send it again. And in the future, flag it so I know it's important."

Somehow she'd turned her mistake into mine. How did she do it? I sat down at my desk and re-wrote the memo, seething as I hit every key. Then I wrote my column and turned it in. It was time to get out of here. As I was leaving, I ran into our new managing editor, Charlie. We didn't get along, especially lately, and generally I tried to dodge him. But this time I was glad I didn't. Charlie asked me to do a feature on Sydney Vander Venter. This was right up my alley, so to speak. Gave me an excuse to poke around in something I was curious about anyway.

That night, about nine o'clock, I got another excuse. Sonny, the barrel-chested head honcho of the South Side HOGs, called me at home.

"Francesca, we're pissed," he said. I could tell. The usually chipper Sonny sounded as sour as a flat beer. "Every time we turn around, there's another cop asking questions. They follow us around at work, at home, at the store, at the bar. It's harassment, I tell you. It's got to stop. We want to talk to you."

"I'll be glad to talk. But I don't know what I can do."

"We'll tell you when we see you."

"Want me to meet you at a bar tonight?" I said.

Sonny sounded shocked. "Of course not. We got work in the morning. We'll meet you for coffee at Uncle Bob's at five-thirty."

"In the morning?" I said, horrified. I hate getting up early.

"Yes. Only time we can all talk to you is on the way into work."

I rolled out of bed at 5:00 A.M., threw on some clothes that might have matched, and pulled into

Uncle Bob's at 5:28. God, it was cold. No wonder I never got up at this hour. My early appearance stunned the staff and, for once, my egg wasn't waiting for me. All the bikers but Gilly were already assembled at a big round table, drinking coffee. They looked less exotic than they did Saturday night. Crazy Jerry looked sane and sadly concealed in a well-pressed khaki uniform. Sonny wore navy coveralls. Stephanie had traded her lace body stocking for jeans and a blue flannel workshirt over a white T-shirt. Jack, the late Sydney's boyfriend, wore the same outfit except his T-shirt was black. Probably in mourning.

Just as I sat down, Gilly with the gut walked in. He was the only one wearing anything that looked vaguely like a biker outfit. He had on black jeans, biker boots, and a faded T-shirt. He started to take the empty chair next to Stephanie, but she snarled, "You are not sitting near me in that T-shirt, asshole."

I couldn't understand why Stephanie was so upset. The shirt had some sweat stains, but they were hardly noticeable. Sonny looked puzzled, too. Then Gilly turned around so we could all read the other side. It said, "If you see the back of this shirt, the bitch fell off." Crazy Jerry made a manful effort not to laugh. Sonny snickered. Gilly sat next to him.

Sonny was the group spokesperson. "We're being harassed by the police," he began. "We can't go anywhere without them stopping us and asking questions. They're coming to our jobs, and that doesn't sit well with my boss. They're talking with everyone who knows us, and that's also embarrassing."

"You bet," said Gilly. "They talked to my wife *and*

my girlfriend. This bullshit is cutting into my income. How am I gonna sell anything with cops around?"

"What do you sell?" I asked.

"Uh, small appliances and such."

Right. I bet he specialized in TV sets and CD players that fell off a truck. He fell silent and stared at his coffee. I broke the silence by asking Jack "Why did Sydney take her Jeep to the ball? You said she wanted to ride home on your Harley."

"She did," Jack said. "The cops asked me that question too. She had to see her lawyer, so she met me at the ball. I was supposed to take her home."

"What about her car?"

"She thought we could pick it up the next morning. Stupid woman thought it would be there too."

Jack must have remembered at that moment that Sydney was dead and he was supposed to be sorry. "Where were you and Sydney living?" I persevered.

"She left Ladue and had an apartment on the South Side—Juniata near Spring. Nice big place, new rehab, cheap rent. Moved right after her husband dumped her. I moved in with her a few weeks ago."

"Is that where you went after the ball?"

"I just rode around until three A.M., going no place in particular, because I was so honked off. I mean, I'm sorry the woman is dead, but damn, she made me look stupid. And she's still making me look bad."

"Jack took a lie detector test and flunked it," Sonny explained. "That's why the cops follow him like Mary's little lamb."

"I flunked it because I'm on methadone," said Jack,

saying each word slowly. He was angry and just barely keeping his temper under control. "I told them that when I took the test."

Might as well spread the fun. "What about you, Jerry?" I said. "The police say there's an important time span you can't account for."

Jerry looked uneasy. He shifted in his chair, stared at his hands, and mumbled, "I was around. I didn't hear them paging me. Musta been in the john or something."

He was lying. I knew it. So did Stephanie. She said, "Hmpf. Have to be deaf not to hear them calling you." Exactly my thought. Stephanie gave Jerry a look that would burn the hair off an ordinary man.

"Where were you, Gilly?" I said. "Cops said you were missing for at least an hour."

"I was in the car with my wife, getting a little nooky," he said.

Sonny snorted. Jack giggled. Stephanie looked at him like he was a loathsome life-form. Which, come to think of it, he was.

"It's the God's honest truth," Gilly said, sounding like a liar.

"The point is nobody has a decent alibi," said Sonny. "Stephanie was at the ball all night, but she could have slipped out for ten minutes and killed Sydney."

"I wanted to murder the bitch with my bare hands. But I didn't," Stephanie said.

Sonny jumped into the conversation pool again. "We're innocent, Francesca, and we want you to prove it."

"What!" I said, finally fully awake. "I can't do that."

"You've got to," Sonny said, and the others looked at me like Oliver Twist's tiny pals. "We were set up. The murder was made to look like a biker did it. If a biker really did beat Sydney with a drive chain, he—"

"Or she," said Gilly, glaring back at Stephanie.

"Wouldn't be able to ride the bike home," Sonny said, "unless the killer brought an extra chain. There were no bikes left after the ball. And none of us had a reason to kill Sydney beforehand, so we wouldn't bring an extra chain. She and Jack were real lovey-dovey. Stephanie, Jerry, and Gilly didn't even know she existed."

"Yeah, but the cops think if you didn't kill Sydney because you hated her, you killed her because her husband hired you."

"No biker would murder a Ladue lady at the Leather and Lace Ball," Sonny said. "We don't want that kind of notoriety."

"We'd have offed her at her South Side flat and made it look like a burglary," Gilly said. "Could have picked up a new TV and a CD player, too," he added wistfully.

Sonny and Stephanie glared him into silence. "We know you can do this, Francesca, because you solved the drag queen murders," Sonny said.

I didn't want to think about that. "I didn't solve those murders, I stumbled into the middle of them and made things worse."

"The killer got caught, thanks to you. Now we need your help," he said. "You asked us for a favor and we got you into the ball."

Payback time. "Okay," I said. "Our new managing

editor wants me to do a Sunday feature about Sydney, anyway. But I'm not making any promises."

"Thanks," Sonny said. "I knew you'd do it."

"Don't thank me," I said. "You don't know how wrong I was last time."

Dead wrong.

3

"**G**o Away."

I could read the words, but I couldn't believe them. I looked again. They still said "Go Away."

The *Gazette* actually wanted to call its new travel tabloid "Go Away."

"So, what do you think of our prototype?" Charlie the managing editor asked me.

I thought it sucked. But I also thought I'd better not say that. I knew what I was supposed to think. Charlie, the little slimewad, was standing in his conference room beaming like a proud papa. The man almost looked human. He was wearing his best blue suit and most sincere tie. He did everything but hand me a cigar when I went to look at his newborn.

Six months of meetings and God knows how much money had produced this misbegotten thing on the long mahogany conference table. It was a mishmash of bold, clashing colors, busy layouts, and hard-to-read headlines. It violated every principle of newspaper layout and design. The pages bristled with pointless lines, boxes, takeout quotes, and other graphics gewgaws. Stories were jumped two or three times. Photos were small and skewed at odd angles. Text was squeezed into skinny columns, then stretched across the page for no reason.

There wasn't a staff-written story in the section, just empty words off the wires. One particularly embarrassing example began: "Hollywood has discovered the magic of Montana. You should, too." The story named some movie stars with homes in Montana. It forgot to mention how much the natives hated Hollywood types. The illustrations were six postage stamp–size celebrity photos and one picture of the Montana mountains at night. "The *other* stars come out after dark in the magic of Montana," the cutline gushed.

Advertisers would love it. Readers would do what the section advised: Go away. In droves. But they wouldn't saddle up the family van for magic Montana. They'd cancel their subscriptions. Charlie was planning to turn the Monday paper, our lowest circulation day, into a tabloid with this special travel section as the lure to boost readership. It wouldn't lure a canary to the bottom of a bird cage. The question was, why would Charlie, who'd tried a number of underhanded tricks to get me fired, want my opinion on his pet project?

I bought some time by staring thoughtfully at the prototype, but I had to say something soon. Charlie was still smiling expectantly.

"Is this a MacCreedy design?" I said.

"You can tell!" Charlie said, looking pleased.

I sure could. Only MacCreedy produced such empty, fussy work. He was a sour eggplant–shape man, who hated everyone who wasn't as unhappy as he was. Fortunately for MacCreedy, the people working on his sections were absolutely miserable. He made sure of that. MacCreedy had already midwifed four sections. Two were dead, one was limping sadly, and one was gasping its last. We expected the plug to be pulled on the St. Louie Woman section any day. This was a new women's section that looked remarkably like an old women's section. It served up wire service stories on child care, fashion, and household hints. A "Look Inside" column had cute articles about how local celebrities decorated their houses, written by freelancers for thirty-five bucks. No wonder the section was dying. St. Louis women were too sophisticated to swallow rewarmed hash.

MacCreedy was never blamed for the sections' failures. He was smart enough to get out after a new section was started. It was turned over to an eager but doomed editor. Then MacCreedy simply sat back and sniped at the poor sap with memos. "I want to call your attention to the following errors in today's section," his memos always began. "On page one, there should be a two-point rule under the masthead, not a one-point. The column on page two should have a takeout quote, but it should not be boxed. The column on the facing page should be boxed without a takeout quote. In the story on page four . . ."

Readers didn't give a rat's ear about the size of the rules. I doubt if they noticed. But the bosses did. They praised MacCreedy's nitpicking memos for their attention to detail. The new section editors were so bogged down in pointless—or one-point—graphics details they didn't have time to worry about the content. They also didn't have any staff. Most of these ballyhooed new sections simply had an editor, a copy editor, and all the wires service readers could eat. No money was spent on reporters. The budget had already been used for ads to promote the section. But maybe this time the *Gazette* would do it right.

"So, how many reporters will this new section have?" I asked.

"We'll have a copy editor and an editor," Charlie said. "The local reporting will be done by freelancers." For thirty-five bucks. So the *Gazette* didn't have to pay the staff overtime.

"The travel stories will be wire service. We'll also take freelance from *Gazette* staffers," Charlie said, as if he was handing out bonuses.

"We get thirty-five bucks to write 'How I Spent My Summer Vacation'?" I asked. Oops. That sounded a little sarcastic.

"No," Charlie explained. "We'll pay *you* twenty-five dollars. But we'll give you the opportunity to write off a portion of your vacation on your taxes." The *Gazette* and the IRS. They made a terrific team.

"But no new staff," I said.

"Francesca," Charlie replied, "we have one of the largest news staffs for a paper our size in the nation. I couldn't justify more people."

It was true. We had an enormous staff. But we also had one of the highest ratios of editors to reporters. We had more assistant city editors than we had news photographers. Photographers took pictures for the paper. Editors produced nothing but memos—and more confusion. But that was something else I couldn't say. Charlie already hated me.

Instead I said, "The section name is unusual." I thought that sounded remarkably subtle.

"We wanted to appeal to the young, hip reader," Charlie said, patting his old, fat gut.

"I thought most travel was done by older readers who have money and leisure time. Are you concerned the Go Away name will offend them?"

Charlie shrugged. "We may lose a few old farts," he said, obviously not including himself in that category. "But our focus groups indicate the name has high appeal in the eighteen-to-thirty age group. We need younger readers."

So we offended our older ones. And didn't get the young hip readers, either. They could get better info off the Internet. But that was something else I couldn't say. Evidently Charlie thought I'd said enough, anyway.

"I don't like your attitude, Francesca," he said, but he sounded avuncular rather than angry, which should have warned me the sawed-off sleaze was about to pull something sneaky. "You have lots of theories about how a newspaper should be run. You have lots of criticisms. But you have no practical knowledge. That's why I'm putting you on our Voyage Committee. Our publisher has hired one of the finest consultants in the business to help guide us into the next century. You're always complaining that we have only white males on these committees.

Well, Francesca, you're our official female newsroom representative. The first meeting is this weekend."

"What?" I felt like he'd punched me in the gut. Except a punch in the gut would have been quick. This was going to be slow and painful, like having my arm sawed off with a dull knife.

"Charlie, I'd be wasted on that committee," I said, overcome with modesty for once. "Also, I have a four-day-a-week column to write. And you want a special story on the Vander Venter murder."

Charlie handed me a thick envelope. "Stretch yourself," he said, giving his creepy little smile. "Consider this a sign of my confidence in your ability."

Consider this a trap so Charlie could get rid of me once and for all. I left his office fuming. At my desk, I pushed aside a pile of old *Gazette*s, mail and phone messages, and opened the envelope. There, on creamy stationery that must have cost my next raise, was a letter from our publisher.

"Dear Citizen of *Gazette*ville," it began.

Dear citizen? The publisher didn't know the name of his best-read female columnist?

"We are about to sail into the twenty-first century on a Voyage of Discovery that we hope will take us in new directions. You, as a member of our Voyage Committee, will be one of the people at the helm of the Good Ship *Gazette*. This committee is hand-picked from the paper's newsroom and business people."

Terrific. The two groups that are traditionally at each other's throats will be locked in a conference room together. The business department felt they could get this newspaper going if they could just make the effete, arrogant snobs in the newsroom understand that there has to be some connection between ad content and news content. The newsroom believed the business department couldn't sell the fine product we created. All they knew how to do was sell out. The ad reps were always trying to find sneaky ways to persuade writers to do nice stories about major advertisers, including questionable car dealers and siding contractors.

The letter blathered on. "We will take you all on a Voyage of Discovery to learn about yourself and your newspaper.

"Our objective is not to improve circulation, but to improve the internal dynamics so that the paper will naturally improve as the committee goes on a voyage of personal discovery. We must improve the product and the profits, while engendering the capabilities for enthusiasm, innovation and community involvement."

I groaned. This looked like weeks of what I had a low tolerance for: bullshit meetings. For me, being on this voyage was more dangerous than sailing on the *Titanic*. I looked around for my life preserver. Thank God, there she was. I spotted my mentor, Georgia T. George, assistant managing editor for features, going into her office on Rotten Row. I called her number. "Georgia, you won't believe what that little reptile Charlie has done now," I began when she answered, but she quickly cut me off.

"Francesca, I know how you really feel about Charlie," she said soothingly while I stared at the phone. Why was syrup pouring out of it? This didn't sound like my funny, foul-mouthed mentor. Had she been taken over by the pod people? "Your blood sugar must be low," she said, much too sweetly. "I want you to have a relaxing cup of tea at Miss Lucy's Lunchroom. Promise me you'll be there in ten minutes."

She hung up before I could ask what the heck got into her. Tea? At Miss Lucy's? Tea never sullied Georgia's lips. She drank scotch, and like most of the newsroom staff, would rather mud-wrestle naked on live TV than go to a tearoom. A light finally dawned. That's why she wanted me at Miss Lucy's in ten minutes. So we could talk without running into anyone from the *Gazette*.

Miss Lucy's was just around the corner from the *Gazette* but light-years away. It was staffed by sweet elderly women in ruffly pink uniforms who called you dear and seemed to mean it. I ordered oolong and cress sandwiches for two, because I'd read about them in English novels. The oolong tasted like ordinary tea and the cress sandwiches tasted like buttered grass.

"Your ass would have been grass if I hadn't shut you up," Georgia bellowed when she steamed through the tearoom's candy-pink door a few minutes later. The tearoom was empty, but the sweet pink lady pouring the oolong looked so shocked, she slopped tea into my saucer. She apologized and fluttered back to the kitchen to get me another cup.

Georgia settled into a spindly pink chair, smoothing the wrinkles on one of her expensive, ugly suits. The woman had a genius for picking corporate clothes that looked all wrong on her. Her elfin face and slight figure were lost in boxy suits the color of fungus. Maybe she thought it was the only way to be taken seriously. Maybe she was right. She usually was.

"I couldn't talk to you because the fucking phones are bugged," she said, lowering her voice an octave. "The company is also monitoring the effing e-mail and reading the frigging files on computers. Charlie announced it at the morning meeting today. Said it's the first step toward getting rid of the deadwood."

"Sounds like a worthy goal to me," I said.

"That's exactly what management wants you to think," she said sharply. "But your definition of deadwood is different from theirs. With your smart mouth and high salary, you could be Charlie's next target."

"I should know you can't count on management to make a sensible decision. The *Gazette* is notorious for promoting goofoffs and driving off talent. Charlie chased off a really fine black reporter by giving her dog assignments. Now she's a war correspondent at the *Washington Post*. But Charlie told everyone she was awful and didn't work hard while she was at the *Gazette*. Even I believed him. I didn't realize it was because he gave her such awful stories."

"*Gazette* management specializes in divide and conquer," Georgia said. "If the staff is at one another's throats, they won't notice management is reaming their asses." The sweet pink lady had returned while Georgia was making that speech. She was so startled she oolonged on my wrist.

"I'm so sorry," the tea lady said, and pulled out an embroidered handkerchief to mop up the spots on my sleeve. She turned pinker than her uniform at

Georgia's language. Georgia was a newswoman of the old school. When she started at the paper, women were automatically sidetracked into the society section. Georgia talked her way out of covering society stories and into a serious city hall beat. She used a two-pronged approach. First, she convinced management she was a good reporter by getting scoops. Second, she used language so foul her editors were afraid to let her near a so-called society lady.

When the pink lady went back for another fresh cup for me, Georgia said, "Now, what's the problem?"

"Charlie put me on the Voyage Committee," I said.

"That's good," she said.

"That's bad and you know it," I said.

"Only if you open your big mouth. I've warned you about that."

"But I hate long meetings," I said. Even to me, this sounded whiny. "They're hot-air machines. I listen to the bullshit and get restless and the next thing you know I say the wrong thing."

"Then let this be a test of your willpower, Francesca," she said sternly. "It's about time you developed some. This committee can make your career. You'll be very visible. The publisher will be there— it's his personal project—and he can see how intelligent and charming you are."

I snorted and nearly ruptured my sinuses.

"I mean this, Francesca. It could be your showcase. The paper is sinking half a million bucks into this Voyage of Discovery."

I was outraged. "What! That's obscene. They could

spend that money on staffers and stories and have a really good paper."

"That outburst is an example of exactly what I mean," Georgia said, fixing me with a glare. "Learn control. We both know that Charlie expects you to lose your temper in front of the publisher and damage your career. There's only one way you can hurt Charlie: Keep your mouth shut. Except when you have something positive to say. Besides, you won't be alone. I'm on the committee, too. I'll be with you."

"But this committee is useless," I said. "We just had an expensive survey taken last year. We had a focus group study two years before that. We had an in-depth telephone survey three years before that. The Voyage Committee will make the same recommendations the other surveys have made for the last thirty years. They'll say the paper needs younger readers. It needs more women readers. It needs reader involvement. It should have lighter, brighter, shorter stories. It needs more local stories.

"The surveys all have the same conclusions. And management always reacts in the same dumb ways: We'll have to do a silly series of 'Tell Us What You Think' features. Write a bunch of boring celebrity interviews. All stories will have to have a local angle, and we'll go crazy trying to find one. Last time we went through this, Japan was hit with a major earthquake and the only way we could get that news into the paper was to interview two local families who had relatives living there. Reader response to all these changes will be underwhelming. In a few months, the paper will slip back to its old ways."

Georgia clapped when I finished. "No shit, Sherlock. Tell me something I don't know," she said. I could feel her sarcasm etching into me like acid. "Francesca, idealism is embarrassing at your age. The *Gazette* is a mediocre paper because it's run by mediocre people. And it will continue to be that way, unless one of them wises up and says 'Damn I'm dumb, I think I'll fire myself.' Mediocre people only hire other mediocrities. I know this Voyage Committee will go nowhere. The answer is already predetermined by the consultants we hired. There are consultants who recommend you beef up your features and local stories and the ones who recommend you improve your hard news. The *Gazette* hired soft-news consultants, and they will make exactly the recommendations you said. The publisher knows that. He's not buying an unknown quantity."

"You're not mediocre. Why do you work here?"

"I'm fifty-five years old. I have a fourteen-room penthouse overlooking Forest Park and a private office at the *Gazette*. I have a nice salary, good bennies, and an impressive title. I like my life in St. Louis. I couldn't work out of our Boston headquarters and live this well on my salary. Does that answer it for you? Now, can I go back to work?"

"One other question. What's corporate casual? We're supposed to wear that the first Voyage Committee meeting."

"Something preppie. Khaki slacks and a Polo shirt will do fine. No black leather or thigh-high boots."

"Oh. You heard about those?"

"Babe made you sound like you moonlighted as a dominatrix."

"At least I'm not boring in his reports to management. I don't know why they want to bug our phones and monitor our e-mail when they have Babe spying on everyone."

"They're gathering solid evidence of insubordination," she said. "So remember that when you e-mail your pals or talk to anyone on the phone."

I had one last question and I had to know the answer. I didn't care if she laughed at me. "Georgia, is there really no hope for the *Gazette*? Will the paper ever be a major national newspaper again, the way it was fifty years ago?"

She looked at me with pity and patted my hand, a rare gesture for a tough woman like Georgia. "The *Gazette*'s glory days are dead and gone. The paper's old and tired. It's had a monopoly for too long. It forgot how to fight, except with its own employees. Now all the consultants in the world can't turn it around. You know what our former mayor said about the *Gazette*?"

Probably something unprintable. The ex-mayor was as foul-mouthed as Georgia. The two were old cronies, who liked to sip scotch and swap city hall stories in his law offices.

"Hizzoner said 'That newspaper couldn't sell whores on a troop ship.'"

There was a resounding crash as the pink lady dropped my teacup on the floor.

■

They looked like a golf foursome ready to tee off, which I guess was the perfect illustration of corporate casual. The big four at the *City Gazette* were sipping coffee and waiting to embark on their Voyage of

Discovery in Conference Room B at the Chesterfield Executive Center.

The publisher was surrounded by his three courtiers: Simpson Tolbart the chief operating officer, Charlie the managing editor, and Roberto the city editor. I could tell that the publisher was the biggest bigwig in this group. He was wearing the kind of gaudy golf clothes only really rich guys can wear without anyone laughing out loud. And loud was the operative word. His pants were bright green and his golf shirt was canary yellow. Simpson, the *Gazette*'s number-two man, looked only slightly less ridiculous in yellow-and-green plaid pants and a pale-yellow golf shirt. Charlie wore a red Polo shirt that matched his nose and red plaid pants. Roberto, the lowest man on this big chiefs' totem pole, was wearing the most normal clothes: a powder-blue golf shirt, khaki pants, and penny loafers. His face was fixed in an obsequious smile. As the publisher and Simpson talked and Charlie nodded sagely, Roberto's head bobbed up and down in agreement like one of those toy dogs in a car window.

Georgia, looking ten years younger in a sea green Lacoste outfit, waved me over to her group. A breakfast buffet had been set out for us. There were mounds of strawberries and melon slices, miniature bagels on silver trays, iced bowls of whipped butter, cream cheese, and strawberry cream cheese, and huge urns of coffee, decaf, and hot water for tea. I poured myself a cup of decaf and sugared it heavily to ward off all that healthy food. It was the ungodly hour of seven-thirty on a Saturday morning, and I felt awkward in my pink golf shirt and khaki pants.

Normally I'm a Donna Karan creature. Wearing this preppie stuff made me feel like I was forced to talk slowly in a language I didn't understand well.

"You've met Tucker Gravois," Georgia said, indicating a mild-looking gray-haired type with not one but two old St. Louis names. The man sounded like a street intersection. He also sounded like old money, which you would want for a vice president of business operations in St. Louis, where connections counted. Tucker was a pretty decent guy for a business type, and we always had congenial conversations when we met in the *Gazette* elevators.

Next to him was our very own Steel Magnolia, Yvonne "Just Call Me Vonnie" Cutte, our multimedia director. We exchanged curt nods. Vonnie saved the honeyed Carolina accent for the men. I'd tangled with her when she did a promotional ad for my column. She complained to the *Gazette* photographer that the picture he took of me was "too sexy." I found out later from my friend Tina that Vonnie had the same complaint about her promo photo. Tina looked good and photographed even better. Imagine Whitney Houston with a computer. Tina had star quality. Vonnie scuttled Tina's ad, saying the budget was blown. Tina didn't care. She didn't need the limelight. But we both wondered if little old Vonnie had her own private campaign to make the *Gazette* women writers look like schoolmarms.

Those were the principal members of the Voyage Committee, along with four eager young yups from the business side, who were named Brittany, Courtney, Scott, and Jeremy. I couldn't tell them apart, because they all had short blond hair and said yes a lot. They stood in a little covey near the coffee urn.

Promptly at 8:00 A.M. a ponytailed guy in work boots, blue jeans, and a chambray shirt arrived. "Good morning," he said with irritating chipperness. "I am your Voyage Captain Jason."

"I'm getting that sinking feeling already," I whispered to Georgia. She shut my mouth with a laser glare.

"Before we begin," chirped Jason, "I have a little gift that symbolizes our Voyage of Discovery." He pulled out a big cardboard box from under a skirted buffet table. Then he presented each of us, starting with the publisher, with a nylon navy backpack with the Voyage of Discovery ship logo on it. He handed them out reverently, as if they were platinum-plated.

"We don't want you carrying old baggage on this journey," Jason said, smiling earnestly. "We want you to make fresh, new discoveries about yourselves and your colleagues. That's what our backpack with the special ship logo represents."

"I thought it represents the fact that the paper is totally at sea," I whispered to Georgia. She kicked me. Hard.

We were sitting around a big dark walnut conference table. The room was done in soothing mauve and gray. Jason spurned the walnut podium. He stood at the head of the table, hands in his jeans pockets. He looked at ease yet in command. The publisher was hanging on to his words as if they were solid gold. Considering what this was costing the *Gazette*, I guess they were.

"As your captain on this voyage, I must warn you.

You're in for some heavy weather. We've done some preliminary research, and the Good Ship *Gazette* is lost in stormy waters. It's leaking circulation faster than ever before in its history, particularly in the West County suburban corridor, which is the most desirable area for the advertisers. We're losing women readers and we aren't bringing in young readers. Our analysis, plus the results of several years of surveys and focus groups, shows that readers feel the paper is lacking in structure and identity and that it is elitist, arrogant, and out of touch with the community."

Hmm. Maybe Voyage Captain Jason wasn't all wet after all. So far, I'd agreed with everything he'd said.

"Our internal surveys of the staff were even more disturbing. We found a staff that is distrustful of management and one another. Section heads refuse to assist each other. Staff members are encouraged to dislike their colleagues. This is not a good working atmosphere, people. This is not a sharing and caring environment where creativity can be nurtured. These kinds of conflicts can sink a corporation."

Way to go, Captain. Everything you said would float my boat.

"It's going to take a lot of work to get the Good Ship *Gazette* back on course," he said. "It's going to take the cooperation of you." He pointed dramatically at our publisher.

"And you and you," he said, pointing at the two money men, Tucker and Simpson.

"And you and you and you and . . ." He made sure we all got the point.

"We need the high Cs here—Cooperation and Creativity. And to help develop these two vital life-enhancing and business-building qualities, we are going to have our first exercise in teamwork. Francesca, what do you think would be a good, fun learning game for *Gazette* people to play? Choose a popular game, now."

Game? I didn't play games. Wait a minute, what was that game I used to play with my suburban cousins? It was about buying and selling. Was it Scrabble? No, it was . . .

"Monopoly!" I said brightly. There was an awkward silence. Shit. Bad choice. Some said the *Gazette* already played Monopoly. The city's two other daily newspapers were dead.

Georgia came to my rescue. "Poker is a good learning game," she said. "I learned it when I covered city hall, and it taught me everything I needed to know about people."

It was just the right thing to say. "I heard the mayor lost his shirt playing with you," Tucker said, smiling.

"Not true, it wasn't strip poker," said Georgia, and everyone laughed. I hoped my Monopoly remark was forgotten.

"Those are good games," said Jason, sounding like he was talking to a gifted kindergarten class. "But I was thinking of something a little more basic. A way of going back to our beginnings, when we first learned to play." He reached again under the table skirt and pulled out a giant box of . . . Tinkertoys.

"I'm going to divide you into teams of four. Each team will build something that represents their concept of the *Gazette*. You'll have twenty minutes. Sit on the floor now. We need to start building from the ground up. I realize some of you must be thinking 'What does that silly man have in mind? These are kids' toys!' "

I was thinking something similar, only not so clean.

"I promise you. This only looks like a childish exercise. It is actually a childlike activity. That is an important difference. This is the best way I know to teach you teamwork," Jason said.

■

"I swear to God, Lyle, we actually sat on a conference room floor and played with Tinkertoys for two hours yesterday. What was that idiot thinking?"

"Which idiot?" asked Lyle.

"Good question. I meant Voyage Captain Jason, but the publisher sat there and lapped up that foolishness. That's one emperor who doesn't realize he's running around naked."

Naked. Yes. I was distracted by the hunky young man who ran past us in Tower Grove Park, with teeny shorts and tons of muscles. I'd always loved St. Louis's fall days, and this one was particularly beautiful, even without the nearly naked jogger. Most of the trees still had their leaves, and this year they were a blaze of fiery red and gold. Tower Grove was a nineteenth-century Victorian walking park, a perfect place for lovers to stroll and talk on a warm Sunday afternoon. We passed the lily ponds, paused to watch a giggling bride and groom pose for pictures near the fake Roman ruins, and then walked up to a little gazebo with a roof like a Chinese pagoda.

And all the while we sampled this sun-drenched beauty, I griped about the Voyage Committee. It was one reason I'd agreed to see Lyle when he called. I missed talking to him after I flounced out of his place last Saturday. He was so smart, and he listened.

"I can see why you're discouraged," he said. "It doesn't sound like this group is going to solve the *Gazette*'s problems. And the paper does have problems. Do you know my students call it News Lite, because they don't think it has anything worth reading?"

"No, I didn't. I suspect the paper will be even emptier when this committee gets through with it. This is going to be a long voyage," I said with a sigh. "And besides these Voyage Committee meetings, I still have to write my column and do that special feature on Sydney Vander Venter. And if I write about Sydney, I have to go to one of my least favorite areas in St. Louis—Ladue."

"Ladue is an attractive older suburb," Lyle replied. He wasn't from St. Louis, so he didn't have my built-in attitude. "All those big trees and big houses."

"And small-minded people," I said.

"Oh, come on. Not everyone in Ladue is a snob. Don't you have some friends who live there?"

"Yeah, I like them. But I still can't stand the place."

"Why?"

"I hate the rich."

"You do not. I'm rich. You don't hate me."

No. But right now, I didn't exactly like him, either. When he stood there and smiled like that, I wanted to slap him. I was in a foul mood after spending yesterday on that Voyage Committee.

"Come on, tell me why you hate the place," Lyle said, and punctuated his taunt by kissing me on the nose. I swatted him away, like a pesky fly.

"It's insular. It's stupid. It's smug. There's a whole Ladue attitude. They think they can run the city and do whatever they want and they don't have to follow the rules like the rest of us."

"Those are prejudices," Lyle said.

"Based on fact. Remember when I did that story on the county health department's vector control service—we call it Rat Control in the city? Well, a woman called up and asked what she could do about the night squirrels. Vector control said they didn't know what night squirrels were.

"'My gardener told me about them,' the Ladue woman said. 'They only come out at night. They look like squirrels with long skinny tails.'

"'Those are rats, ma'am,' said vector control.

"'Oh, no,' she said. 'We don't have rats. We live in Ladue.'"

"A funny story, I admit," Lyle said. "But still not enough evidence. Why don't you start with some research on Ladue?"

"Okay," I said. "I'll go to the downtown library tomorrow and find the facts to back me up."

"At least you'll know why you hate the place."

4

Some barflies get thirsty at the whiff of an old-time bar. There's something about the smell of stale beer and Pine-Sol, and I do feel at home in a saloon. But I lust for libraries. They were my home away from home. My parents argued a lot. I would sneak off to the library and hide out there in the silence with my peaceful books. I liked the suburban library with the blond bookcases, the big glass windows, and that peculiar greenish aquarium light. The librarians wouldn't let anyone talk to me or hurt me. I'd sit there, feeling safe and protected, hoping my parents would quit fighting by the time I got home. If the bedroom door was locked and I heard their bedsprings squeaking, I knew they were making up and everything would be fine in the morning. If they were still arguing, I would sneak upstairs to my room, shut the door, and read my books on my bed until I finally fell asleep. I'm surprised my ribs didn't cave in, sleeping on some of those fat tomes.

After my parents died and I moved in with my grandparents in the city, I hung out at the library near my grandparents' city store. The Carpenter Branch Library smelled dark, old, and mellow. It was different, but I liked it. My favorite, though, was the main library downtown. It was built in 1912, when St. Louis was still a mighty river city and wanted a book palace for its people. Cass Gilbert, the same guy who designed the U.S. Supreme Court, designed an opulent library. Every time I went in the place, I took my own tour. The main room was oval and done in a warm, soft pinkish gray marble. It had molded plaster ceilings, a huge oak counter, and carved church pews to sit in while you waited for your books to be brought from the stacks.

Today I wanted History and Genealogy, another grand room with a ceiling modeled after an Italian palace. It had helpful librarians. I called and told them what I was looking for, and they assembled everything they had on Ladue. I took the pile of books and files and sat at a long oak table, next to a husband and wife who were researching their family tree.

The librarians dug up good stuff. I couldn't wait to tell Lyle what I found. He wanted facts on why I didn't like Ladue, I'd give him facts. Hah. Old and new, Ladue was one strange place. It had no public pool, no tennis courts, or recreational facilities. If you wanted those, you had to join a country club. Ladue had the highest concentration of private clubs in the area, places that excelled at keeping more people out than they let in. They included the St. Louis Country Club, the Log Cabin Club, the Bogey Golf

Club, the Deer Creek Club, Old Warson Country Club, and the Racquet Club Ladue.

Ladue believes we're just jealous, which we are. They also say Ladue isn't as rich as everyone thinks. Huntleigh Village, a tiny St. Louis suburb of 392 people, has a median family income of more than $135,000 a year. Ladue families, on the average, scrape by with around $121,000. Ladue has 108 people living below the poverty level. Huntleigh has none. Not one person. So why don't we pick on Huntleigh? Why aren't we calling it elitist and snobbish?

Because Ladue has this attitude, see. It has more to do with Ladue minds than Ladue money. Ladue likes to sue the socks off people—for reasons that would have the rest of us shrugging and turning away.

Only Ladue would sue a respectable cohabiting couple, because the city had a rule that more than one family couldn't live in the same house. Ladue won that lawsuit, too. Took it all the way to the Supreme Court. My hairdresser friend told me the suit had a curious outcome: a gay couple living in Ladue were worried they were next. So the older one adopted the younger. They now commit incest, with the blessing of the city.

Then Ladue turned around and sued Margaret Gilleo, a woman who was worried about war. She put up a yard sign that said, SAY NO TO WAR IN THE PERSIAN GULF. CALL CONGRESS NOW. The sign was the size of a FOR SALE sign, but Ladue carried on like she was advertising X-rated videos. Gilleo thought she was guaranteed free speech. She challenged Ladue's sign ordinance in federal court—and the ordinance was struck down as unconstitutional. Ladue then adopted a new sign ordinance, which wasn't much different from the first. And Margaret taped a sign the size of a piece of typing paper in a window that said, FOR PEACE IN THE GULF.

For that modest wish, Ladue sued her all the way to the Supreme Court. Ladue lost that one. Some Ladue-ites complained to the press that the sign was tacky. Evidently, it was not tacky to have Americans die in the desert. But it was tacky to mention the problem in a Ladue yard.

That was Ladue for you—so self-absorbed in petty city politics, it forgot there was a world out there, where people died. My Ladue friends keep telling me "We're not all like that. Some of us are normal," and I believe them. Because otherwise, Margaret Gilleo wouldn't have fought the good fight for free speech. She would have put her sign away and shut up.

Some people say this rash of lawsuits is a recent thing. But it's not. Ladue has been getting itself in stupid public scrapes for years. My favorite example was back in the 1940s when Ladue had a ghost library. St. Louis County wanted to set up a county library district and tax everybody ten cents per hundred dollars of assessed valuation. But some municipalities in the county already had thriving libraries, so they were exempt. Ladue did not have a library—until it looked like it would have to pay that ten-cent tax. Then people quickly donated a bunch of old books, and Ladue got a subscription to *Life* magazine. These intellectual treasures were kept at a fire station. Ladue said it had a library and voted to tax themselves one cent to maintain it, and save nine whole pennies. Except the courts didn't let Ladue get by with it. This cheap trick was labeled "a new low in political subterfuge" in the newspapers back then. Ten years later, Ladue donated its ghost library to the prisoners at the county jail.

There was a lot more like this, including a nostalgic interview with an old Ladue resident who bragged he drank the best bourbon at a Ladue eatery all during Prohibition. He said a disgruntled employee tipped a prohibition officer that the place had 250 cases of booze stashed in an old cistern. The restaurant owner put three hundred dollars down on the bar and the agent forgot about the stash. This charming tale of bribery was repeated in an adoring newspaper article.

I'd been hearing Ladue stories like these all my life. But Lyle wasn't from St. Louis, so he didn't absorb these attitudes with the beer-perfumed air. Now I had more than an attitude. I had facts about why I did not like Ladue. So what did this information tell me about Sydney or the Vander Venter family?

Nothing. But I knew someone who could tell me: Endora. She was the *Gazette*'s Ladue specialist. Endora had been at the *Gazette* so long she didn't quite rate an office, but she had a three-walled windowless lair where the Family section petered out into the no-man's land between Sports and Food. The ergonomically correct pastel pods we sat in never came back this far. Neither did anyone who was on the fast track for promotion. In this cramped, airless space that nobody wanted, Endora had accumulated two battered gray desks piled with yellowing newspapers and old books, a three-legged bookcase (she used a brick to prop up the fourth side), an assortment of straggling plants, a phone, and an old, slow computer.

Endora sat on a straight-back wooden chair that would have crippled an ordinary person. She was handsome in a horse-faced, WASPy, don't-give-a-damn way. She let her hair turn gray and she pulled it straight back in a ponytail. Her strong body had softened and thickened and her face had more lines than one of her daddy's railroad maps. But on her it looked good.

Endora was the last survivor of a robber baron who made his money in nineteenth-century railroads. Like the Vanderbilts and the Rockefellers, he kept his fabulous fortune one step ahead of the law and became a pillar of society. He built a huge stone-and-marble mansion on Portland Place, with a two-story Tiffany window and fireplaces from a French chateau. About 1924, when gloomy Victorian palaces were unfashionable, his son—Endora's grandfather—moved to Ladue, so he could be closer to his favorite country clubs. Grandfather was good at investments. His son, Endora's daddy, inherited Grandfather's gambling streak without the old man's shrewdness and eventually lost most of the family fortune at the gaming tables. When he was down to his last half million, Daddy skipped with his secretary for Mexico. They did not take the train.

Endora's Mummy, who always did the right thing, quietly pined away, with a little help from the liquor cabinet. But Endora was healthy as a horse, and, alas, she rather resembled one. With no family money, a lumpy figure, and outrageous opinions, it was doubtful she would ever marry. There was almost nothing left after the family home was sold off and Daddy's debts were paid. Something had to be done. Her grandfather's friends let her live in a charming guest cottage on the old Gravois estate. The cottage was big enough for a family of four. Then they got her a job at the *Gazette*. Endora, the product of the best private schools (she hung her Vassar degree in the guest john, in case we didn't know) wasn't a bad writer. The editors soon found her enormously useful. Endora covered all those touchy stories that had Ladue-ites on the phone squealing to their lawyers and had their lawyers on the phone threatening to sue the *Gazette*. Writing about Ladue was financially and emotionally draining before Endora, and the paper avoided it whenever possible. But there were times when they couldn't, especially when one of their suits made federal court. That's when Endora proved to be worth her considerable weight in gold. She wrote stories with such wit and style, you actually thought she said something. Everyone was happy. Ladue had one of their own reporting things the way they wanted, and the *Gazette* staff didn't have to tangle with Ladue. On the rare occasions when Endora overstepped herself and offended someone there, nobody complained to the *Gazette*. Her invitations simply dried up for a while. She never failed to get the point. A few younger writers at the *Gazette* groused because Endora seemed to do so little. The rest of us realized her true worth. Endora was getting up there and we dreaded the day she finally retired.

At first I thought Endora was not in her lair today. Then I saw her behind a screen of wilting philodendrons she kept on the bookcase. Someone must be dumping *Gazette* coffee in the poor things again. She was at her desk, reading a book. She looked up from her paperback novel. "Yeah, Vierling, what can I do for you?" she said in a voice that could be heard on the other side of a hockey field. She always called me by my last name. It sounded very private school.

"I've got the Sydney Vander Venter story," I said. "I don't know why they didn't assign it to you in the first place."

"Because you were there when she was killed," she said. "Anyway, Wendy stuck me with the Shop Till You Drop section about stores for the St. Louis super-rich. You know that's like walking on goddamn eggs."

"I don't envy you," I said. I meant it. Some of that area's biggest advertisers were not the most fashionable stores. Endora had to steer a delicate course to please editors and advertisers. "If anyone can carry it off, you can." I meant that, too. I was on a roll, telling the truth twice in a row. I'd better quit while I was ahead. "I'm looking for information about Sydney. What can you tell me?"

"Let's see . . ." She stared straight ahead, as if the answer were written on her dingy wall. I knew she was going through the Ladue data bank in her head. "You know Sydney came from an old St. Louis family. A minor branch of the Gravois. Made their money in shoes, back when St. Louis was known for shoes, booze, and blues. The Gravois family had some money then, although most of it's gone now.

Not as much as the Vander Venters—they must be worth twenty million minimum—and that's not counting the business."

"That much? And I heard Sydney's mother-in-law Elizabeth was a tightwad."

"Elizabeth," Endora said, and smiled. "That woman is a hoot. She's the real brains of that family, you know. Elizabeth lives well, but she's not ostentatious. Quality of life is what's important to the Vander Venters, mother and son, and I admire them for that. She has another house in Maine, a fifty-foot sailboat, and I think she still has her place at Palm Beach, too.

"Anyway, you asked about Sydney. Her father left her a small trust fund. Sydney went to Stephens College, you know, because she could take her horse to school with her."

"Did the horse learn anything?"

"Very funny, Vierling. Don't go South Side on me. I'm trying to help. I think Sydney married Hudson right after college. I know she was a model Ladue wife: devoted to her son, played bridge and tennis, chaired the right charity events, weighed the same at forty as she did when she married."

"Did she fool around on Hudson?"

"Not that I ever heard. But he screwed around on her all the time. Mostly wives of friends. It was pretty quiet until he met Brenda and dumped Sydney."

"Why did he dump the perfect Ladue wife?"

"Because she *was* the perfect Ladue wife. Hudson got tired of living with—and, let's face it, maintaining—all that perfection. Sydney was expensive. I heard he met Brenda at Tom Schlafly's Saint Louis Brewery. You know it?"

"Of course. They have wicked french fries and sticky toffee pudding. Lyle likes their porter."

"Hudson told me about the first time he had lunch with Brenda. It was strictly business. Nothing was going on then. Brenda ordered a beer, a cheeseburger, and french fries. Sydney would never do that. She starved herself. Always on a diet. If she did eat anything, she'd go on about how many fat grams she consumed until your eyes crossed. Well, after her cheeseburger and beer, Brenda said, 'That was good. Think I'll try the oatmeal stout.' Hudson had never been around a woman who acted that way. He said that's when he fell in love. I felt sorry for Sydney, but virtue is its own punishment. She spent her whole time talking about her kid, her worthy causes, and her diets. I can see why the poor guy dumped her. Plus, I heard Brenda was pretty good in the sack. Sydney looked like she'd clank if you got on top of her." An attractive, skinny woman wouldn't get much sympathy from Endora.

"What would have happened to Sydney if they'd divorced?"

"Hudson hired a real shark. If Sydney was lucky, she might have been able to get a house in Chevy Chase."

"Where's that? Isn't Chevy Chase a suburb of Washington, D.C.? I couldn't imagine Sydney living anywhere but here."

Endora looked at me like I lived on another planet. I guess I did. "Chevy Chase is a subdivision in Olivette, right on the edge of Ladue. The southwest corner of Price Road and Bonhomme. It's where divorced Ladue wives go when they get a bad settlement. If you live in Chevy Chase, you are still in the Ladue school district, so your kids can go to Ladue schools. A lot of Catholics and Jews live there, too. It's mostly brick-and-frame houses, built in the twenties. You'd probably like it, but it would be a comedown for Sydney."

I'd probably like it, because I was too dumb to know any better. After all, I grew up Catholic. Endora had no idea she'd just insulted two religions. Talking with Endora could set my South Side teeth on edge. She gave me the names of two of Sydney's friends, but one lived in Chicago. She also gave me her son's new address, although Endora didn't know the phone number. Then her phone rang, and Endora had an excuse to dismiss me. "I have to go," she said. "I've been expecting this call. Come back if you need anything."

It was only after I got back to my desk that I realized Endora really hadn't told me much, except that Hudson had a lot of affairs and a lot of money. Both were ways of bragging. Endora really was one of them. If I was going to find out anything, I needed to talk to someone who knew Ladue but didn't live there.

Who did I know who would fit that description? I opened my brown leather Filofax and began paging through it. It wasn't until I got to the Ps that I found the right person: Jinny Peterson. Jinny was an engaging redhead who lived in Kirkwood. If *Father Knows Best* was shot today, it would be set in Kirkwood, and Jinny's white clapboard house with the black shutters, red front door, and—I swear—white picket fence, would be perfect. Jinny might be just a little too sexy for the fatherly insurance agent, Jim Anderson, though. Besides, she had a sense of humor, and I didn't see Jim living with any woman who might laugh at him. Jinny was on half a dozen boards, from KWMU, the public radio station, to a battered women's shelter, and a children's museum. She didn't have major money. What Jinny contributed was time and hard labor. She would make zillions of calls, find volunteers, and volunteer herself.

She also loved to swap information. It was too detailed and too accurate to be ordinary gossip. Jinny knew everyone, and if she didn't, she'd call around until she found someone who did.

She answered her phone after two rings. "Help!" I said. "I'm supposed to write about Sydney Vander Venter's murder. I need background information on the Vander Venter family."

"Well, I knew her as someone to nod to at charity events," she said. "She was always nice—which is a word no one in Ladue uses. Too middle class, my dear. I can give you lots of gossip about the mother-in-law, Elizabeth."

"Just what I need. I'm going to try to interview her."

"Then come on over," Jinny said. "I've just made a cheesecake and I'll put on a pot of tea."

People who lived in *Father Knows Best* houses also bake. Jinny's home, like anyplace you'd want to live in St. Louis, was only twenty minutes from downtown. She lived in the West County corridor that *Gazette* advertisers lusted after. Kirkwood was a more

generous and less exclusive community than Ladue.
It didn't expect its citizens to join country clubs. It
provided them with a public swimming pool, a community center, a recycling center, and recreational
programs for the kids. It had big old homes with
wide summery porches, shady trees, and old-fashioned gardens. Unlike my neighborhood, Kirkwood
had no slums, no panhandlers, and its drug dealers
didn't wear scary, baggy clothes. I would have died
of boredom if I lived there. But Jinny loved its pretty
perfection. Half an hour after I called her, I was in
her kitchen, which had blue ruffled curtains. She put
a plate of cinnamon-sprinkled cheesecake and a teapot on the maple table. It was my week for tea.

"Why is your teapot wearing a sweater?" I asked.

"That's a tea cozy," she said. "It keeps the tea
warm." Even the tea was cozy here. I was fascinated
by this normalness.

"I figured you'd be good to talk to because you
know Ladue," I said, "but you don't live there."

Jinny shuddered. "God forbid. I view Ladue with
jaundiced amusement."

"Just what I need. Along with another hunk of
cheesecake, please. Tell me about Sydney's mother-
in-law, Elizabeth. Endora avoided the subject."

"Probably scared of her," Jinny said seriously.
"Queen Elizabeth has the power of banishment."

"That's her nickname, huh?"

"Not to her face, no one, not even her husband,
ever called her Liz. By the way, I heard her late husband was gay. Just a rumor. I don't have a single fact
to back it up, but I happen to believe it's true." Jinny
graded her gossip. She'd tell you if it was Grade A

reliable information, Grade B rumors mixed with facts, or simply wild speculation.

"She looks formidable," I said. "She's a prime example of old Ladue money, right?"

"Absolutely. Elizabeth lives on the grounds of the St. Louis Country Club, which as you know is one of the most exclusive addresses in Ladue. I heard from several *very* reliable sources that Southwestern Bell moved its headquarters from St. Louis to San Antonio because that country club refused to admit Bell executives."

"You can't mean that. The telephone company would hurt the St. Louis economy and uproot all those people for a ridiculous reason like that?"

"It wasn't ridiculous to them. We're talking social life or death. One Ladue woman told me, 'That's why we have Old Warson Country Club, for corporate people.' Whether it's true or not, people out here believe that story, which is almost the same thing as being true."

"How old is Elizabeth?" I asked, subtly steering the conversation back to the topic.

"She says she's sixty-two, but she went to school with my friend Carol, and Carol says Elizabeth is somewhere in her late sixties. She dresses like the real Queen Elizabeth in expensive, dowdy clothes. The last time I ran into her was a perfect example. She was going to the Women's Exchange in Ladue, probably for a liquid lunch: martinis and their fresh vegetable soup. She was wearing Barbara Bush pearls and a powder-blue Adolpho suit made to look like Chanel. I think the pearls were fake, but the alligator handbag was real."

"One reptile calls to another," I said.

"Oh, but her lizard brain is sharp. Although Elizabeth rarely goes to the firm's office, I hear she is the real investment genius in that family. When her husband was alive, she used to advise him regularly. She never forgave him for not taking her tip about buying a local wonder-drug company in the sixties, and she'd often remind him of his error in public. Her son did not make his father's mistake. Hudson follows her advice religiously. In fact, he does everything his mother says. Carol told me Elizabeth even has a key to his house and drops in when she feels like it—poor Sydney. What a life she must have had with that husband and that mother-in-law. Naturally, Hudson has a key to his mother's place and frequently lunches or takes tea with her, on those days when she's not lunching out or playing tennis or bridge."

"I heard Elizabeth was so tight she squeaked. But when I asked Endora, she sidestepped the question."

Jinny rolled her eyes. "Tight? That woman throws pennies around like manhole covers. I was brought up to know how to save a buck, but this woman is beyond shame. I was at a lunch for the battered women's shelter, and Queen Elizabeth was there. She ate the salad, then called for extra rolls and asked for them to be boxed with her chicken entree and potato. She actually told people she would have them for that night's dinner!"

"No! With her money?"

"Yep, yep, and wait till you hear this. Carol, my friend who went to school with her, told me Elizabeth charged her housekeeper, Cordelia, seven dollars for a leftover ham in the refrigerator when she went to Europe for three weeks."

"You're making that up."

"I am not. Cordelia was outraged. She told Carol's housekeeper."

"Who told you. Well, did Cordelia buy the ham?"

"Sure. It was a whole ham with only a slice or two out of it. It was still cheaper than she could get it at Schnucks." Jinny lowered her voice, the cue that her next bit was really good. "Now, a writer friend who must remain nameless told me this one. He said Elizabeth had deviled eggs as one of the hors d'oeuvres at a party for an English horn soloist. The soloist was a guest artist at the symphony, staying at her house. At a party after his performance, a maid in a black uniform passed the eggs and little puff pastries and things around on a silver tray. The writer was invited to the party. The writer came back to interview the soloist in the morning, and Elizabeth served the musician those same deviled eggs for his breakfast. Isn't that the limit?"

"Eeccch. Recycled eggs. With all her millions she couldn't pick up some bagels and fresh fruit at the store?"

"How do you think she keeps her millions?" Jinny asked. "Here's another good one. Last year, when I worked at the Charity Designer Resale Show, she donated a ballgown with sweat-stained armpits and a waterstained hemline. Elizabeth said it was an Oscar de la Renta—which it was, although it was older than God—and demanded a tax write-off of $2,000. We had a special meeting about it. Finally we gave her the tax letter, because no one wanted to offend someone as powerful as Elizabeth, but we refused to put the dress out for sale. We have standards. It was too shabby."

"If she's so tight, what's the secret of her power?"

"Elizabeth is very good at getting other people to donate to her pet charities. She also makes highly visible donations to local charities. She knows exactly where her money will be the most welcome. She gives away about a hundred thousand dollars each year, usually in $10,000 amounts. You can make a real hit if you give $10,000 to KWMU—that's major money for public radio—or the University of Missouri at St. Louis, Lindenwood College, or the zoo. Her name appears in the symphony programs as part of the Slatkin Circle, and she always donates in their $10,000 to $14,999 category. You can bet she gives exactly $10,001 to qualify for the circle."

"She sounds shrewd."

"Exactly. Elizabeth is smart, clever, cold, and most of all, cheap. Never forget that last one. It's the key to everything."

"South Siders are frugal, but we'd be embarrassed to be that cheap. We'd never skimp on food for guests—or ourselves, for that matter."

"South Siders know how to do things," Jinny said. "They can fix toilets, clean houses, repair cars and run computers, and they get paid for those skills. Elizabeth's family hasn't held a real job for generations. Their money works for them. Anything happens to it, they don't have the skills to work at Steak 'n Shake. All they know how to do is hang on to every nickel. That saves them from a fate worse than death—a job."

Jinny said this with such feeling, I knew she wasn't just talking about South Siders. Elizabeth chaired the committees and took the credit in the newspaper stories, but it was people like Jinny who dealt with the caterer for the fund-raiser, tried to find employment and child care for the women at the shelter, and tried to fire up the legal system so the women would have the needed restraining orders, separation agreements, and child support.

"One more story," said Jinny, "and then I have to throw you out and start fixing dinner for the Mister."

That was another reason I couldn't live in *Father Knows Best* land. I didn't have a dependable schedule. Lyle would starve to death if he waited for me to have dinner on the table when he got home.

"I've saved the best till last," Jinny said. "I wouldn't believe this story if I hadn't heard it from my friend Pat. She deals in antiques. She was on Highway 67, on her way to the antique stores in Alton, Illinois, and she passed the Discount Barn in West Alton. She saw Elizabeth there."

"Elizabeth was at the Barn? You're making this up."

"I swear. Pat recognized her from her picture in Babe's column. She knew she had to be somebody because the woman had the only Buick Park Avenue in the Discount Barn parking lot, and she was wearing a black wool pantsuit with pearls and a silk scarf."

I choked on my tea. The Barn's regular customers drove pickups or big, old clunkers. Designer duds at the Discount Barn were jeans and a clean T-shirt. The Discount Barn is the last frontier of shopping, the third world of discount stores. It sells purple bathtubs, cheap carpet, and wallpaper by the pound. Also odd lots of auto and motorcycle parts, and offbeat bargains like cucumber soap and Jimmy Swaggart sermons. My rehabber friends couldn't live without the place, but they're looking for buys on plumbing, paint, and paneling. I like it because it's so wacky. Your average West Countian wouldn't be caught dead at the Barn.

"Let me guess. She was buying a plywood bathroom vanity."

"She was buying auto supplies. Pat pulled off the road to get a better look, because she knew she had a scoop. She said Elizabeth was ordering some kid to load up her trunk with cases of windshield solvent, antifreeze, and motor oil. She had three cases of Exxon motor oil. Pat thinks Elizabeth is so cheap she changes her own oil. Can you imagine?"

"No. I go to the gas station to have my license plates put on. I wonder how much dust the Barn's dirt driveway left on her car?"

"Won't make any difference. She'll have her yardman wash the car. And while we're talking about driveways, my husband is going to be in mine soon."

So it was time for me to go. I thanked her for the tea and the good talk. All the way home I wondered what it would be like to live with a man who wanted dinner on the table at the same time every night.

■

I was primed to talk to Queen Elizabeth, but I was still surprised she agreed to talk to riffraff like me. She briskly told me I could have ten minutes at eleven o'clock tomorrow morning. That was the only time she had available. Ever. She also gave me directions to her house on the St. Louis Country Club grounds. I wrote them down, turned off of Upper Barnes Road like she said, and got lost anyway. I expected that. It's easy to get lost on the winding roads around there. I passed the country club, the polo field, and parts of the golf course several times, and even I had to admit they looked fabulous, as they say in Ladue. Nice, too, as we say on the South Side. It was another golden late-fall day. I enjoyed watching the sunlight through the Ladue leaves. I enjoyed it even more because I knew those leaves drove Ladue nuttier than a nest of squirrels. With all those trees, the city spent ungodly amounts on leaf pickup and collection.

Her house was typical for the area: a six-bedroom white frame colonial revival with black shutters and a lot of lawn. It didn't look that rich. But I knew I was in a different world from the moment the door opened. Cordelia, the housekeeper, answered the door. She was a grandmotherly woman with mocha skin, gray hair, and a comfortable figure.

"I better take your coat and put it under lock and key," Cordelia complained. "Coats are disappearing around here right and left. Right and left. The burglars track in mud, too. Come right in this house and take an old lady's coat."

There was Elizabeth, in another one of her formidable suits. But she wasn't acting like a queen. She was trying to placate her "treasure," Cordelia. "I am sorry your coat was misplaced," she said to Cordelia. "I said I would buy you a new one."

Cordelia was not afraid to talk back to Elizabeth. I guess she'd been with her too many years to be awed by her. She snapped back, "It wasn't 'misplaced.' That coat was stolen. I thought I was working in a good neighborhood here, but I guess you can't count on nothing no more."

I stood there in the sunlit, slate-floored hall, while the two women bickered. I could have been a hat rack for the attention they paid me. It was funny. They were both about the same age and size, but Elizabeth had been surgically nipped and tucked. It didn't make her look younger than Cordelia, just unnaturally smooth, like a statue.

"It could not have been a burglar, Cordelia," Elizabeth was saying. "Nothing else was missing from this house, and I am sure they would steal more than your five-year-old winter coat."

"Huh! There were some good years left in that coat," Cordelia said, but she and Elizabeth finally remembered I was there. I hoped the five minutes they spent arguing didn't count against my ten. Cordelia took me into a sitting room that had to be Elizabeth's famous green room. It was painted pale green to highlight a pair of really ugly Meissen vases on the mantel. Endora had told me about those. She said I should also look for a Philadelphia highboy that may or may not be of exceptional quality and two late eighteenth-century tilt-top tables. I found them all. They were supposed to be from her husband's family. Endora didn't mention the two 1960s Waterford lamps with raw silk shades turning slightly yellow on the tables. She also told me that the rug on the floor was from Elizabeth's family and it was "seriously good." She didn't say anything about the serious hole in the rug. It was mostly covered with a three-legged table. Jinny told me to compliment the rug and see how long it would take Elizabeth to tell me it was a prized overall pattern. So I did.

"Nice Kirman," I said.

"Yes, it is," said Elizabeth. "It is not one of those with a center medallion but with a prized overall pattern."

Less than two seconds. And the way she said it, I was sure her family climbed Mount Everest to buy that rug. The rest of the furniture was mostly Baker reproductions from the last time she had the house redecorated—almost thirty years ago, when her husband was still alive. I'd heard serious furniture collectors sneer at Baker reproductions, but they looked pretty nice to me.

I also noticed that the upholstery was worn and the curtains were sun-faded. My grandmother wouldn't have had them in her living room. I know this was supposed to be old money, and Elizabeth was saying she didn't need to impress me with expensive new curtains. But what's the point of being rich if you live like you're poor?

There was nothing worn about Elizabeth's manner. She was in full command of everything but Cordelia. "I agreed to see you this once," she said frostily. "I wish to inform you that my son and grandson will not speak with you at all. I do not want to discuss my late daughter-in-law, except to say that her unfortunate end is what happens when you associate with the wrong element. The city is no longer safe for our kind of people."

Wow. Talk about cold. That woman could flash-freeze beef. I didn't think I'd ask her what she admired about her daughter-in-law. Oh, why the hell not? "I am sorry for your loss," I said. "Perhaps you could tell me what you admired about Sydney for my story."

"I prefer not to discuss my family in the newspaper. If Sydney had stayed where she belonged, caring for her home and family as a proper wife, this would not have occurred."

She wasn't going to tell me anything. She was going to throw me out in two seconds. Since I had nothing to lose, I answered back. "I thought Sydney tried to do that, until your son threw her out for another woman," I said.

"Cordelia!" commanded Queen Elizabeth. "Please bring Miss Vierling's coat and show her out." The audience was over. Cordelia gave me my coat and the bum's rush, and I was out the door before I knew it. I wondered why Elizabeth had me drive out there. She could have delivered that message by phone.

I went back to work at the *Gazette* and tried to call Hudson at his office. His secretary said he was in a meeting. I started calling every fifteen minutes, which must have driven the woman crazy. Finally, after two hours and eight calls, Hudson himself picked up the phone. "Miss Vierling, do not call here again. I will *not* meet with you. I *will* call your managing editor if you persist in calling my office and badgering my secretary." He hung up. The boy got all his charm from his mother.

No point in calling the son, Hud Junior. I'd better try to track him down in person. It was, of course, twenty minutes away, in Richmond Heights, an older brick neighborhood on the edge of St. Louis. I knocked at the door of the apartment where Endora said Hud was now living, but no one answered. Next I went to the Clayton coffeeshop where she said he worked. It was called Has Beans. It sold the usual array of coffee, sweets, and bottled juice. A long blond wood counter had a collection of crumbs and crumpled napkins and a pile of newspapers and magazines. The place looked like it had had a rush of customers but was suddenly empty. Hud was cleaning up behind the counter. He wore a black-and-brown Has Beans T-shirt. He was a handsome blond kid with dark circles like bruises under his eyes. He didn't look like he'd been getting much sleep. His eyes were red rimmed, and so was his nose. He wiped the crumbed up counter with a kind of twitchy energy, but at the core he seemed listless. Was this someone in deep mourning? Or someone on drugs? I couldn't tell. In the 1980s, I'd worked for an editor at the *Gazette* who was a cokehead. He was also a relative of the managing editor, so nobody did anything about him. The coke gave him a curious flattened personality. The cokehead editor finally went to L.A., to break into movies. Since he didn't have any relatives there, it didn't happen. It took me months to tumble to why my editor had these odd mood swings. I was never any good at figuring this stuff out.

"May I help you?" Hud said politely.

That was my cue. I told him I was doing a story about Sydney.

"Listen," he said desperately, "you can't quote me.

My dad would kill me, and he's already mad at me now."

"I'm sure he's not mad at you," I said, trying to be soothing. "This is a difficult time."

Hud stared at me, as if weighing his options. "Talk to Aunt Jane in Chicago," he said, scribbling a phone number on a coffee-stained napkin. "She'll give you good stories. I can't talk anyway. I feel too bad."

For a minute, he looked like he was going to cry. "I never thought it would turn out this way. I was royally pissed at my mom because she put me in rehab, and I wanted to show her she couldn't run my life, so I moved in with Eric for a while. But I always thought we would make up and I would see her again." Then Hud couldn't stop the tears. "She really did care about me. My father never gave a damn, but she did. Now there's no way I can make it up to her. I wish I were dead, too."

He looked so miserable. I felt so helpless. He was right. Nothing could undo this. He could never tell that broken figure I saw in the alley that he loved her and didn't mean it. But I didn't say that. That would be stupid. Instead, I said something stupider: "The best thing you can do is go back to school and get your degree. That's what your mother wanted more than anything." Hud looked at me but didn't say a word. He blew his nose and wiped his eyes. I felt like an interfering old lady. Two kids in black jeans and T-shirts came in and ordered double espressos.

"I have to go," Hud said. I was glad for an excuse to get out of there. Back in my car, I realized that Hud had told me nothing, just like his father. But the

kid could be a lot slicker than Dad. I felt sorry for
him, and wanted to leave him alone in his grief.

■

Endora said Caroline was Sydney's best friend in St.
Louis. I called Caroline first. She was so terrified I
might ask her to come into the big bad city that she
invited me to her Ladue home. She lived in Fair
Oaks, one of the second-best addresses in Ladue, although it looked pretty snazzy to me. The house was
a brick-and-stone fake Tudor about fifty years old. It
had a slate roof and leaded glass windows and a yard
with fair-size oaks, of all things. Blue pots of bronze
chrysanthemums brightened the front steps.

Caroline answered the door. She could have been
Sydney's sister. She was blonde and very slender. I
could count the bones under her tennis bracelet. She
was wearing an outfit that would have better suited
her daughter: Pappagallo flats, a silk T-shirt, skimpy
A-line skirt that showed off her knobby knees, and a
matching zippered jacket. It was a soft grayish color,
so I guess she was in mourning for her friend.

At first glance, her living room seemed more impressive than Elizabeth's, but even I knew the furniture wasn't as good. It was just better pulled together
by the decorator. It had an Oriental rug about the
size of a school auditorium and a couch longer than
a city bus, except buses weren't upholstered in soft,
silky beige. My South Side soul longed to protect it
with some nice slipcovers. Caroline sat me down on
the couch and asked if she could get me something
to drink.

"Anything but tea," I said.

While she went for Evian water, I struggled to get out of an avalanche of pillows on the couch. There must have been twenty of the things, some as small as a toaster, others almost the size of the couch cushions. After I fought my way free, I started counting all the knickknacks on the little tables nearby: three family photos in flowered silver frames, a Limoges basket filled with potpourri, two pairs of gilded wooden candlesticks, a blue-and-cinnamon porcelain bowl, a millefleur paperweight . . . I was still counting when Caroline returned with my water.

"I am sorry about your friend, Sydney," I began.

"It's been so horrible," she said softly. "None of us can believe it. She was a neighbor, you know. We played golf and tennis at the club and car-pooled our boys to Burroughs. Last December we cochaired the Winter Gala for Greiner's disease. Sydney had fabulous ideas for flowers, just fabulous. We had to have it at this hotel, and the room was dull, dull, dull. But she had the flower centerpieces cascading from the ceiling, and she took those awful hotel chairs with the metal legs and covered them with fabric and then tied the fabric on with contrasting colored bows that picked up the colors in the candles, and it was the most beautiful room you ever saw. Everyone commented on the transformation. It was a super success. Sydney was also good working with the caterers. You never had rubber chicken at any party of hers. And she knew where to buy super things. She bought me that little Moroccan treasure box."

She pointed to a lacquered box on a table where I hadn't counted the things yet.

"But then Hudson said he wanted a divorce, and everything changed," Caroline said, sounding sad. "She wasn't fun anymore. She was angry all the time. She couldn't lunch or shop or anything."

I guess not. If Sydney was being financially destroyed by her husband's lawyer, she probably didn't have money for pretty, pointless bibelots. That Moroccan box might buy a good chunk of a lawyer's time. And if her husband had smashed her perfect life, then Sydney should be angry.

"And that's when you stopped seeing her?" I said. Caroline must have heard the disapproval in my voice.

"I didn't see her much after she started dating that biker," she said defensively. "He had . . . tattoos." Caroline said the word like it was a loathsome disease. "Then Sydney got herself killed. But that's what happens when you go to the city."

I wondered if everyone in Ladue believed that you died if you went to St. Louis. I wondered if anyone really cared about Sydney. Was Sydney worth caring about? So far, all I knew was that the woman was one hell of a shopper. There had to be more. Maybe I was asking frivolous questions. I tried a serious one. "What did you admire most about Sydney?"

Caroline smiled. She was on safe ground again. "Sydney *always* dipped her fork in her salad dressing," she said.

Hey, it's something I'd want on my tombstone.

5

"I never did like that woman," said Sydney's best friend, Jane.

I agreed. I always agree with people who have sharp knives in their hands. Besides, Jane was right. Caroline was a heartless ditz.

"Caroline doesn't have the brains of a zucchini," said Jane, beheading a zucchini on her cutting board, then gutting it, or whatever you do with a dead zucchini. Jane kept telling me this was a simple recipe, but she couldn't fool me. I was in her kitchen. The woman had an asparagus steamer, pudding molds, and a pasta machine. People with hardware like that did not have simple recipes.

"I never did see what Sydney saw in Caroline," Jane said. "But Sydney had the ability to get along with people, even that awful mother-in-law of hers."

Jane gave the zucchini another whack, then began rummaging in the refrigerator like a bear in a park trash can. Her refrigerator was crammed with fruits, vegetables, meats, cheeses, bottles, and jars. I didn't have that much food in my fridge if you totaled its lifetime contents. This could be a long search.

I wandered into the living room and looked at the view of Lake Michigan. The lake stretched out, an endless smoky blue-gray, trimmed with darker gray clouds. Jane's living room seemed a continuation of the view, only warmer. St. Louis still had warm fall days in November, but Chicago was bitter cold. The wind clawed at the windows but didn't get in. I was only an hour by plane from St. Louis—even the ultra-cheap *Gazette* would spring for a one-day trip to Chicago—and Jane was my last chance to get a fix on Sydney for my story. I went back into Jane's kitchen, lured by the good smells. I could see why she was a popular Gold Coast caterer. She was out of the refrigerator now and eviscerating a fat purple eggplant.

"When did you move to Chicago?" I asked.

"Ten years ago," she said. "I refused to be one of the Ladue divorcées who live in genteel poverty in Chevy Chase."

"I heard about that place," I said. "I got so curious I went to see it. In my neighborhood, people could work all their lives and not achieve that kind of poverty."

"Touché," Jane said. "The rich have refined ways of making themselves miserable. There is nothing wrong with Chevy Chase, except I'd have to live there with my friends' pity. But I didn't want to cling to a scaled-down version of my old Ladue existence. I wanted a new life. I'd always liked the energy of Chicago, and my kids were in college. So I moved here.

The nice thing about this city is that anyone, rich or poor, can have an apartment by the lake."

"This section of Lake Shore Drive doesn't look too shabby," I said.

"Oh, it's not," Jane said. "But I didn't live here when I first moved to Chicago. After Rob dumped me, all I had was a small settlement and an outdated degree in English. After years of hosting dinners for Rob, I decided I could make dinner for other people. I went to cooking school and then worked at a caterer's to learn the business. Now I have my own company. I'm still serving dinner, but now I'm paid for it."

Jane looked successful, happy, and twenty pounds heavier than Sydney and Caroline. She was no longer a Ladue lady.

"Do you miss your old life?" I asked her.

"I miss some of my old friends, especially Sydney." Her face started to crumple, but she did not cry. "But she's dead, so it doesn't matter whether I live in St. Louis or not. There were things that I liked about my life there. But I don't miss it."

"What can you tell me about Sydney?" I said. "I don't have a clear picture of her." What I did know made her death seem no great loss.

"Sydney was closer than a sister," Jane said. "We did everything together. We met in college. We were bridesmaids in each other's weddings. We both married St. Louis boys. We both got pregnant the same year and had our boys a month apart. We both did the suburban mom routine together. Because of Rob's law firm, I think I entertained even more than she did. I still remember my first dinner. Rob was up for partner, and he wanted to impress everyone. I tried something exotic—lobster and shiitake mushrooms in puff pastry, and a lovely field greens salad before you could buy field greens at the supermarket. You'd have thought I was trying to poison my dinner guests. The women were all on diets and wouldn't touch the lobster because of the pastry and cream sauce. One of the senior partners picked a baby oak leaf out of the salad. He'd never seen edible oak leaves before. He said, 'So, Rob, did you rake the yard before dinner?' Rob was furious at me. I learned my lesson. Next time I served beef tenderloin and Caesar salad. Rob had the partnership and I had a reputation as a good cook."

Jane set aside the eggplant and began dismembering a chicken. Now I knew why I didn't cook. It was too violent.

"Sydney's dinners were exquisite. She could serve a salad and it looked like a sculpture. Of course, her degree was in interior design. She never had a career, but she would have been good. She paid attention to the details, always. She kept her guest room ready for a constant flow of out-of-town visitors for Hudson's company, and it was lovely—fresh flowers, heated towel bars, Porthault sheets. All her creativity went into these things. You'd say it was wasted, I guess. But we didn't think so back when we got married. The unspoken agreement—and perhaps the problem for women our age was that it was unspoken—was that Sydney would give up her career to help Hudson's career. She made sure their son, Hud, went to the proper schools. She took him to all the games and activities, and attended all the parent-teacher conferences, because Hudson was too busy. She was a very good mother. When she found out their son was using coke at parties, she insisted he go to a drug rehab clinic. Hud Junior was furious. He saw coke as a recreational drug. All his friends used it. She took his drug use seriously. She and the boy were estranged over the rehab issue. Hud dropped out of college, but I always thought it was just for a semester, to scare her. His father promptly cut his allowance until he went back to school. Hud calls me from time to time. I'm still Aunt Jane, and with his mother gone, he needs a shoulder to cry on."

"I tracked him down at Has Beans, the coffeehouse where he works," I said. "He seems pretty upset by his mother's death."

"He is, and his family is no comfort. Hudson is like hugging an iceberg, and Elizabeth is no warmer. That poor boy is alone."

"Do you think he's off drugs?"

"Hud's problems are not for publication," she said, pointing the knife at me. I felt . . . chicken.

"I'm not interested in nailing a kid in the newspaper. But it might help if I knew." Help what, I couldn't say.

"He says he is," Jane said. "I don't know. I hope so. Sydney was miserable when he dropped out of school."

"You said Hud's friends used coke. Is that true?"

"There's a big drug problem in Ladue. You have too many bored kids with too much money."

Jane washed her hands in the sink, as if she were finished not only with the chicken but the whole subject. She arranged a vegetable still-life on the wooden cutting board: four floppy pale-green heads of lettuce, purple onions, weird mushrooms that reminded me of my college days, red tomatoes on a green vine, and a pottery jar of garlic cloves. She peeled the cloves, halved them, and rubbed them on the inside of a wooden salad bowl the size of a small tree trunk. I watched in silence and considered what Jane had told me.

The Sydney she knew was nothing like the tipsy troublemaker I saw at the Leather and Lace Ball. I didn't recognize Caroline's silly spendthrift, either. I couldn't make all these Sydneys match up.

"Is your Sydney the same woman who dipped her fork in her salad dressing and bought cute things that cost a fortune?"

"Oh, she did that, too," Jane said, tearing apart a lettuce head with her bare hands. "A good Ladue wife is obsessed with dieting and shopping. Sydney never gained an ounce, and she could find cute things we couldn't. But she had a serious side. She was a loving mother and a good wife. Not that Hudson noticed. The real woman in his life, at least until he met Brenda, was his mother, Elizabeth, and she ruled the roost."

"Was Sydney in love with Hudson?" I asked. I didn't know how anyone could be.

"I'm not sure," Jane said. "They'd been married a long time. I thought Hudson was short-tempered and demanding, and probably drank too much. Sydney made excuses for him. She said he wasn't like that when they were first married. She said his mother spoiled him and his secretary kowtowed to him. She said his bad behavior wasn't his fault, because Hudson was under pressure at work. I thought she was too tolerant, as usual.

"I know Sydney would have stayed with Hudson. She liked their life and she liked their money, and she lived with the hope that he'd change back into the man she imagined she married. But one day Hudson came home and announced he wanted a divorce."

"To marry Brenda the lawyer, right?"

Jane rolled her eyes and ripped into more lettuce. "I saw her only once, but I heard all about her. Brenda was ten years younger, ten pounds heavier, and six inches taller than Sydney. Brenda didn't diet. She drank beer—an exotic act for a woman in Ladue. To me she looked like a man-stealing yuppie, but Hudson found her wildly exciting.

"Sydney was stunned when Hudson said he wanted a divorce. She was paralyzed. She pretended nothing had happened for the longest time. Sydney believed Hudson would come to his senses and drop Brenda. Meanwhile, Hudson hired a divorce shark to make sure that Sydney got nothing. He was cruel. He declared war on his own wife."

Jane declared war on a tomato, savagely slicing until the cutting board ran red.

"Sydney was helpless," she said. "She didn't know how to fight. She was a woman who believed in the system, and it betrayed her. Her husband and his bloodsucking lawyer wanted to strip her of everything. Until it happens to you, you can't understand what it's like. There are rich wives who wind up homeless, literally living under a bridge after their divorce."

"Don't they have lawyers?"

"Hah!" Jane said, slashing another tomato. "Lawyers are part of the problem. A divorce for someone in Sydney's circumstances can cost thirty thousand dollars or more. A woman can go bankrupt trying to pay off her own lawyer.

"The first thing Hudson did was cripple her financially. He made sure she couldn't get her hands on their joint assets. Before he announced the divorce, the sneak cleaned out their safety deposit box, although she didn't know this until later. She couldn't find any of their salable stocks and bonds, the deed to their place in the country, anything. Sydney was sure he was hiding their assets, but she didn't hire an equally aggressive lawyer to fight him. She didn't know how to find one. At first, she treated her husband's betrayal as if it were some terrible failure on her part. She was too ashamed to talk to other women who'd been divorced. We could have steered her to someone good. Instead, she got Elliott Tedley. She knew him from their dinner parties. Elliott talked a good game, but he was not a fighter. He knew Hudson had the money, so Hudson would have the power. Elliott could have asked the judge to have Hudson pay Sydney's legal fees. But Elliott didn't want to upset Hudson. Then he wouldn't be invited to the Vander Venter parties.

"The final blow came at a meeting in Hudson's lawyer's office. Sydney called me in tears and told me all about it. If she'd called me earlier, I could have helped her. At the meeting, Hudson's attorney announced he had canceled all Sydney's charge accounts and put their joint checking account in

Hudson's name. This left her with no money to fight back. He said Sydney would be given a small cash settlement and a little alimony for two years, until she was 'rehabilitated.' Then, when she was self-supporting, Sydney would get no other money. After all, Hudson's business was not doing well.

"Sydney sat there in the lawyer's office, speechless. Then she said, 'Rehabilitated? Like I'm some kind of . . . of convict? And then I'll be turned loose to go to work when other women my age have had a twenty-five-year start on their careers, and I've been at home? You owe me more than that, Hudson. I never asked for this divorce. I gave up my career to advance yours. You owe me.'

"Hudson said, 'I owe you nothing. And that's what I have to give you. I am simply an employee of the firm with a few shares of stock. Mother is the main stockholder, and my partners are the other major shareholders. Mother is the real investment genius in the family. You don't even deserve what you're getting. You sat on your ass for twenty-five years while I supported you in style.'

"Sydney said, 'You couldn't have had a career if I didn't take care of our son. You wouldn't have been able to travel if I didn't stay home with him when he was sick, and car-pool him to school, and . . .'

"Hudson interrupted with 'And you did a fine job. The damned kid's a dropout and a drug addict.'

"She said, 'Because his father was never home!'

" 'Oh, spare me the cheap psychology,' Hudson said. 'There is no money, and that's that. You can't get blood from a stone.'

" 'Turnip,' Sydney said. 'It's blood from a turnip.

And if the business is doing so badly, why use it to lease a BMW and a Lexus, travel to Europe, pay our club dues, and buy season tickets to the Opera Theatre and the symphony?'

" 'Those are legitimate business expenses,' he said, 'but you'd never understand that because you've never taken any interest in the business.'

"Before she could answer, her lawyer, the gentlemanly Elliott, took her aside. He counseled her to accept Hudson's offer and not upset him, or she would get even less. This made Sydney even angrier. Hudson was lying. He had plenty of money. She knew it and he knew it, but she would have to spend her money to prove it. Elliott was flapping around telling her not to get angry or Hudson's attorney could use her blowups against her. You'd be surprised how many male divorce judges think women are unstable.

"Elliott's advice only fueled Sydney's fury. She'd been fired from her life, like a maid who dropped the china.

"Sydney left that meeting seething. She couldn't believe Hudson had really canceled all her charge accounts. But then she called around. They were all gone. Except for one. Hudson forgot Botanicals on the Park, the fashionable florist on the South Side. Sydney was one Ladue lady who actually braved the city. She drove to Botanicals and bought six thousand dollars' worth of fabulous things. There were so many, and I can remember only a few of them. I know she bought a dozen damask throw pillows at sixty dollars a pop. A Sheffield rug. Porcelain vases, bowls and plates, at one hundred dollars apiece. Rat-

tan chairs and ornamental tables. A pine cupboard—
that was over a thousand dollars right there. Mirrors
with gold-leaf frames, cut-glass rose bowls, a darling
footstool trimmed with tassels. She thought of everything, even potpourri and scented candles, place
mats and napkins. She had fun things, too. I remember a sweet little monkey lamp, lion sconces, and the
most luxurious leopard throw."

"Sounds like a real zoo," I said.

"You're laughing, but this was her revenge on Hudson: one last superb shopping spree. Then she drove
up and down the streets on the South Side, until she
saw an apartment she liked on Juniata, just west of
Grand. She rented it on the spot. She had a little
money from her trust fund, and Hudson couldn't get
that. She furnished her whole place from Botanicals,
except for the bed and some other necessities, and
Hudson had to pay for it. She even sent herself bou-
quets of fresh flowers—until the first bill came, and
Hudson closed that charge, too. Many of her friends
wouldn't go to her new home because it was in the
city, but I stayed there on a visit to St. Louis. I
thought it was an interesting area, with lots of little
shops, ethnic restaurants, and coffeehouses. Naturally, her lawyer had advised her against moving out
of their house in Ladue, but Sydney had had enough
of Elliott's advice.

"After the spending spree and the apartment hunt,
she went to Uncle Bob's Pancake House, a few blocks
away. She had read about this twenty-four-hour
gathering place where interesting people eat themselves into a syrup-induced stupor. Sydney was determined to experience so-called real life."

"Is that where she met Jack? I wondered how she stumbled across him."

"She told me how she met him. She was in a rebellious mood. She went to Uncle Bob's and did what no Ladue woman would do: She ordered a Belgian waffle, dripping with whipped cream and butter. That was more calories than Sydney eats in a week.

"Then, having committed the ultimate Ladue sin, Sydney flirted with this guy at the next table. He took her for a ride on his Harley. They literally rode off into the sunset together. Sydney was entranced. A week later Jack moved in with her. Jack sounded sleazy to me, even through her glowing descriptions. She may have even loaned him money, but she never told me straight out. It was just an impression I got. I didn't care for Jack, but he had to be more fun than a stick like Hudson."

I was beginning to have some sympathy for this Sydney. But what about the Sydney I saw? I asked Jane, "Your friend Sydney sounds like a fine person. Why did she behave like such a jerk at the Leather and Lace Ball, chasing every man there?"

"Have you ever been divorced?" Jane asked.

"Nope, I've never been married," I said. Not likely to be, either. Jane hit my sore spot.

"Then you can't understand. You go through this period of about six months where you go crazy, absolutely crazy. Inside, you're bleeding all over your soul. Outside, you're acting like a slut, sleeping with every man you meet, including the dishwasher repairman, the meter reader, and guys you pick up in bars. You can't believe you're behaving this way, and you can't stop. Then, one day, if you're really lucky and you don't meet Mr. Goodbar, you wake up and wonder who you are, and who is this strange man in your bed, and change back into your old self.

"Sydney was still in the bleeding-all-over stage. She had this image of bikers as wild, and so she acted wilder."

"She acted stupid," I said. "She acted like a rich idiot. You don't go after another woman's date." I sounded surprisingly bitter.

"Francesca," Jane said mildly. "How would your friends act at one of Sydney's perfect little dinner parties? In Ladue, their clothes would look just as garish as hers did at the biker ball. When they started drinking Busch beer and telling jokes, they would seem just as crude. She didn't belong in their world, and they wouldn't belong in hers. She was just in a stage, a passing phase. I knew in a few months Sydney the tough-talking biker chick would go away, and Sydney my sweet, sensible friend would return.

"Already, Sydney was starting to make good decisions. First, she fired her lawyer. Elliott had the nerve to send her a bill for five thousand dollars for two months' work. Work! The man did nothing but cringe in front of Hudson and charge her for it. I knew a thing or two about lawyers' bills. I noticed a lot of initials, and realized he'd put three other lawyers on her case. Then they charged her for sitting around and talking about her. I asked if she'd authorized three more lawyers, and of course she hadn't. I got her bill cut in half. Then I talked her into retaining Susan Huddlan, a feminist attorney. Susan excelled at going after husbands like Hudson and finding their hidden assets, and she wasn't interested in dinner at the Vander Venters.

"Sydney and Susan demanded more information about the firm. Hudson insisted that it was privately held and he didn't have to release anything. Sydney combed through old credit card bills and income tax returns, looking for clues. Two days before she died, she called me. She was so excited. She found out her husband had been making frequent trips to a safety deposit box at another bank. She couldn't get into the box, but she had an idea he was using it to hide some assets. She had another lead, too. Hudson claimed that he was an employee and his mother was the principal stockholder in the firm. Sydney thought Hudson had used an elaborate series of devious transactions to transfer most of his shares to his mother, so he could be only a salaried employee. Sydney was on that paper trail."

"How'd she find out about it?"

"She wouldn't tell me. She said it wasn't good for me to know. The last time I talked with Sydney was the day she died," Jane said. "She said her problems were going to be over soon. She and her lawyer had this really tough strategy. They were getting ready to subpoena Hudson's partners for their financial information. That would have been intensely embarrassing for someone as private as Hudson. He couldn't stand to have his partners dragged into his marital problems. Sydney was sure he would hand over the financial information she needed for a fair divorce settlement. She said she had a 'breakthrough' thanks to her boyfriend, Jack. She thought that was funny.

She giggled every time she said the word break-through."

"Do you think she meant break-in?" I said, remembering Jack's somewhat doubtful occupation.

"I doubt it. Everything at Hudson's firm was on computers. Jack was a whiz with engines, but I don't think he knew much about computers. She didn't, either.

"I told her to be careful. I thought she was playing a dangerous game. She wouldn't take me seriously. She said, 'Relax. It's in the can.' Those were her last words to me—'It's in the can.' Then she laughed."

"Do you think Hudson murdered his wife to avoid an embarrassing divorce?"

Jane quit cutting to consider the question. "Hudson? He was mean and cold, but I don't think he had the guts to murder anyone—particularly not the way Sydney was murdered. Too messy. I could see him hiring someone to kill her, though. Hudson thought he could buy his way out of anything."

Jane's words seemed to carry more weight with a knife in her hand. But I had to cut and run. I had just enough time to catch my flight, if I caught a cab now. I thanked her and dashed outside into the cold.

My plane flew back through the same gray-blue clouds I had admired from Jane's window. When I was in them, they quickly lost their appeal. The plane creaked, bucked, and bounced, and once it dropped like a stone, for I don't know how many feet. People screamed, drinks spilled, and a baby cried. I wished I could howl right along with the kid. I was scared, and not afraid to admit it. The seat belt sign never went off the whole time. The flight attendants quickly threw our overturned drink glasses into plastic bags and buckled themselves in for the duration of the seventy-minute flight. I hung on to my chair arms, as if that would hold the plane up in the air, and tried to distract myself by thinking about my talk with Jane. The interview was difficult, personally as well as professionally.

Jane had given me the clearest motive for murder yet: Sydney was about to embarrass her husband. She would hit him where it hurt most—in the wallet. Hours after she told Jane that she had the information to nail Hudson, Sydney was dead.

I was haunted by her story. Sydney's husband had set out to destroy her after twenty-five years of marriage. He was a respected businessman. He could have made a decent settlement if he wanted to get out of their marriage, but he turned on his wife like a hungry rat. What made a man do that? How could a woman tell? How could I tell?

Lyle wanted me to marry him. I loved him, but how did I know he wouldn't turn out like Hudson? What guarantee did I have? The promises made at the altar? They sure didn't help Sydney. And Lyle wondered why I was afraid to get married. Sydney's story just confirmed what I already knew: A wedding was an invitation to death and disaster. For my parents, marriage was a nightmare. My nightmare.

If you live in St. Louis, you probably know the story: When I was nine years old, my mother killed my father and then shot herself. I found them when I came home from school. I knew things were wrong because my dad's car was in the driveway, and he never got home this early. Also, the back door was unlocked. I walked in and heard this odd drip, drip, drip sound, like a leaking faucet. There was no one downstairs. That was wrong, too. Usually about that time of day, Mom was fixing dinner, and she had the TV or the radio going. I called their names as I went upstairs. The drip sound came from Mom and Dad's bedroom. I wondered if it was a busted pipe.

I kept calling their names, but no one answered. I went in their room. The drip sound was blood, dripping off the light fixture. Dad's, I think. They were both lying on the bed, and at first I thought Mom had a new red bedspread. Then I realized it was blood. Their blood. Dad had been having an affair with my mother's best friend, Marcy, and Mom went kind of crazy when she discovered them together at a New Year's Eve party. I thought when Marcy and her husband, Tom, moved away, Mom would stop screaming at Dad, but she only seemed to get madder. She screamed and screamed and . . . Suddenly I realized the person screaming was me, and I was running in the street and a neighbor came out and caught me.

After that the police came, and then the newspaper and TV reporters. My parents' deaths became a big scandal—a suburban fantasy gone horribly wrong. There was even a picture of me that ran in *Life* magazine. It showed me at their grave, in my little blue coat. Everyone thought I looked heartbroken. My big secret was that I was glad they were dead. My mother took out her rage at my father's infidelities on me. I learned early that the way to fight back was not to cry when she hit me. It made her crazy. Once she beat me with a hairbrush until it broke but I never cried, not once. She did. When the brush broke, she threw herself on the floor and sobbed. I watched her. I felt triumphant. I knew I'd won. I also knew that the bond between us was broken forever. I was five years old.

I loved living with my grandparents. They didn't drink like Mom and Dad, or have bad fights. Grandma never hit me like Mom did, or make me wear my cousin Linda's castoff clothes. The South Side was much more interesting than the suburb I grew up in. So I lived with Grandma and Grandpa happily ever after. Except for the dreams that started with the dripping, dripping, dripping . . .

Something was dripping on me now, something warm and sticky, and I felt the scream rising in my throat. Then the sandy-haired businessman wedged in the seat next to me said, "I am so sorry. My bourbon spilled when the plane gave that last lurch. I should have turned in my glass when the flight attendant came down the aisle, but I needed a drink on this flight."

I could tell by his glowing nose that he needed a lot of drinks. I told him it was okay, and it was. This suit was going to the cleaners, anyway. Then I went back to brooding. Lyle said everyone wasn't like my parents, and our marriage could work. But what about Sydney and Hudson? He wanted to marry another woman, so he tried to ruin Sydney financially. He may have even killed her.

What chance did I have with Lyle, when better matches than ours fell apart? Sydney and Hudson had everything going for them: a common background, money, education, connections, plus a bright, handsome son, and yet their marriage failed. Lyle and I were so different. He had family money and went to private schools. I had a blue-collar background, a state school education, and an ugly scandal in my past. How could we live together happily ever after after that? How could I give up my independence and my apartment? Okay, my grandparents' apartment. I hadn't changed a thing since their deaths. Even the plaster fish blowing gold bubbles in the bath were the same ones Grandma dusted. No matter how much I loved Lyle, that apartment was my retreat, my safe place, and I couldn't give it up. Not even to marry him.

The captain interrupted my thoughts with an announcement. "Ladies and gentlemen, we apologize for the bumpy ride today. We'll be on the ground in about ten minutes. . . ."

I just hoped we would be on the ground in one piece. Right now, my love life was as bumpy as this flight. Lyle and I made up after the Leather and Lace Ball, but things weren't quite the same between us since that night. We still seemed slightly out of sync. But he was meeting me at the airport, and I was glad.

When the plane finally touched down at Lambert International Airport, the passengers applauded. I found my briefcase, pulled my coat out of the overhead compartment, and tried to straighten my suit. The skirt had more wrinkles than a sharpei puppy, my jacket was sticky from my seat mate's sloshed drink, and I stank of fear and spilled bourbon. I didn't care. I just wanted to go home and take a shower.

Lyle was waiting for me at the gate. He folded me

in his arms and kissed me as if I'd been away for a week.

"This *is* a welcome home," I said.

"I've been thinking," he said. "You're right. I've taken you for granted. So tonight I'm making this a romantic evening."

I smiled and hugged him, but all I could think was "What bad timing." I'd never felt less romantic. Lyle talked all the way to the West End, telling me funny stories about his students and his neighbors. We could always talk to each other, even during the worst times. The lights were on at his town house, and it looked warm and inviting. He unlocked the door, and his big gray cat, Montana, greeted me solemnly. Monty had green-gold eyes and a perpetually worried expression. I didn't think I liked cats, but I liked him. I dropped my briefcase and scratched his ears and tail until he twirled around happily. Lyle stood there patiently until I looked up and saw a dozen red roses on the dining-room table.

"Red roses," I said. "My favorite."

But I felt oddly disconnected, as if someone else were admiring them. Lyle lit candles and popped the cork on a bottle of cold champagne. "Sit down," he said, and I plopped down on his couch. Monty curled up next to us and purred. Lyle kissed me again. He tasted of coffee and champagne, but he must have noticed I wasn't responding, because he stopped and said, "What's the matter?"

"I'm sorry. Bad flight. I'm not much fun tonight." Lyle studied me, looking concerned. Monty jumped up in my lap and looked worried, too.

"You need food," Lyle said. "I should have realized

that. I have some of my special tenderloin. Would you like me to fix you dinner?"

I realized I wanted to go home and see him another night, but I didn't say that. "Not a whole meal," I said. "Just a sandwich." He made one big enough to feed everyone on the plane from Chicago. So when he wasn't looking I took it apart, reassembled it, and slipped most of the meat to Monty under the table.

Lyle brought out coffee and strawberries and more champagne. I poked at the strawberries and let the coffee go cold and the champagne go flat while Lyle carried on the conversation. I listened with half an ear. Until I heard him say "Francesca, I know you're tired, and I promised myself that I wouldn't bother you with this question, but I have to know. I can't stay in limbo like this. I love you. I want you. I'll make you happy. Will you marry me?"

I wanted so badly to say yes. But I was so afraid. How could I trust him? My father wasn't faithful. Jane's husband dumped her. Sydney's husband wanted to destroy her, and maybe he succeeded. No man seemed faithful. I loved Lyle, I really did. I just didn't feel safe. The silence hung between us. I could have said I loved him and I was frightened. I could have told him about my grim interview with Jane. I could have said this wasn't a good time to ask. Instead, I blurted out, "Do I have to give up my apartment?"

Lyle recoiled as if I'd slapped him. His face reddened and his mouth tightened. "Yes," he said impatiently. "It's time to let go of living in the past."

"I can't," I wailed, and I sounded so desperate,

Monty came over and brushed against my hand to reassure me. Lyle did not. He sounded exasperated.

"You can't because you don't want to," he snapped. "You want to spend the rest of your life mourning parents who didn't love you."

"My grandparents loved me," I said, sounding more like a contrary child than a woman. Monty paced back and forth between Lyle and me, looking worried.

"Your parents didn't," Lyle insisted. "Congratulations. You've re-created your family. You've managed to duplicate their lack of love by working for the *Gazette*—a paper you make richer while it treats you as badly as your parents did. Your editors are jealous of your success and do everything to hold you back."

"But my readers love me," I said. I sounded pathetic. I was too big to whimper.

"Like your grandparents, they are beside the point," he said brutally. "When are you going to wake up?"

"Right now," I said. I could feel my fury rising, wiping out my fear. "You want me to give up everything I care about. Maybe *you're* the jealous one. I'm the celebrity. No one ever heard of you. I'm not going to quit my career and keep house for you. I can't live without my work."

"I'm not asking that," Lyle said, raising his voice. "I want you to stop clinging to the things that hurt you. You're talented. You can work anywhere. Leave this city where everyone knows your past. Leave this loser newspaper. Go where you're appreciated. I'll follow you. I'll go anywhere you want."

"Then go to hell," I screamed back. "I don't need

your pop psychology. Quit practicing psychiatry
without a license. Your degree is in English."

Monty stood between us and meowed loudly. We
ignored him. I grabbed my coat and my briefcase
and stormed out of Lyle's place. He didn't try to stop
me. He didn't say anything. He turned his back on
me and walked out of the room. I let myself out and
slammed the door. I walked for several chilly blocks
before I realized I didn't have a car. Fortunately, the
Inn at the Park was nearby. I found a cab there and
directed the driver to take me home.

Home. Home to the South Side, where I belonged.
Home to the familiar comfort of my grandparents'
apartment. Lyle and I were finished. I didn't need any
man. I didn't need marriage. I didn't need anyone. I
wrapped myself in my grandmother's brown-and-
yellow afghan and cried myself to sleep.

6

The next morning I felt dead. I even looked dead. After a night of restless sleep, my skin had a corpse-green tinge, which set off the bright-red zit on my nose. But I guessed the zit was proof I was alive, no matter how dead I felt. Dead people don't get pimples. They also don't get bags under their eyes and puffy red eyelids from crying. Damn Lyle. He wasn't worth crying about. I wished my burning anger could dry up my tears.

Since I felt half dead, I might as well spend some time with people who were all dead. I'd try for a morning at the morgue. I had to know if Sydney's autopsy revealed anything about her killer. I was in luck. Cutup Katie, a pathologist who'd helped me out at the medical examiner's office on another case, had assisted at Sydney's autopsy. Katie's boss did the autopsy on a celebrity like Sydney, but Katie was there to assist. She invited me to the autopsy, but I refused. The cops had to tough out autopsies, but I didn't. I knew I'd disgrace myself and pass out. I offered to take Katie to lunch to talk about the results, but the local citizenry had been industriously stabbing and shooting one another, and Katie couldn't break free for several days. This morning I called her again to bug her for an interview.

"If you can get here in twenty minutes, I can talk to you for a while," Katie said.

Of course I could get there in twenty minutes. Everything in St. Louis was twenty minutes away, and if it wasn't, we didn't go there. I'd even have time to rummage in the refrigerator for breakfast. I found a jar of garlic cloves, a bottle of ketchup, and a grapefruit. I'd eat the grapefruit and get a healthy start on my day. I picked it up, and my thumb went through the squishy skin. One side was green with mold. So much for a healthy start, unless you counted the penicillin growing on the grapefruit. Well, I'd skip breakfast. I wasn't hungry, and there would be less to hurl—always a consideration for a morning at the morgue.

I'd better call my office. I got Louise, the Family department secretary, and told her where I'd be that morning. I could almost see her comfortable middle-age body and home-permed hair hunched over the phone and her morning mug of coffee.

"The morgue? What an awful way to start your day," she said. Louise was always sympathetic.

"Going to the *Gazette* would be even worse," I said.

"You got that right. The publisher's secretary told me Charlie may announce more changes today, and I should watch out. I'm worried."

"You? Louise, you run that department. Why should you worry?"

"Everybody here worries these days."

"The body count is piling up," I said. "I just want to survive this next round. But I'm sure you're safe." Her phone started ringing again, and Louise hung up quickly. I used to love the newspaper business. Now, with all the changes, the newsroom was as jittery as a bunch of junkies who couldn't score. The camaraderie was gone. The staff was worried and surly, and utterly without hope.

I put on some makeup and a dark suit that made me look like an undertaker's assistant. Ugh. I took off the white blouse and put on a red blouse that matched my eyes. If I didn't force some color in my face, someone at the morgue would shove me in a drawer and put a tag on my toe. I drove downtown in a daze, trying not to think about Lyle or the turmoil at the *Gazette*. The day was damp and cold as a tomb, and low-hanging gray clouds added to the gloom. At least traffic was light. I found a parking spot on the city lot next to a lumbering gold car that reminded me of Lyle's beloved gold tank, Sherman. This car had a bad case of cancerous rust, and I felt a malicious glee, as if it were eating Lyle's body instead of the car's. What was the matter with me?

The first thing that hit me about the morgue was the smell. It was a hospital odor mixed with strong disinfectant and a faint hint of spoiled meat that I knew was not somebody's old sandwich. The guard showed me to Katie's office, a grand word for a closet with a desk. Katie would join me shortly, he said. I opened her door carefully, hoping I'd see nothing gray and creepy floating in glass jars. I couldn't face pickled diseased organs and dead babies.

Katie's small room was soothingly ordinary. There were fat, dignified brown and red medical books on shelves, framed diplomas and honor society certificates on the walls, a golf putter in the corner, a potted plant on the desk. No jars of preserved innards. No fleshless skulls or stray bones. Nothing unusual except one shelf with a curious combination of everyday objects: three toy trucks, a hot sauce bottle with a broken string around the neck, a vibrator, a bed knob, a light bulb, and a 1950s blond wood chair leg with a big screw at the end.

I was examining the chair leg when Katie came in the door. Katie called herself plain, but she was too smart and funny to fit that description. She was about thirty-five, with brown eyes, short brown hair, and a sturdy, muscular build. Katie was a country girl who drove a pickup and liked to play pool and golf. She was embarrassed about the golf, because it was such a doctor cliché. At least she refused to join a private club. She played on the city course.

Katie had only one major fault. She forgot the effect her job had on civilians. Today her lab coat was covered with brownish-red stains that made my stomach leap up and bounce off my rib cage. I started babbling so I wouldn't think about what fluids were coloring her coat. I pointed the chair leg, screw-end first, at the odd accumulation on the shelf.

"What do these have to do with medicine?" I asked.

"Oh, that's my collection of weird items removed from rectums," she said. "I did some time in the emergency room. You wouldn't believe what people get stuck in their lower anatomy and then have to go to the hospital to have removed."

I thought about where that chair leg had been and dropped it on the shelf with a shudder. I wondered what a six-inch hook-and-ladder truck could do.

"Nobody died from this stuff?"

"Nope. Not unless you can die of embarrassment. But it was touch and go with the hot sauce bottle. If that broke, the guy would have been mighty unhappy."

"Maybe we should talk about Sydney's autopsy. It might be less disgusting."

Katie fished a file from her desk. "Give me a minute to look this over," she said. "I want to get the facts straight. These celebrities can come back to haunt you."

"Especially in your line of work," I said, but Katie was immune to death puns. She skimmed the autopsy report and then started talking about Sydney.

"Someone was sure angry with her," Katie said. "She was attacked with a motorcycle drive chain, which was found next to the body. It made a nasty weapon. My guess is the victim was caught by surprise and hit upside the head first, which stunned her. She recovered enough to try to fight back. But by that time the killer was whipping that chain around pretty fast—maybe thirty or forty miles an hour. The victim had serious front and side damage to her skull. It looks like the killer got a lucky shot and drove the nasal cartilage right up through her brain, which probably killed her. But the victim also had considerable damage to the right temple. Either injury is fatal, and whoever did it kept beating her after death. There's not much left of what used to be a fairly pretty face. Good face-lift, too. Anyway, the woman's death was violent. It takes the big three to get someone this mad: sex, drugs, and money."

"Must be sex," I said. "That family has plenty of money."

"There's never enough," Katie said. "Especially if you're rich. The victim may have been rich, but she didn't live well. She was malnourished."

"You're kidding. She lived in Ladue. Nobody goes hungry there."

"She did," Katie said. "She was too thin."

"You can't be too rich or too thin," I said. "Thin is healthy."

"Not that thin. Did you ever see how skinny her arms were? The woman barely had enough muscle to swing a tennis racket. She didn't have any strength to fight off her attacker. She couldn't run much, either. She had bird legs. I've seen parakeets with more meat on them. You could see the bones in her legs and the cartilage in her knees. Heck, her knees were bigger than her tits. They're the only things that stuck out on that woman. I call that too thin.

"There was almost no fat on her organs, another bad sign. Also, her liver was atrophic and yellow."

"What's that mean?" Sydney's organs sounded like they would be rejected by the better class of supermarket.

"It had shrunk to half its normal size. I had the top half of her body X-rayed and found accelerated bone loss for her age. She had the beginnings of osteoporosis. In twenty years, her Escada outfits would be hiding a dowager's hump. Her face, what was left of it, had too many lines in it for her age. The woman had too much sun and not enough food. Her stomach was empty. It must have been that way often."

"She lived on salads. Her friend said she always dipped her fork in her salad dressing. It was a skill I wanted to master."

"Forget it, Francesca," Katie said. "The woman was a fashion victim. What her diet was doing to her insides wasn't pretty."

Katie looked at her watch. "Time for me to go back to work," she said.

Me, too. But I couldn't face the *Gazette* yet. Maybe I should add some healthful fats to my diet at Uncle Bob's. I didn't want face wrinkles. I could try something really daring—a pecan Belgian waffle. But I'd have to act quickly when I got on the parking lot, or I'd be eating my usual scrambled egg and toast. I pulled into a parking slot under the kitchen window and knocked on it until Tom the cook looked up.

"Tom, no egg today. I want a pecan Belgian waffle," I said.

"I've prayed for this day," Tom said. "I knew you'd order real food sometime instead of that skinny-ass egg. You eat like an old lady, Francesca."

"I've changed. Give me the biggest waffle in the house. Bring on the butter and the syrup."

Tom smiled. Nothing makes a cook happier than someone who eats. By the time I sat down in a booth, Marlene was coming out of the kitchen with a hot, puffy waffle topped with a full ice-cream scoop of whipped butter. She set it on my table, along with a pitcher of warm syrup. As I poured the syrup and watched it puddle into the waffle holes, Marlene said, "What's the reason for the change? First time I've ever seen you order anything but your egg and toast."

"I spent the morning at the morgue hearing about a dead woman who was too rich and too thin," I said.

"Neither one is my problem," Marlene said, running her hands over her generous hips.

"I was afraid I wouldn't get to Tom in time," I said. "It's tough being a regular here. You choose your usual, and you have to be faithful to it for life. Well, I am about to stray." I picked up my fork, ready to plunge into the golden syrupy goodness.

"Speaking of faithful, Mayhew was in earlier this morning asking for you," Marlene said. I thought I detected disapproval in her voice. I put my fork down.

"We've been talking about a story, Marlene."

"All he could talk about was those leather pants you wore."

"I was working."

"At what?" Her sarcasm dripped like the maple syrup.

"Jeez, Marlene, I was at the Leather and Lace Ball. Then Sydney Vander Venter was killed and I was one of the people who found her body. Mayhew interviewed me about it, and I talked with him about the story I have to do on Sydney."

"He's married, Francesca. He has two darling little girls."

"I know that."

"Well, he forgets. Especially after he solved that last big murder. His name was all over radio and TV and now he's a big deal. I always suspected he fooled around, but he kept it quiet. Now he's bringing his girlfriends into Uncle Bob's. Had that trampy-looking blond Sheila in here the other morning. It makes me mad. Upsets some of the other waitresses, too. They go to church with his wife. She's a sweet woman. It's disgusting."

"My interest in Mayhew is strictly professional," I said, looking at my waffle with longing.

She raised one eyebrow. "Yeah? I've seen you eye him like you're eyeing that waffle. I'd say you're both looking for trouble."

That did it. I wasn't going to sit there and be accused of adultery before noon. I threw down my napkin and some money. "I can leave them both alone," I said, in one of the stupidest exit lines of my life.

I left the waffle untouched, grabbed my coat and my briefcase, and flounced out, furious at my old friend. It was not my week for long-term relationships. As the door shut, I heard Marlene say "Francesca, wait . . . what's the matter with you?"

■

I should have waited. Instead, I went to the *Gazette* on an empty stomach, always a mistake. Charlie's latest announcements had been posted, probably right after I talked with Louise. The newsroom had time to settle back into its usual sullen self. The staff had already discussed the current changes—or they were too afraid to say any more at the office. Only a small knot of people was still gathered around the bulletin board by the men's room, where the new changes were posted. No one said anything. I started reading. The first change on the list looked good. Grady, the son of a nasty and long-retired *Gazette* managing editor, had been given the title of ultimate doom—Director of Special Projects. Good. Translated, that meant Grady had six months to get his résumé together and get out. The *Gazette* was infested with relatives of old editors. Most were snotty and superior, and forgot they didn't get their jobs on their innate talent. But they were an obedient bunch. They always did what management told them, no matter how slimy the task. Following orders must be genetic. I wouldn't miss Grady.

But there was more news, and it was bad. A respected political reporter was taking early retirement. So was an editorial writer who had the guts to stand up to Charlie.

One name jumped out at me. Louise, mainstay of the Family section, was being transferred to the morgue, effective immediately. Charlie was getting rid of Louise? She ran our department. She kept track of the staff. She always had our vacation paychecks on time. She handled countless irate readers with courtesy. She warned us when Charlie was on the warpath. And now she was being sent to the morgue, where the newspaper files were kept. What an insane move. Louise didn't know computers, and at fifty-five she'd have a hard time learning them. This was a terrible mistake.

I was so upset by Louise, I'd overlooked another name on the list. Albers, head of the Family copy desk, was taking early retirement. Albers smoked a pipe that smelled like a burning landfill and bored young interns with tales of his Pulitzer Prize–nominated investigation of the Grey Gates Inn nursing home "when I was a young cub reporter like you, thirty years ago, heh, heh." But Albers sent six people to prison for cheating the elderly residents. He was an old-time newspaper man, and he handled my copy with care.

Who was taking Albers's place? Did I even need to look for the name? There it was—Peggy. She'd won. She'd gotten rid of Albers. I studied the list again. It didn't look like she'd nailed the other decent copy editor yet. Monahan had survived this cut. As I headed toward the Family section, I didn't hear the sounds of joyous celebration at Peggy's promotion. I heard what I always heard since Peggy joined us—a loud, ugly fight. This one was about my column. I'd had a funny interview with the mayor. He talked about almost getting arrested as a teenager because he tied up rush-hour traffic on Kingshighway with a Chinese fire drill. Did kids still jump out of the car at a stop light, run around it, and jump back in? We used to think it was hilarious at sixteen.

"And I still say *Chinese fire drill* is offensive to our Asian readers," Peggy was saying, in her shrill voice.

"And I still say that's ridiculous," Monahan shouted back. "You've carried political correctness to the point of stupidity. But I know how we can settle it. I have a friend who grew up on mainland China. He runs a restaurant now in my neighborhood. You can ask him if the term is offensive."

"So what?" Peggy sneered. "It would be only one male opinion. There are quite a few other Asians, you know."

"It's hard to poll more than a billion Chinese people by press time," I said, butting into the argument. It was my column Peggy was going to mutilate.

"I think I better take that section out to be safe," Peggy said.

"God forbid we actually say something in this newspaper," I said. "If it goes, I'll take it out myself. You're way too thorough at removal."

She glared at me and tossed her hair. She knew she'd just been insulted. She'd already forced out one good copy editor. Now she was going for two. The staff's name for Peggy was Cruella, for Cruella de Vil. She once condemned three Dalmatian puppies to almost certain death in the animal shelter gas chamber when she pulled their "Pet Pick of the Week" photo to run the picture of a hunky surfer. Peggy had long red nails and dead black hair like Cruella, but she was much plumper. She was tightly packed into glamorous clothes that looked ridiculous on her. She wore chubby heels like a cartoon character.

Cruella thought of herself as a sex symbol. She did sleep with a lot of men, mostly married ones. Charlie and our former managing editor, Hadley Harris, had both done the deed with her. So had a *Gazette* ad salesman who strayed when his wife was out of town. The salesman ungallantly told Babe, our gossip columnist, that Cruella was a flop in the sack, but it could be he simply wasn't inspired that night.

All this would be funny, if she wasn't forcing out good people. Peggy was ambitious, but she aimed low. God knows why, but she wanted to be head of the Family copy desk. Doing the horizontal bop with Charlie and Hadley had helped, but that wasn't enough. She wanted her own people on the desk. To get them, she had to get rid of two veterans, Albers and Monahan, and both were too close to retirement to fire. Peggy loaded Albers and Monahan down with work, criticized them constantly, and made them work holidays, deftly shifting their schedules so they were never paid overtime. Three months ago Albers inherited a little money from his mother. Now he was taking early retirement. One down, one to go.

Monahan was made of sterner stuff. He was a real war correspondent, a tough man who spent his youth in the godforsaken jungles of Vietnam. He was a good writer, but he had a taste for the booze, which he could keep under control when he wasn't pressured too much. He was riding out his last years on the copy desk, and it was a safe, easy berth. Writers liked him to work on their stories because he had a deft hand with other people's prose. He always improved my copy and caught my errors. He also told me when he thought I did a good job. Praise was scarce at the *Gazette*. Peggy, on the other hand, slashed my copy, criticized me behind my back, and, worst of all, added careless errors. Fortunately, I kept copies of my columns and exposed her shoddy work. After that, she hated me, but she usually left my columns alone. Most other writers let her do what she wanted to avoid the strife.

Peggy was determined to get rid of Monahan, and he was determined to stay. He dug in at his desk like it was under enemy attack. I knew Peggy tried all the tricks on him that she used on Albers, but Monahan held out. Today Monahan looked like she was getting to him. His gray hair was hanging in his eyes instead of neatly combed back, his shirt was wrinkled, and his tie was crooked. A lot of newsmen looked like that all the time, but not Monahan. He was always neat. Something was bothering him. I didn't think Albers's retirement came as a surprise. It had to be something else. Monahan jerked his head toward the back hall and walked away from his desk. I waited a minute and followed him out. He was angrily pacing back and forth by the old freight elevator.

"Cruella's outdone herself this time," he said through clenched teeth. "Now she's adding outright lies to her other tricks. I can fight anything but lies. Damn her." He was so angry, he balled his fist up and hit the wall.

"Let's meet after work and talk about it," I said. "Maybe we can think of some way to stop her."

"We can't meet at the Last Word," he said. Too many people listened in on conversations at the newspaper bar. "How about Crusoe's on Osceola? It's near your place and not too far from mine. I get off work at five. I'll see you there about five-thirty." I agreed to meet him there.

I'd been in the building half an hour and still hadn't reached my desk. Louise was hiding out in the back hall, too, pretending to wash her coffee mug in the janitor's sink. She didn't bother hiding the fact that she was crying. I could hear the department phones ringing and ringing, but for the first time ever Louise didn't rush over to answer them. I put my arms around her, as if there had been a death. Well, there had. Louise's career was dead. "Louise, I'm so sorry. This is a stupid move."

She sniffed and wiped her nose on a tissue. "How can they do this to me? I've worked hard for this paper for twenty years. Now he's turned on me. Charlie wants rid of me."

Suddenly it fell into place. It didn't make sense to have Louise work with computers—unless the *Gazette* wanted her out. Then it was a clever move.

"Why does the paper want to force you out?" I asked.

"Because I'm too old," she said. And started crying again. "They want a younger image for the section."

"Charlie said that?"

"Charlie wouldn't bother talking to someone as unimportant as me. He had Smiling Steve do it," she said, and started crying again.

Smiling Steve was assistant managing editor for scummy stuff. His official title looked better on a letterhead, but that's what Steve did. He'd been second in command for three managing editors, including Charlie. He was an affable-looking man who would slice off your head while he smiled. Steve desperately wanted to be managing editor. He never understood that carrying out the company's petty crimes barred him from the job he coveted. Great editors could commit great sins, but they couldn't harass harmless secretaries like Louise. The publisher would no more promote Smiling Steve than he'd invite the guy who sprayed his place for roaches to dinner. Despite his fancy title, Steve was simply someone who did unpleasant but useful things.

Poor Louise had stopped crying and started talking again. "Steve stood by my desk with that smiley face of his. I knew he was up to something. He made small talk until I almost couldn't stand it, I was so nervous. Then he said the paper was transferring me to the morgue because I was too old to work in the Family section. Too old to answer the phone! You know what really hurts? I'm the same age as Smiling Steve."

"Louise, he can't say you're too old. That's against the law," I said seriously. "I know a good EEOC lawyer. Please let me set up an appointment for you."

She shook her head. Her shoulders sagged. Suddenly she did seem old. I'd never seen lively Louise look so defeated. "Francesca, I am too old to fight. You know my Bob has heart trouble. I don't know how long I'll have him here with me, and I don't want to have our time together eaten up with a lawsuit. I can't risk losing our health insurance, even if I won later. The *Gazette* got me. I'm transferred out of the only job I've ever cared about. Friday is my last day in this department. I start in the morgue on Monday."

We both saw Wendy the Whiner coming down the hall. I couldn't stand to talk to that woman, on top of everything else. I abandoned Louise and finally reached my desk after forty-five minutes of *Gazette* crises. I had a stack of letters propped up next to my phone. Thank God for my readers. My love life was dead and my job was insane, but my readers were delightful. They kept me going. I read some of the letters and laughed out loud. The best was from Muffy O'Toole. She had a hilarious story about how the family cat, Brownie, seized a chipmunk raiding a bird feeder on her back deck. Her toddler boldly went over and pulled the chipmunk away. The toddler and the cat got in a tug of war, and the chipmunk ran up inside the baby's fashionably baggy pants, like something in a Warner Bros. cartoon. Just like the cartoon, no one was seriously hurt. The cat was disgruntled, and the chipmunk lost the fur on the tip of his tail, but the tiny animal was back on the deck the next day, eating from the bird feeder. Muffy identified him by the bald spot on his tail.

The phone rang. It was Sonny, my biker friend, and he sounded unhappy. "Hey, Francesca, you got any news for us?"

"Still looking into things, Sonny."

"God, I hope so. Francesca, you got to do something. The cops are thick as mosquitoes in a swamp. We can't do nothing without running into one."

"I need to find one particular person, Sonny, who'll give me some information. I promise I'll spend tomorrow tracking him down. Meanwhile, have you seen Jack?"

"Nobody has," he said. "Jack's skipped."

I said good-bye to Sonny, but with a sinking feeling. If Jack didn't show up to defend himself, he was going to stay on Mayhew's list of suspects—and I wasn't sure he didn't belong there.

By the time I finished making phone calls and answering letters, it was past five o'clock. Time to go meet Monahan at Crusoe's, a dark, newish bar with comfortable booths and a younger South Side crowd. Monahan was already there.

"Hi, doll," he said, and waved me over to his booth. I didn't mind Monahan calling me that. The man always sounded like a 1940s movie, but he believed women were equal at the office. I liked his attitude better than a lot of younger men who called me Ms. to my face but tried to keep me in my place.

Monahan was drinking blackberry cordial, a strange sweet drink for a war correspondent, but no one ever questioned his courage. The small glasses were lined up in front of him. I counted three. Not a good sign. I sat down and ordered a club soda, a burger with fries, and potato skins slathered with sour cream. Since I wouldn't be seeing Lyle any time soon, I asked for extra onions on everything but the club soda. Might as well enjoy being alone.

"Cruella's out to get me," he said. Monahan wasn't being paranoid. It was a fact. "Look at this." He pulled out a *Gazette* memo. "I printed this out. I found it in her computer queue this morning, when I was looking for some extra medical columns."

The memo was labeled "confidential" and addressed to Charlie. Peggy spent several paragraphs flattering Charlie. Then, after complimenting him for his good judgment in promoting her, Peggy got to Monahan. The memo said:

> I am extremely concerned about the performance of copy editor Monahan. I believe he is alcohol-impaired, and it is affecting his ability to perform his duties. I have verbally warned him about serious errors on several occasions, but he has not responded, except with denials and abusive comments. I do not think an uncooperative attitude such as this is the kind of thing we need at the new *Gazette*.

"What does she mean, she's given you verbal warnings?" I asked.

"She told me I made two obvious mistakes. In one of my headlines, 'condom' was spelled 'condum.' In another headline, 'surprise' was spelled 'suprise.' I don't make mistakes like that. I told her she was nuts. You know my work, Francesca. I'm careful."

"Yes, you are. Besides, you use spell check, so those kinds of errors are easily caught."

"I think she's adding those mistakes, but there's no way I can prove it."

"Yes, there is. I have a friend at the *Gazette* who's good with computers. Jim can call up the audit trail and check it. It will show who is making these mistakes. Then, if it's her, we'll have proof she's trying to ruin you."

"She is. That's exactly what she's doing. I'd like to wring her fat neck . . . aw, shit, sorry, doll." Monahan had squeezed the stem on his cordial glass in his anger and broken it. Purple liquid spilled on the tabletop. I grabbed some paper napkins and mopped it up. "Maybe I should go home and get some sleep," he said, "I don't feel so good." He didn't look so good, either. Monahan's hands were shaking, and his skin was pasty white overlaid with cherry red. He was drinking too much and he looked sick. Maybe he was making the mistakes himself. I didn't know, and I wouldn't until my computer maven checked the audit trails. But I did know that Peggy was getting to Monahan. Something had to be done soon, or Monahan would give up.

"Don't worry," I said. "I'll talk to Jim the computer expert tonight, before he goes on duty. He'll find out if she's adding errors. We'll talk again tomorrow. How about a ride home? You look like you're a little under the weather."

"Thanks, doll, I need the walk," he said. "I'm a lot

better now that I know I'm going to hear Cruella shriek."

"We'll get her," I said. "Tomorrow, everything will be different."

It was. For both of us.

7

The next morning, I was back at Uncle Bob's for breakfast. I wasn't going to have my usual this morning. I was going to eat crow, and I knew it would be tough. Marlene was not waiting with my scrambled egg and a side of sarcasm. Instead, she greeted me at the PLEASE WAIT FOR A TABLE sign with freezing politeness. "Would you like a table or a booth, ma'am?" she said, as if she didn't recognize me.

"Marlene, I'm sorry."

"Are you?" she said. "I don't know who was in here yesterday, but she certainly was a touchy bitch. Wasteful, too. I threw away a perfectly good breakfast."

"I'm sorry," I said. "I don't know that person, either, but I think she's a real jerk and I want to apologize for her. Look, I acted badly. I know it's no excuse, but I've just broken up with Lyle. This doesn't seem to be my week for getting along with anyone. I'm sorry."

"I'm sorry, too," Marlene said, defrosting immediately. She could never stay angry for long. "Sit down and have some coffee. I can tell this is tearing you up. You look awful. What went wrong? I like Lyle. I thought you made a good couple, but it's your decision."

"He was pressuring me to marry him," I said.

"Men are such romantics," Marlene said. "Sleep with them a few times, and they want a commitment."

I laughed. It felt strange, but good. "It's a little more than that. He thinks I love my job more than I love him."

"So? Men can get away with that. Why not women? Why shouldn't Lyle be grateful that you work your ass off? You'd think he'd want a good provider." I thought of Sydney, married to cold, hardworking Hudson, spending his money on useless things and chauffeuring their son on a lonely round of required activities. I didn't laugh this time. "Somehow, I can't see Lyle lunching on gin and lettuce at the Women's Exchange and buying cute things for the house," I said.

"And I can't see you working less than ten hours a day. Ever. Hasn't he realized that yet?"

"I'm not going to change," I said. "Why can't he accept me as I am? Lyle says the paper doesn't love me, and all I'm doing is making it rich while the editors mistreat me."

"So?" Marlene said. "All companies do that to their employees. Everyone knows that. At least everyone who wasn't born with a silver spoon in his mouth, like Lyle. The point is—do you love your job?"

"I do, I do," I said, and laughed, realizing I'd said part of the marriage vows. "I guess I *am* married to my job."

"Who cares? Do you think you make enough money?"

"I could make more if I worked someplace sane. But I like the freedom I have, and that's a good trade-off. Management sucks, but my readers make putting up with the editors worthwhile."

"Then you aren't being taken advantage of," Marlene said. "Maybe you and Lyle just need time to think things through."

"He hasn't called," I said, trying to keep my voice from wobbling.

"And have you called him?"

"After what he said? I've got some pride."

"Then you're both taking time to think it over. That's not bad. Meanwhile, I have a column idea for you. You know my friend Laurie?"

"The name's familiar, but I can't place her."

"Perky little brunette. Used to be married to Mr. Family Value."

"The guy who has those awful ads on late-night TV peddling insurance?"

The ads showed Mr. Family Value sitting stiffly on a blue-flowered couch in his South Side living room. He wore a cheap sleeveless shirt and a mustache that looked like a piece of brown shag carpet. The woman he called "my sweet wife, Susie" was posed nervously next to him, as if she expected the couch to be repossessed at any minute. A fat baby drooled happily in her lap, until the end of the commercial, when the kid reached up and yanked Mr. Family Value's mustache—something the whole city was dying to do.

Marlene intoned with a look of fake sincerity, just like Mr. FV, "Remember, you need value—Family Value—so you know your loved ones are financially safe. Put your family first. Give your family something to hold onto, owww!"

That was the best part of the ad, when the baby grabbed Mr. Family Value's hairy mustache. I was sure that thing on his lip was a fake, until the baby pulled on it. It seemed obvious the kid wasn't following the script, but Mr. Family Value's ad agency must have talked him into leaving that bit in. They were right. The kid's unscripted move made the ad wildly popular. It entered into the local folklore with other classic local late-night ads, right up there with "Wanda, the queen of carpet" sitting on top the Gateway Arch.

According to Marlene, sweet Susie was Wife No. 2. "He left his first family in the lurch. He walked out on Laurie and their two kids, so he could marry Susie, a woman he met at church—don't you love it? He decided he didn't want to pay child support, even though Laurie had a court order. The city is notoriously lax about enforcing those orders, and Laurie's tired of having to pay her lawyer to get money that's supposed to be hers. This morning, when his Family Value insurance office opens at ten, she's going to do something about it. You might want to be there."

It was nine forty-five. I paid my check and walked out to Ralph, admiring his sleek Jaguar beauty in the morning sun. We made it to Mr. Family Value's insurance office on Hampton, in the heart of St. Louis Hills, by nine fifty-five. It was in a neat yellow brick building from the late 1940s. St. Louis Hills was a section of St. Louis that had remained almost unchanged for half a century. The lawns were still neatly manicured. The redbrick houses were scrupulously cared for. On Sundays you could drive down the streets and smell the roasts cooking in the ovens. People here still had old-fashioned standards. They would certainly be shocked by the sight of tiny Laurie, in a pink shirtwaist and blue coat she must have stolen from June Cleaver, in front of the Family Value Insurance Office with a hand-lettered picket sign. "What about Family Value for your first family?" the sign said. "Mr. Family Value Owes $9,983.62 in child support for the children he abandoned."

Laurie walked sedately back and forth on the sidewalk, while a crowd of neighbors gathered and read the sign. They were mostly well-dressed matrons and businessmen in suits, and they thoroughly disapproved of this spectacle on their street. Promptly at 10:00 A.M., Mr. Family Value and his mustache got out of a shiny new blue-green Buick.

"Laurie! What is the meaning of this?" he barked.

"Read the sign," she said sweetly.

"I'm calling the police and having you removed. This is illegal," he said.

"Not as long as I stay on the sidewalk," she said.

"It's libelous," he screamed. The crowd didn't like him yelling at tiny Laurie. There was a low, angry murmur. Laurie refused to be bullied. I was scribbling frantically.

"Not as long as I'm telling the truth," she said.

"That is the exact amount. Here's the most recent court order." She held it out to the crowd. A woman with steel-colored hair and an equally steely expression put on her half-glasses and examined it eagerly, then passed it onto her neighbor carrying an NPR tote.

"I have to do something," Laurie said calmly. "I can't make the payments for our children's Catholic school tuition." Mrs. Steel frowned. Score another point for Laurie. This Catholic neighborhood would be doubly shocked by a father who deserted his family and wouldn't pay for a proper religious education.

"Laurie, I told you I was short of money," he said, but now he was pleading.

"You have money for a brand-new Buick," Mrs. NPR Tote said.

"Disgraceful!" Mrs. Steel said. They both shook their heads.

"So much for Mr. Family Value's family values," said someone else in the gathering crowd, but it was hard to tell where the remark came from. Everyone was making disparaging comments. Mr. Family Value was starting to sweat, even though the morning was chilly.

"Susie better watch her sweet self. She could be next!" Mrs. Tote said. "And that cute little baby will have nothing to hold on to. Is this your family value?"

"Family Value! Family Value!" the crowd chanted while Laurie marched back and forth. Traffic was slowing down on Hampton to watch. A police car pulled up, followed by a four-wheel drive vehicle belonging to a TV station. I was enjoying this.

"Laurie, sweetheart, let's discuss this inside," he said in a wheedling tone.

"Let's talk about it in front of witnesses," she said firmly. "I'd especially like to talk to that nice TV reporter." Mr. Family Value's eyes were wide with terror as he saw the cameraman open the back of the vehicle. This station did not carry his commercial.

"I'll write you a check!" he yelped, as if he'd been stung.

"Better hurry," Laurie said. "I think he's getting ready to shoot."

The crowd cheered as Mr. Family Value wrote a check for $9,983.62, right there on the sidewalk. It made a great shot for the TV cameraman. After he left, Laurie was only too happy to talk to me. "I said I wouldn't talk to that TV reporter if he wrote the check, but I never mentioned anything about the newspaper," she said. Mr. Family Value said nothing to me but "no comment," which only made my job easier. I'd bagged a column before noon.

I found a pay phone at the Target store. I didn't want this call to go through the *Gazette* switchboard. Jim Grove, my computer maven, had done some electronic snooping for me last night. He told me to call him at home after eleven this morning. Jim worked deep in the *Gazette* computer room, a windowless, white-floored, temperature-controlled room. But he didn't look like your typical pasty-faced computer nerd. Jim was a sailor who happened to like computers. The income from his grandfather's patent malaria medicine, Grove's Tasteless Chill Tonic, allowed him to indulge his passion for boats. He had a vintage 1966 power boat, a fifty-footer with a wood cabin lovingly crafted by Carolina cabinet-makers. One summer he took it from Florida to Nova Scotia, a memorable five-month trip. I'd never seen the boat, but I saw a photo of Jim on deck. The man had great legs.

Jim was enough of a free spirit he'd help prove Monahan's innocence—if he was innocent. I thought of his shaky hands and wondered if Monahan was making those mistakes himself. I was almost afraid to call Jim, but I did. He answered on the first ring.

"Morning, Francesca," he said cheerfully. "I found what you wanted. Monahan was absolutely correct. He sent the first story to the Family desk, the holding desk for edited copy, at one-oh-four, and 'condom' was spelled correctly. At one-sixteen it was changed to 'condum' by someone logged in to terminal 22. That's the Family copy chief's desk. Same story, different times for 'suprise.'"

"Cruella set him up," I said.

"Whoever was sitting at terminal 22 at one-sixteen on that date set him up. I've saved you a printout."

"It was Cruella. She always takes an early lunch. You got her, Jim. I can't wait to tell Monahan. I'm on my way into the office."

I found Ralph right where I'd parked him. That car was such a pleasure to drive. Too bad it was not a pleasure to go to the *Gazette*. The place was positively poisonous since Charlie took over. Today the newsroom was strangely silent. Now that Charlie was managing editor, it was often quiet. But that was a sullen quiet, like a classroom with a mean teacher. This was different. This silence had a shocked quality to it. People stood around in little groups, talking softly. Whatever was wrong, it was bad. When I got back to the Family department, I didn't hear any bickering on the copy desk. I'd prayed for that silence, but now it seemed unpleasant and brooding. Family Editor Wendy wasn't around, as usual. The phones were ringing, and Louise wasn't answering them. She was sitting at her desk, crying.

"What's wrong?" I asked her.

She got out two words before she cried again. "It's Monahan."

"What's Monahan?"

"He had a stroke. He probably won't make it," Louise said. I was shocked and numbed by the news, but not surprised, not really. I remembered the way his hands shook and the waxy white over red color of his skin.

"When did it happen?"

"Last night at ten-thirty. His poor wife called this morning. He's not expected to live out the week, poor thing. He was such a nice man. The last of the real newsmen. As far as I'm concerned, when Monahan dies, the old *Gazette* is dead."

"And I know who killed it," I said. I didn't say anything else. Now I'd probably never be able to tell Monahan he didn't make those mistakes. I wished I could have called Lyle and talked with him about what happened. He knew how much I liked Monahan. But we weren't talking. So I did what I always do when I'm unhappy. I threw myself into my work. I wrote my column about Laurie. Then I started on my story about Sydney's life and last days, and how a Ladue lady went from society soirées to biker balls. As I was pawing through my notes to find

another interview, I found a notice on my desk that
added to my misery. There was another meeting of
the Voyage Committee next week. I groaned. I had to
spend more time in the company wind tunnel. I
needed to get out of the newsroom right now. Too
many things were going wrong: Monahan was dying.
The Voyage Committee was meeting. Could things
get any worse? Oh, yes. Much worse. On my way out
of the newsroom, I ran into Charlie. A close encounter with my boss was never pleasant, but he had a
weasely grin that let me know he was up to something nasty.

"How's Lyle?" he asked, while the reporters sitting
around us pretended to type on their computers. I
knew they were pretending because Charmaine, the
one closest to me, kept hitting the same four keys.

"Just fine," I lied.

"I saw him at lunch at O'Connell's the other day.
He must like chicken."

"Usually he has their burgers," I said, wondering
why we were discussing Lyle's eating habits at an
Irish bar.

"He was lunching with a student," Charlie said.
That slice of grin again. Like a knife in my gut. "Very
pretty blonde. Young. Looked to be almost twenty
years younger than you. She was hanging on his every word. Hanging on him, too. Everyone was talking about it. Just thought you should know about his
little lunch."

"It's okay, Charlie," I said. "I know he eats."

I heard Charlie laughing as I walked away and pretended I didn't care. That conversation was Charlie's
payback. He was notoriously unfaithful, and I'd let

him know more than once what I thought of his tom-cat behavior. Naturally, Charlie wouldn't pass up Lyle's little slip with a student.

Damn Lyle twice over. He was going out with a student! Lyle was forty-nine years old. What could he say to a nineteen-year-old girl? Of course, maybe he wasn't talking to her. Maybe when he was in bed with her he didn't see the cellulite I had on my thighs, or that sag around my midsection, or . . . the hell with that. There was only one thing to do when I felt like this. Head for a bar.

I picked one to suit my mood: South Side Annie's on Delor Street. Annie was a sixtyish woman who weighed about ninety-seven pounds, and most of that was her haystack of sprayed blond hair. She didn't look big enough to lift her unfiltered ciga-rettes. But Annie once blew away two holdup men with a shotgun. As far as Annie was concerned, they gave her two reasons for the instant death penalty: Both pulled weapons on her, and one used the line she hated most in the world. He sneered and said, "Annie, get your gun?" She did. She kept it within reach under the bar.

Their deaths were ruled justifiable homicides. No charges were filed, and South Side Annie's became one of the safest bars in the city. In the afternoons, the neighborhood seniors drank cheap beer at her place. At night, when they toddled home to bed, bik-ers drank there. I was hoping I'd see Streak tonight. He owed me a favor. I'd looked up some information for him. His nephew wanted to know about his fa-ther, who died a hero in Vietnam. I tracked down the old stories in the *Gazette* files and found some duplicate photos. Streak owed me, and I was going to cash in. I needed information. I got the feeling the bikers weren't lying to me, but they weren't telling me everything I needed to know, either. Maybe Streak would be able to fill in the gaps.

I sat at a back table, in my yuppie beige pantsuit, chugging club sodas, eating a cheeseburger, and watching drunks try to get the big prize in the claw machine: a neon-pink stuffed bear. Annie could have kept herself in smokes for a month with the quarters they dropped in that claw machine, just while I sat there. A paunchy fellow named Billy came over and tried to hit on me, but Annie called out, "Billy, get over here," like he was two years old, instead of fifty-two, and Billy obeyed. After Annie shot those guys, most men did obey her. No other man was dumb enough to try to bother me, and I sat there for three hours.

Finally, after eight-thirty, when I wasn't sure I could force down one more club soda, Streak came through the door, his gray streak glinting in the neon beer signs. Tonight he was wearing black jeans and a Daytona Bike Week T-shirt with a huge faded gold eagle. It set off the panther tattoo on his bicep nicely. I waved him over and offered to buy him a beer. He went up to the bar and bought his own Busch, then sat down with me. "What brings you here, Francesca?"

"You. I'm here to collect my favor. Shouldn't be too difficult, Streak. I'm just trying to find out what's going on. I promised Sonny I'd look into what happened at the Leather and Lace Ball. I don't think a biker killed Sydney Vander Venter, either. But I'm not getting straight answers from some of them, so I can find out who did."

"I'm not sure I know what you need, Francesca. But ask me some questions."

"I need to know what Crazy Jerry was doing at the time of the murder," I said.

Streak started laughing, as if my question amused him. "Sorry, Francesca, I can't betray a brother. Jerry and I, we go all the way back to Nam. But I'll give you a hint. Ask him that question sometime when Stephanie isn't around and you might get an answer."

"When can I see him without her? They live together, right?"

"They do, although I'm not sure how long it's going to continue. She was pretty pissed at him after the Leather and Lace Ball, and he gave the lady reason to be upset. However, if you stop by the factory where he works about three-thirty, quarter to four, some afternoon, you should see him coming out when he gets off work. He rides his Harley most days and parks it up near the side door." Crazy Jerry worked at a furniture factory near my house, so tracking him down would be easy.

"Okay, fair enough. But I know Gilly wasn't a Vietnam vet. Can you tell me what he was doing? He says he was with his old lady, but nobody believes him."

"For once that guy is telling the truth, but he lies so much, who's going to believe him? I drove Crazy Jerry home, because Steph left without him and he was too shook to drive after that society lady was found dead. While walking to my pickup, I passed Gilly's car, and the windows were all steamed up. I wasn't going to look, but there was this break in the steam, and I saw him with a blonde. Do you know much about Gilly? The story won't make much sense unless you do. See, he and Mabel still live together, but they really can't stand each other. She says if they divorce, she gets his left nut or his Harley, whichever hurts more, and I don't have to tell you the answer to that. So they have this kind of truce. She has a show husband who takes her to church and dances and her relatives' for dinner and pays the bills, but she does her thing and he does his. He has some girlfriends, but he's careful not to have them around Mabel. So I just turned my head away when I saw Gilly with the blonde, except something about her looked familiar. Finally, I sorta peeked in and I'm sorry I did. There was Gilly in the backseat with his own wife. They saw me, too. It was embarrassing for all of us. He must have been really drunk to hit on Mabel, and she must have been drunker to say yes. Naturally, no one believes him."

"So Gilly got caught cheating on his girlfriend with his wife. I think that's a country song, isn't it? Well, we cleared one biker suspect. Let's go for two. Where was Jack, Sydney's boyfriend? He says he was just riding around after he left the Casa Loma, but nobody saw him."

"Can't help you there, Francesca, I don't know where he was after he left that night."

"Do you know where he is now, so I can ask him?"

"No. Haven't seen him. Haven't seen anyone who's seen him."

"Do you think he did it?"

"Don't know. Can't help you with that one, either."

Streak was clearly losing interest in the conversation. He was definitely gaining interest in a redheaded woman drinking beer out of a bottle. Some men were suckers for beer-drinking women. Lyle, for one. Wonder if his little college student drank beer out of the bottle. At her age, she probably drank milk out of a bottle. Wonder if I'd ever quit thinking about Lyle.

"That's okay, Streak, you've been a big help already," I said. Streak finished his beer and ambled toward the bar in the direction of the redheaded beer drinker. I paid my check and left. At home, I checked my answering machine. No calls. Not that I was expecting to hear from Lyle, but you'd think he might at least let me know when I could come pick up my clothes and stuff I'd left in his closet. I hadn't moved in with him, but when you sleep over at a guy's house a few times (okay, more than a few) things just kind of accumulate. Heck with him. There was nothing I needed there. If Lyle wanted my things out of his house, he could call me. Or he could throw them out. I didn't care. Just like I didn't care that he didn't call. So why did my heart beat so fast when the phone rang? And why was I so disappointed when it turned out to be Jack, even though I'd just told Streak I really wanted to track him down?

"This Francesca Ver-ling?" Jack said, mispronouncing my name. He spoke slowly and carefully. I wondered if he had a buzz on.

"It's Veer-ling," I corrected. "Where are you, Jack?"

"Doesn't matter," he said. I could almost hear the shrug. "I got some information about who killed Sydney."

"Oh?" I used my most noncommittal oh.

"Yeah, I got some papers that will prove who murdered Syd."

I wasn't noncommittal anymore. I was excited. "When can we meet?" I said.

"When you got the money," he said. "You can have them for twenty-five thousand dollars."

Incredible. This slob wanted to sell me the name of Sydney's killer. "The *City Gazette* does not believe in checkbook journalism," I said loftily. The *City Gazette* did not believe in opening a checkbook, ever. The paper made Sydney's mother-in-law look like Donald Trump. Those cheapskates wouldn't pay twenty-five thousand dollars for one reporter, much less for one story. They wouldn't give that kind of money for Jimmy Hoffa's body and Elvis's current address. But I couldn't say that, so I took the high road instead. "Are you selling me the name of Sydney's killer?" I said.

"Yep. This will do it."

"You have no shame. You lived with that woman. You borrowed money from her, and now you want to make money off her dead body. You're disgusting."

"Hey, Sydney didn't mind having me commit a crime to get these papers," he said. "It was me that got them, and it would be my ass thrown in jail if I got caught, and this time they'd throw away the key. But I did it for her. You can afford morals, Miss Newspaper Lady. You get a paycheck every week. Me, I can't make a living with the cops buzzing around me like flies on shit. I owe my lawyer and I owe rent clear back to August, and if I don't sell these papers, I gotta sell my Harley, and that I just ain't gonna do, not for Sydney or anybody else. This will be enough money to get me out of town for a while."

"I don't have any money, and I wouldn't pay you if I could," I said. Jack was a sleaze. I'd never figure out what Sydney saw in him.

"Fine with me," he said. "I got somebody who's willing to pay. We're meeting Saturday at midnight. I just wanted to give you first crack at it, out of respect for Sydney and all. If you change your mind, give me a call."

"Yeah, right. Don't hold your breath underwater waiting for my call." I hung up the phone. What an idiot. Did Jack really think I'd believe someone would give him twenty-five thousand dollars cash at a midnight meeting? Did he think I still read Nancy Drew? Jack was bluffing. If he knew anyone with bucks, Jack would have sold those papers by now, and he wouldn't bother calling me. He didn't have a buyer. How could he? The *Gazette* was the only newspaper in town. No local TV station would pay his price, and this wasn't a big enough story to interest a network TV tabloid show.

The phone rang again. I was popular tonight. Maybe I was even popular with Lyle. But the next call made me forget about Lyle and Jack both. It was Monahan's wife. "My husband died about an hour ago," she said in a flat, emotionless voice. "I just wanted to let you know, because my husband thought a lot of you."

"I thought a lot of him, too, Mrs. Monahan," I said softly.

"I know you did," she said, and I could hear her voice slipping. But Mrs. Monahan was as tough as

her husband. She fought back the tears and told me
Monahan would be laid out Saturday and Sunday
and buried Monday morning after Mass at St.
Philomena's, an old city Catholic church in my
neighborhood. It was a good church for Monahan's
funeral service: traditional and dignified.

I drifted through Friday, stopping in at the *Gazette*
just long enough to pick up my paycheck and check
my messages. I had contributed twenty bucks for
Louise's going-away gift, but I didn't have the heart
to hang around for the party in the company cafete-
ria that afternoon. It would be sadder than
Monahan's funeral. I couldn't believe that this was
Louise's last day in our department already. Monday
she would be working in the morgue. Nobody
claimed to know yet who would be taking her place.
I left a message for the mystery receptionist that I
would be at Monahan's funeral Monday morning. I
had a good excuse to leave the *Gazette* that afternoon. I planned to track down Crazy Jerry as he was
coming out of work. And I was in just the right trou-
blemaking mood to do it. The furniture factory was
in a small, hidden-away industrial area at the foot of
Utah Street. Unless you really knew South St. Louis,
you'd never find it. It was a big pale-green aluminum
building with a blacktop parking lot. I didn't go inside. I spotted Jerry's Harley parked near the side
door and pulled my Jaguar in back of it, making it
tough for him to get out. Jerry was one of the first
ones out of the building, freshly showered and wearing his biker leather, this time with jeans under the
chaps. A couple of guys whistled when I got out of
my Jaguar. To get the best results, I'd worn a short

skirt and high heels. Jerry looked terrified. He knew he'd have a hard time explaining this meeting to Stephanie.

"Francesca, what are you doin' here?" he said, looking around guiltily at the guys starting to pour out the door.

"I need a straight answer. What happened at the Casa Loma? The faster you tell me, the faster I'm out of here," I said.

"Nothing happened," he said.

"You asked for it," I said, and unbuttoned one button on my blouse and moved closer to him. I heard another wolf whistle. Jerry looked around desperately, as if he could hide under his Harley. I took another step forward and reached for my blouse again.

"Don't!" He yelped. "I'll talk."

Good thing. I had no idea what I was going to do next. I'd be hanging out all over if I unbuttoned anything else.

"You promise you won't tell Stephanie?" he said.

I promised. It was easy. There was no way I could explain this encounter to Stephanie, anyway. She would break me over her knee like a piece of kindling.

"I was in the coatroom on the balcony," he said. "It's never locked. It's used for storage. There's a big old Christmas wreath, old booths, extra tables and chairs and portable coat racks, all kinds of junk."

"Why would Stephanie object to that?"

"I wasn't alone," he said, and hung his head like a small boy who'd been caught. "I was with Bobbi."

"Which one was she?"

"She's blonde. She's sort of big up here," he said, sketching balloon breasts in the air. "She wears these skimpy-lookin' halter tops."

"That described a lot of women that night," I said.

"You'd remember her," he said, and suddenly I thought I did. If the woman I saw in my mind was Bobbi, she had a bigger endowment than Washington University, a skirt even shorter than mine, and black fishnet stockings with red bows up the back.

"We'd been having us a little fun on one of the black vinyl booths in the corner, behind the Christmas decorations. Nothing serious. Bobbi's married and I'm living with Stephanie. But I couldn't say anything about where I was because Bobbi's got a real jealous husband, and Stephanie gets kind of upset." I pictured an upset Stephanie hurling couches and refrigerators like a goddess throwing thunderbolts.

"I figured I was better off pissing off the police than either one of them."

I figured he was right. "So explain how your handprints got on the door."

Jerry squirmed a little and scratched his head endearingly, part of his little-boy-caught act. I kept staring at him. In ten more seconds, I was going for the blouse button again. But I didn't have to. He talked. He'd already gotten past the worst of it. In another minute or two, he'd be rid of me. "I left the coatroom first, when I heard myself being paged for the contest. I looked around for Stephanie, because she was working on the poker run fund raiser on the balcony. I saw her way over on the other side, mobbed with people, so I just slipped over to the door to the emergency exit without her noticing me.

It's real close. Bobbi waited a few minutes and then headed for the ladies' room in the other direction. I went down the back steps to the alley. I was gonna come back into the dance by the front door and say I'd been getting cigarettes out of my truck. Except I came out the alley door and saw Sydney, and she was dead. Real dead." Even now, his face turned pale at the memory. "I've seen dead before, but, man, not like that. I freaked. I leaned up against the door and I guess that's when I left my prints. At first, I thought Stephanie had killed the woman. But then I realized she'd been working at the poker run, and that kept her too busy to slip out and kill someone and besides, she'd have been covered with blood. But it took me awhile to figure that out. I just sat in my truck until I calmed down and realized Stephanie wasn't a murderer. Then I went back into the ball, where I got shitfaced. I wanted to forget the awful sight of that dead lady. I'd just been dancing with her and now she looked like roadkill. Streak took me home in his pickup, and I told him what happened. He didn't tell you, did he?"

"No, Jerry, he didn't. He'd never betray a friend. Thanks for telling me." I left him there in the parking lot. It was a short trip home, but I spent it wondering why smart men did dumb things. Why couldn't Jerry keep his pants zipped? Why couldn't Lyle? If Lyle called, maybe I'd ask him. But he didn't call all weekend. I brooded and ate pizza and cleaned the apartment and climaxed this exciting weekend with Monahan's wake on Sunday afternoon. He was laid out at the old Grand Funeral Home on South Grand, a place where you expected Gloria Swanson from

Sunset Boulevard to come vamping in the door any moment. The Grand had a slightly decayed (if I can use that word about a funeral home) 1920s Hollywood glamour: chairs as big as thrones, torch lamps, and paintings in heavy gold frames. A lot of my South Side relatives made their final public appearance at the Grand. Monahan was in Parlor A. I recognized Mrs. Monahan and two of their adult children surrounded by a flock of graying folks in their sixties: Monahan's friends and family. These were his contemporaries. But where were his colleagues? There wasn't anyone from the *Gazette*. I didn't see Charlie or Wendy or Peggy. Not a soul from the copy desk. Not one of the writers whose copy he had so skillfully edited. Maybe they came earlier. I checked the guest book on an ornate stand by the door. Nope. Nobody from the *Gazette*. Unless they got here in the next hour, no one from the paper would be at Monahan's wake. The walls were lined with floral tributes and prayer cards. The staff was well represented there. I found the flowers from the Newspaper Guild—a huge spray of orange gladioli. The bronze chrysanthemums from the Family department complemented the open bronze casket.

"Francesca!" said Mrs. Monahan, a slender, dark-haired woman in deepest black. "I knew you'd come. Nobody else did from the paper, but I was sure you'd be here." She clung to my hand as if it were a life preserver.

"Nobody?" I said, and wished I could recall the word the minute it slipped out.

"Not one of those cowardly bastards," she said, sounding amazingly like Monahan. "Not his pipe-smoking buddy Albers. Not Charlie, the new caring managing editor. Not his lovely black-haired boss, Cruella. None of the writers who used to sneak around and ask him to fix their copy after Cruella took a hatchet to it. He did it, too, even though there was hell to pay when Peggy caught him. Now that he can't do any more favors for them, they don't bother with him." Her face looked hard and angry and hurt. Then she patted my hand and said, "I'm so glad you could come. Would you like to see him?" as if she were a hostess at a party.

I would rather do almost anything than see Monahan dead, but I said yes and she escorted me to the bronze casket. I got up the courage to look inside. Monahan's hair was combed wrong. It was the first thing I noticed. It really bothered me. I hated the thought of someone as neat as Monahan having his hair combed wrong forever. A permanent bad hair day. I choked back a badly timed laugh. This couldn't be Monahan, looking like a department store dummy in pancake makeup and a blue suit, with a black rosary wrapped around his hands. In his pocket, instead of a handkerchief, were a reporter's notebook and a pica stick, the old newspaper method of measuring. My stifled laugh was in danger of turning into a sob. I knelt on the padded kneeler at the casket, crossed myself as if I still went to church, and stared at a small makeup stain on his white shirt collar for a minute or so. Then I stood up, told Mrs. Monahan how sorry I was, and promised to be at the funeral in the morning. She nodded vaguely, because a weepy woman wearing enough Poison to gas half the South Side had her in a hold like a lady wrestler.

I escaped to the parking lot. The cold air on my face felt good. Poor Monahan. The *Gazette* had used him and forgotten him. He meant no more than any other worn-out piece of equipment. Maybe that was my future there. Maybe Lyle . . . awww, screw Lyle. Unless his book baby was doing that.

It took me a long time to fall asleep, and I woke up with less than twenty minutes to make it to Monahan's funeral Mass. I threw on something dark and slipped into a back pew. St. Philomena's was dim and cool and beautiful, with an ornate altar gilded in the old German style. There was that special smell you get only in older churches: a lingering odor of beeswax candles, hothouse flowers, furniture polish, incense, and dust. The stained-glass windows glowed in the morning sun. A shaft of sunlight spotlighted the bronze casket in the center aisle. Monahan would have loved that touch, even if it was a little corny. Speaking of shaft, there was no one from the *Gazette* at the funeral. Except—wait. In the last pew across the aisle, I caught a glimpse of a boxy gray suit, a black silk blouse, and a yellow head. It was Georgia, bless her. After Mass, I stopped her in the parking lot.

"Georgia, am I glad to see you here," I said.

"Ain't this a load?" Georgia said, cleaning up her mouth for the occasion. "Poor old Monahan. I didn't find out until I got home last night. I was out of town at a Better Newspaper Conference."

"Did you find out what would make better newspapers?"

"Yeah. Quit having useless conferences with consultants telling us that papers need more local stories. I can't believe anyone can make money spouting that tired message. If local news really brought readers, our circulation would be up five hundred percent. We even had to find a local angle to write about the Gulf War. Instead, our numbers are dropping faster than Charlie drops his drawers. Oh, shit, I shouldn't be talking shop at Monahan's funeral. He was a real newspaper person. There aren't many left. I'm going to miss him."

"Me, too. I hope Cruella fries in hell. As far as I'm concerned she killed a good man."

Georgia shrugged. "He stayed because he wanted to. He died on the job and I think he wanted that, too. I couldn't imagine Monahan ever retiring."

"He sure didn't get a chance to try, did he?" I said bitterly. The parking lot was emptying out. Some cars were lining up for the funeral procession. But neither one of us went to the burial. We both had to get back to the office. I wondered who—or what— would be replacing Louise. I could hear the mystery replacement before I ever got to our department. She had a wild high-pitched giggle. I also heard our phones ring wildly and then the department answering machine picking them up. Whatever the mystery woman was doing, she wasn't working. Once I got a look at her, it was no mystery why she got this job and Louise was forced out. The mystery replacement was giggling with Charlie and looking at him as if he contained all the world's wisdom. He was staring down the front of her blouse as if it contained global knowledge. Charlie never wasted time talking to Louise, except to issue orders. Of course, Louise looked at Charlie like he was something she'd scraped off her shoe. Also, Louise would never wear tight black jeans, stiletto heels, or a slick shiny blouse cut to show Dolly Parton promontories. And Louise didn't have dyed black country singer hair. Why did Charlie think this big-haired woman would be able to speak to a younger readership? She probably thought Smashing Pumpkins was something you did on Saturday night after the Dairy Queen closed. Wait a minute. She was wearing eggplant lipstick and brownish fingernail polish, so her nails looked like a handful of cockroaches. Country grunge.

"Oh, Francesca," she said, and the giggle immediately dried up. When she talked to me, she changed her tone. Her voice had an insinuating, superior edge that I don't think the infatuated Charlie heard. "I been lookin' all over for you," she said accusingly, as if I'd been AWOL for weeks. "You should learn to leave a note lettin' me know where you are."

"I did," I said. "I called it Friday. You should learn to answer the department phones. You might find it."

"Francesca, you're supposed to welcome Scarlette and make her job easier," Charlie said sternly.

"Why, Charlie, it looks like you've already done everything you can," I said sweetly. "And I think Scarlette is smart enough she already knows about easy." Hey, she started it. And I liked watching Charlie's face get red. Scarlette knew I'd said something unflattering, but she wasn't sure what it was. She just stood there, her hands on her hips, while Charlie delivered a lecture to her breasts about how difficult I was.

Before I sat down at my desk, I went back to the morgue to say hi to Louise and see how she was set-tling in at her new assignment. She was sitting at the last desk, in front of one of the ancient putty-colored machines. Morris, the nerdy head of the department, was yelling at her: "No, no, no. Hit Shift F-two. Can't you get anything right?" Cool, competent Louise, who could handle six phone calls, two crazed staffers, and the FedEx delivery all at once, looked utterly lost. Her hand hovered uncertainly over the keyboard. I left, before she saw me observing her distress. I hated to see a loyal employee treated so badly, while a worthless piece of trash like Scarlette queened it at Louise's rightful place.

I guess Scarlette and Louise on top of Monahan's funeral were what set me off. That and seeing Peggy joking with Wendy, the world's most worthless editor, and the docile, cowlike creature that Peggy wanted to take Monahan's place on the desk. Peggy didn't waste any time. Monahan wasn't even cold in the ground, and she had his replacement sitting at his desk—a meek little woman who would never argue with her, especially not to save a writer's copy. I stalked over to the copy desk, where Peggy sat, wearing a too-tight black dress to match her long black hair.

"Congratulations, Peggy," I said. "How's it feel to murder a man?" The color drained out of her face, leaving only a bloody slash of lipstick. She burst into tears. I thought it was interesting that Peggy never asked what I was talking about. She knew what she did to Monahan.

Wendy rushed to her defense. "I heard that, Francesca," she snapped. "I won't have you verbally attacking my staff. You've reduced our copy desk chief to tears. You will be disciplined for this."

"You let Peggy harass poor Monahan into his grave, Wendy, and never said a word. You let her sit there and knife the writers every day and you never stopped her. Now this cowardly killer leaks a few tears and I'm in trouble."

"That's enough, Francesca," Wendy said. "I'm making an official note in your file. You're insubordinate."

"Wrong, Wendy. I'm in contempt."

I walked out. I'd always wanted to do that. God, what an exit line. I knew that scene would get me a lecture about team spirit and a written reprimand in my file, but it was worth it. Even Georgia wasn't too mad at me when she found out. I felt like celebrating. I took myself out to a good dinner at my favorite Italian restaurant. I didn't get a chance to sit down and read the morning paper until about ten that night.

So it was a real shock when I opened the *Gazette* and saw that Sydney's boyfriend Jack had been killed in a motorcycle accident. The story said he lost control of his Harley on a deserted road near Elsah, Illinois. The accident occurred sometime around midnight Saturday. The police were investigating the death as "suspicious in origin."

8

Jack was dead. He'd died trying to make money off his lover's murder. The man was a lowlife, but he wasn't a liar. At least, he was telling the truth about those papers he wanted to sell. He really was meeting someone at midnight, someone he thought would give him twenty-five thousand dollars. Who killed Jack? What was in those papers? And what did the papers have to do with Sydney? I was sure these two deaths were connected. Jack's killer had to be the same person who killed Sydney.

If Jack thought this person had twenty-five thousand dollars, then the buyer wasn't any of Sonny's biker friends. They weren't Cell's Angels—doctors, lawyers, and accountants riding their Harleys on weekends, with their cell phones on their belts. Sonny's biker friends were people who'd have to work a long time to get twenty-five thousand dollars. Except maybe Gilly, and he was such a small-time crook, he'd never have that much money in his whole life. As far as I was concerned, that meant Sydney was killed by either her husband or her son, and I'd put my money on the husband. He was mean enough to kill for money, and the Vander Venters had plenty of it.

But how do you kill someone on a motorcycle? Run a trip wire across the road? Drive straight at them in a car until the cycle swerved and lost control? How did you know for sure the rider would die in the accident? Most riders, even experienced ones, wiped out from time to time. They might lose some skin or break some bones, but they survived. That's why they wore protection: leather jackets, chaps, boots, and helmets. Especially helmets. But Jack hated helmets. And he died in Illinois, a state that didn't require motorcyclists to wear them. Did the killer plan that, too?

I wasn't getting anywhere with this speculation. I needed some facts. I needed to talk to Detective Mark Mayhew. I was sure he'd look into Jack's death. He'd be very interested in the sudden, suspicious death of a suspect. I knew where to find him: Uncle Bob's. He was usually there at eight every morning, if he wasn't working on a murder.

I timed it just right. I arrived about eight-fifteen, when he'd finished his waffle and was working on a second cup of coffee.

"Hi, Mark," I said. "Can I talk with you a minute?"

"Sure," he said, smiling. "Pull up a booth."

God, he looked good in the morning. Freshly shaved face. Tiny bit of shaving soap near one ear. Dark hair perfectly combed. I liked the way his pearly gray tie went with his crisp gray-blue shirt and his gray worsted wool jacket. Marlene interrupted these pleasant thoughts with one of her sarcastic comments.

"Should I change your order to over-easy?" she said. That was her cute way of reminding me that Mark was married.

"No, I'll have my usual, while Mark and I talk business," I said, heavy on that last word.

"Of course," Marlene said, letting me know she wasn't buying it. Mark sipped his coffee as if this interchange was over his head. Maybe it was. After Marlene poured me some decaf and plunked down my scrambled egg and toast, I got to the subject. "I saw in the *Gazette* that Jack was killed Saturday night," I began.

"Interesting, isn't it?" Mark said, lazily pouring more half and half in his coffee.

"Real interesting," I replied. "Especially after what he told me Thursday night about Sydney's killer."

Suddenly Mark was not lounging back in his booth. He sat straight up, eyes alert and slightly narrowed. He sounded impatient, even angry. "You know something about this, Francesca? Jack has been dead since Saturday night. You should have beeped me right away. This isn't a joke. This is a murder investigation, and two people are dead, one of them a nice lady who never hurt anyone."

Why did everyone have this urge to lecture me? Marlene, Georgia, Lyle, and now Mark. "Hold it, Mark. I *am* trying to tell you. I just found out late last night that Jack was killed. I came here first thing this morning so I could tell you. So cut the lecture. You're awfully snarly. Is the mayor's office putting pressure on you to solve the Vander Venter murder?"

It was just a guess, but it was a good one. Mark looked embarrassed. He really was a nice guy. Barking at people wasn't his style. "Yeah, they're driving us crazy. And the downtown business types are driving the mayor's office crazy, saying the city isn't fit for decent people, meaning rich white people."

"I saw in the *Gazette* that a special information hot line had been established. Haven't you been getting any calls?"

"Oh, we got calls," Mark said. "Lots of calls. The night of the murder no one saw anything, except one drunk looking out the bathroom window, and all he saw was an old lady. Now people are calling in saying they saw armed killers everywhere. We have tips that there were gangs of black males with AK-47s roaming Cherokee Street, lone white men lurking in the alley with shotguns, and suspicious characters with Glocks walking on all the side streets around the Casa Loma. One caller even claimed the killer was on the roof of the Casa Loma. I'm surprised Mrs. Vander Venter managed to get herself murdered. The area was so crowded with suspicious persons, I don't know how the killer ever got her alone."

"So all these tips are worthless."

"Probably. But we'll have to check them out anyway. And it will set us back even further. Meanwhile, the real killer is getting away with murder. I hate that. I hate what murder does to the family. At least when the killer gets caught the family gets . . . well, maybe not justice, but closure."

I'd heard Mark talk about this before. The agony of

the bereaved families ate at him. Murder had an ugly domino effect on everyone it touched. Afterward, family members' marriages often failed, and so did their health. They were driven half mad by the knowledge that someone they loved died brutally. They pleaded with Mark for assurances that the victim didn't suffer—assurances he couldn't always give. I didn't think Sydney's murder bothered her husband much. But I remembered her son, with the lost look and the dark circles under his eyes. Were those the marks of grief? Or guilt? Anyway, I told Mark about my phone call from Jack. He listened carefully, then asked a lot of questions, beginning with "Why didn't you call me when he called you?"

"Because I thought he was bluffing, Mark," I said. "Meeting someone at midnight with twenty-five thousand dollars sounded like a bad movie plot—just the kind of thing Jack would make up. I thought he was trying to get money out of me with some kind of scam."

Mark's other questions, from "What time did Jack call?" (around 10:00 P.M.) to "Was he drunk?" (probably), were easier to answer. I didn't know where Jack was calling from, but since I didn't hear any bar noises or car noises, I assumed he wasn't calling from a saloon or a pay phone on the street. Which meant he was probably calling from a house or apartment, and my guess was it wasn't his place. The police were looking for Jack, and he hadn't been seen for a few days.

"Now it's your turn," I said, when he finally stopped asking questions. "What can you tell me about Jack's death?"

"You know I can't tell you anything about an ongoing investigation, Francesca," he said. He looked sort of cute when he was serious.

"I'm not asking you to," I said, just as seriously. I looked pretty cute that way myself. "All I want is what's on the public record, anyway: the autopsy and the accident report. I can get them if I flash my press pass. It will save me a trip." Actually, I don't have a press pass. Reporters in cities like St. Louis usually don't. All I had was my *Gazette* ID, which I'm supposed to show to get into the building, but never do. No one's ever asked for my press pass.

"I guess I can give you that much," he said. "The Illinois state police say the accident took place on a two-lane highway near Elsah that's usually deserted late at night. It's mostly farmland. There was a farm produce stand about a half mile north of the accident, but it closes after Halloween. Jack was heading in that direction. It may even have been the meeting place, if what you say is true. It's about the only place to turn off on the road, except for a few farms. The state troopers found evidence that a car was parked on the side of the road about a hundred yards north of the accident, and they got one good tire cast. The accident was a bad one. The road looks like a roller coaster there, and it has a couple of sharp curves, the way farm roads do. Plus, there was fog that night. The Jersey County sheriff called in the Illinois state police, and they brought in their accident reconstruction team. They believe someone poured an oil-type substance on the road, to make it slippery."

"Wait. What's an oil-type substance?"

"Oil. Looked like plain, old motor oil. But the re-

construction team can't say for sure until the tests
come back. The killer used a lot of it, too. Probably
two or three cases of motor oil, although they didn't
find any empty oil jugs at the scene. There was the
smeared imprint of a large rectangular object, probably a cardboard box, in the oil-type substance. They
think the killer poured the oil-type substance on the
road and waited until the victim came along. You
can hear a Harley a mile away. Then the killer put
the large rectangular object in Jack's lane."

"In English, that means the killer poured a lot of
motor oil on the road and then stuck a big box in
Jack's way."

"That's what I just said." Mark sounded a little impatient. "The accident reconstruction team specu-
lates that Jack saw the box suddenly through the fog,
threw on the brakes, swerved to avoid it, and skidded
in the oil-type substance. The motorcycle flipped, he
hit his head and died."

I finished the rest for him. "The man who believed
helmet laws suck died of head injuries. I'm surprised
you can tell anything at all about that accident.
Wouldn't other cars driving on the road mess up the
scene?"

"What cars? One or two other vehicles came by in
the other lane. But the accident happened around
midnight in farming country. Even on Saturday
night, a lot of folks around there go to bed at nine-
thirty. It wasn't a road where the high school kids
party or drag race. A drunk or two might take it to
avoid the sobriety checks on the main road, but with
the fog, Jack and his Harley would be hard to see.
They both ended up in the ditch by the roadside.

Jack wasn't found until around six o'clock Sunday morning, when a farmer and his wife were heading into town for church. The Illinois state troopers believe it was a vehicular homicide."

"Jack was murdered?"

"That's what homicide is."

"Maybe the site choice in Illinois was deliberate, so he wouldn't be wearing his helmet."

"Maybe." Mark shrugged. "But I bet he didn't always wear it on back roads in Missouri, either. The state troopers think the killer's vehicle was nearby, ready to finish him off if he survived the crash. Instead, the driver simply folded the box, stepped carefully to avoid the spilled oil, and put the box in the car. It's probably in a Dumpster somewhere, miles from the scene."

"Simple, easy, and neat."

"Not that neat," Mark said. "You weren't at the autopsy."

"You were?"

"I had a personal invitation."

"Aren't you lucky? How'd that happen?"

"The state police ran a check on him, saw he was wanted in serious connection in the Vander Venter murder, and gave me a call. We had some more questions we wanted to ask him about his girlfriend, but Jack stayed out of sight. We would have picked him up eventually. As it was, I got to see what was left of Jack. His brains must have been all over the road."

I flinched and flashed on that bloody scene in my parents' bedroom. It's the real reason I didn't go to Sydney's autopsy. Mark must have seen my face. If not, he saw me grab the tabletop, as if I were seasick and the room was lurching in a storm. Mark knew how my parents died. He didn't mention them or apologize for what he said. He just changed the subject so smoothly I hardly noticed he was doing it. "Even if he had been wearing a helmet and survived the head injuries, he had a broken neck, crushed spinal cord, crushed ribs, lacerated liver and other internal damage, and broken bones, including two broken wrists."

None of these happened to my parents, so they didn't create any bloody pictures. I quit clutching the tabletop. "From the skid marks, the reconstruction team figures he was going seventy miles an hour—in the fog. An accident at that speed is like taking a dive off a seven-story building. Jack should have never been riding. He was so drunk, I was surprised he even made it to Illinois without an accident. I guess Jack was celebrating his twenty-five-thousand-dollar dividend from his Ladue lady early."

"How do you know he was drunk? I thought it takes a day or two to get those tests back." I'd learned a little hanging around Cutup Katie.

"I don't think I'll need to see the test results to confirm he was highly intoxicated. Did you know you can smell alcohol in a dead body, if the person's really been drinking? There's a strong alcohol odor when they open the body up. There's a lot of other strong odors, too. But when they cut Jack open, it smelled like somebody had dropped a bottle of Jack Daniel's. Funniest part was one of the assistants—I don't know if he was a doctor or not, but he was helping out the medical examiner—didn't say anything about the smell. He just said, 'By the way, are we still going out for happy hour?' Cracked us all up."

It was hard to have any sympathy for Jack, but I didn't want to picture him on the autopsy table, with his smashed head and the liquor stink that turned his violent death into a joke.

"I still can't quite figure out how he died," I said. "I guess I don't know that part of Illinois very well." Like most St. Louisans, I was largely ignorant of the state right across the river. You'd think there was a giant fence at the border to stop us. We rarely went over to Illinois, except late at night, when we were looking for some sin. To most of us, Illinois was nothing but the ugly strip of drinking spots, strip joints, and gambling boats along the river. My personal theory was that because we only went there late at night, we couldn't find our way to Illinois in broad daylight, so we never knew that part of the state was full of tidy German towns and hundred-year-old family farms.

"I can show you where the accident occurred, if you want. For a story or something," Mark said, just a little too casually. "We've been having some mild weather these last few days. It's supposed to last through the weekend. We could take my Harley for one last ride this season. Or not."

"Sounds interesting," I said, just as casually. "I'd like to ride your Harley."

"Wear a warm jacket and boots. Even on sunny days, it will be chilly this time of year when we get going. I have an extra helmet you can wear. You still live over Mrs. Indelicato's store, right? I'll pick you up at your place at three."

"It's a date," I said, which created an awkward pause. I started talking again to fill the loud silence. "I'll tell you something about Crazy Jerry that will clear him and Stephanie, but you can't say you got it from me. You can't even act like you know it, or Jerry will figure out how you got that information."

"Francesca, I can't make you a promise like that. This is murder. If you know something, you have to tell me, or I can throw you in jail."

He was bluffing and we both knew it. "I don't have to tell you anything. A reporter's notes are privileged, and even if you got mine, you couldn't read my handwriting. But if I tell you this, you can check it out yourself, if you approach the right people at the right time."

Then I told him about Crazy Jerry and Bobbi, and how Stephanie was busy the whole time working at the poker run on the balcony.

Mark said, "Oh, I knew that."

"You did? How?" So much for my big scoop.

"Hundreds of witnesses saw Stephanie working up there, and we talked to them all. As for Jerry, I figured it out when he wouldn't talk to me in front of Stephanie. Every time I asked him something, he'd sort of slide a look her way and refuse to talk. That was a guilty man, but I didn't think he was guilty of murder. So I got him when he was coming out of work at three-thirty. He talked real quick so his buddies wouldn't see him with a cop. Even plain clothes, they know what I am. It could damage his reputation to be seen in my company."

"Crazy Jerry didn't say anything to me about talking with you."

"Did you ask him?"

"No." I wondered how Mark figured out so fast that Jerry was sneaking around on Stephanie. Maybe because Mark was smart. Maybe because it took one unfaithful man to catch another. Maybe I didn't want to think about that. So I said, "And you know where Gilly was?"

"With his wife, he says. The trouble with Gilly is he says a lot of things. You just don't know which ones to believe."

"I think you can believe him this time. I talked with a source who saw him in the car with Mabel, but he'd never talk to you."

"I'm not too worried about Gilly. I don't really think he killed Sydney. He's too lazy."

"So who do you think did it? Jack was the only serious biker candidate, and he's dead."

"Is this off the record?" Mark asked, looking around to see if anyone was listening. The booths in front and in back of us were empty. Only Marlene was nearby, busy with the Bunn coffeemaker. Mark started talking. "I think it's either the husband or the son. The son has no alibi at all. The husband, Hudson, seems to have an unshakable alibi: He was at a cigar smokers' dinner at the Progress Club downtown, in full view of two hundred people at the head table at the time of the murder. Every minute of his evening is accounted for except fifteen minutes. Hudson says he was in the men's room, but no one remembers seeing him there. Fifteen minutes is not enough time to get to the Casa Loma and back, but it is enough time to meet with the killer he commissioned. The question is: Who? Who did he hire to kill his wife? Hudson says he's innocent—of course, his lawyer is sitting right there the whole time we questioned him, stopping us every time we asked a question he didn't like, so basically, all we have is his denial."

St. Louis had a lot of private clubs. I didn't belong to any of them, and I had trouble keeping them straight. "The Progress Club is the one at the top of the Petroleum Tower downtown, right? The one with the spectacular view of the Arch and the Riverfront? I was up there at a dinner once during a lightning storm. Greatest light show I ever saw."

"That's the one," Mark said. "Forty-eight stories up. An express elevator from the lobby is the only way to the club on top, besides the fire exit stairs. The lobby is watched by a concierge, and security cameras are at all the exits. The concierge says he didn't see Hudson Vander Venter in the lobby until the dinner broke up, and there's nothing on the security cameras. He didn't run down the stairs or take the elevator down to the lobby to meet anyone. He didn't make any phone calls from his cellular phone. We checked the club phones and didn't find any numbers outside the Clayton–Ladue–West County area for that time period. We found only a handful for the entire evening, and they checked out as staffers calling home. Nobody saw Hudson talking to anyone except other businessmen during the dinner. He didn't even stare down the front of the Rams cheerleader who walked around with the eight-hundred-dollar humidor during the charity auction."

"That sounds suspicious right there."

"We're checking to see if he has any possible connections to the bikers or approached anyone for a murder for hire, but so far, nothing. I'm looking into any possibility for conspiracy, but nothing—" Mark never finished his sentence. His beeper went off. He checked it, excused himself, went to the pay phone, and made a call. "Sorry, Francesca, I gotta go," he said, and headed out the door.

"How's business?" said Marlene, coming by with the coffeepot.

"Mark and I were discussing the Sydney Vander Venter murders," I said with great dignity.

"Mark now, is it? The last case you worked on together, you called him Mayhew. When did you get to be on a first-name basis?"

"When did you get so interested?"

"You're the one who's interested. Tomorrow you're going riding with him on a Harley. Spend a couple of hours with your arms and legs wrapped around him. Very businesslike."

"Marlene," I said. "I don't date married men."

"Yet," she said.

I didn't get mad at her this time. She was just worried about me, that's all. But I was a professional. Just because I found a married man attractive didn't mean I would have an affair with him. I admit that Mark was handsome, and if he'd been single, well, things might have been different. But they weren't. Anyway, this afternoon, I wouldn't have any time for what the nuns at my Catholic grade school used to call impure thoughts. I was going to be trapped in a Voyage Committee meeting that would eat up my whole afternoon. When I finally escaped that colossal waste of time, I'd still have to write my column. Naturally, I wouldn't get overtime. I wouldn't get home until after ten o'clock once again. I guess that's why, on the way into work, I swung twenty miles out of my way and stopped at Nieman Marcus in Plaza Frontenac, where I bought two hundred dollars' worth of fancy lingerie, including a couple of sixty-dollar bras, the lacy ones that give you a WonderBra figure without wires and padding. After perking up the top, I splurged on some silk bikini panties that were sheer in the rear. Sexy. You can always tell the state of a woman's love life by her underwear, and I'd let mine get drab and dingy. I told myself I was buying sexy underwear in case Lyle came back. It had nothing to do with Mark Mayhew's invitation to ride on his Harley.

This Voyage Committee was meeting in another hotel room. I swear, we spent more time in hotels than a convention hooker. What was it costing the paper to sit in a conference room at the Greentree Inn in West County, and drink coffee and tea from big silver urns? We had a perfectly usable conference room at the *Gazette*. But that was downtown. Voyage Captain Jason said to change our minds we had to change our point of view. We needed to spend more time in the West County corridor we wanted so badly for the *Gazette*. As far as I was concerned, they could keep their corridor. I got stuck in construction site traffic on Highway 40 and crawled along the highway, fuming more than the cars. By the time I made it to the conference room, most of the committee was already seated at the table. Since it was a working day, everyone was in sober suits. The publisher was wearing a gray suit like all the other men, but his was so expensive, it positively glowed. His cuff links alone could have bought any house on my street. The publisher presided at his end of the table, with the two corporate money men, Simpson Tolbart and Tucker Gravois, at his left and right hands. Georgia had the next seat down, and Roberto, the city editor, was on the other side of her. Across from them were the interchangeable yes persons, Brittany, Courtney, Scott, and Jeremy. Vonnie the Steel Magnolia was dripping lace at her neck and wrists to let the men know inside her sensible suit was a Southern belle dying to be set free. There was an empty seat next to her that I figured belonged to Charlie, but I didn't see him. There he was, coming across the room with a china cup and saucer, bearing them like a chalice. He reverently set the coffee down before the publisher, then sat down at his place and raised his own coffee in a toast. "To a great man and a great publisher," Charlie said. I expected the publisher to choke on the little toad's flattery. But no, the man was lapping it up. He actually wanted—no, needed— that sawed-off slime to praise him.

Roberto rushed in to pour on more flattery, and the Steel Magnolia added her own honeyed words. "Really, sir, we are just sooooo lucky to have a publisher who cares."

"Oh, yes," the quartet of yes kids chorused.

I was afraid I'd need an insulin injection before this love feast was over. I looked at Georgia. She hadn't said a word to debase herself like Charlie and the others, but she somehow managed to seem part of it. Georgia had an amazing talent. She could pass as a yes-woman without selling out. No wonder she got the big bucks.

Only the arrival of Voyage Captain Jason ended the revolting display. Jason was wearing his uniform—a work shirt that no worker could afford, jeans, and work boots that never saw an honest day's work. I was jealous, I guess. I wished I could think of a scam like this. I could call myself a consultant, but I'd never keep a straight face long enough to collect my half a million dollars. If I had a newspaper mogul and his court on the floor playing with Tinkertoys, I couldn't resist saying "You flunked the moron test, ladies and gentlemen. If you were really fit to run a newspaper, you would have refused to play Tinker-toys. You, Mr. Publisher, know nothing about leader-ship. And the rest of you will do anything to save your miserable jobs."

We would have all deserved that reprimand. After all, I got down on the floor and stuck wooden sticks into little round holes like everyone else. I couldn't imagine what we were going to do at today's meet-ing. Play Ring Around the Rosie? Chutes and Lad-ders? Jump rope?

When I finally bothered to tune in to Jason, I real-ized this meeting was actually instructive. "That's why today, we need to have a serious talk about the newspaper's needs," Voyage Captain Jason said. "Our research division conducted a telephone survey of twelve hundred readers and nonreaders. It con-cluded that the *Gazette* is well read by persons fifty and over. They spend more than forty-five minutes a day reading the paper."

Wow, I thought. Readers actually care about our

stories enough to spend three-quarters of an hour with them. This is good news.

"This is bad news," said Jason, the consultant. "Most people won't make a time commitment that large to a newspaper. The paper needs to develop a younger readership that will spend less time with the newspaper. That is the most effective way for the *Gazette* to have more readers. Also, advertisers want younger readers, not aging ones. The *Gazette* must run more stories about movie stars and pop music to appeal to younger readers. Younger is better, people. Younger is quality. Younger is money. Younger is what your advertisers hunger for. We must think younger, younger, younger.

"Also, we need women readers. Young, childbearing women. Not old, postmenopausal women. Advertisers find younger women desirable."

Charlie snickered. "I do, too."

Jason frowned and went on. Charlie grinned at the publisher. His role as public sexist was to speak for those men who wouldn't dare talk like that anymore—but still thought that way. Charlie's only punishment was a frown from Jason. His reward was an amused smile from the publisher.

"To get these desirable younger women," Jason was saying, "the *Gazette* should devote more stories to fashion and child rearing."

I groaned inwardly. This was the same old stuff. Surely the publisher must realize he'd paid for this message before, and it hadn't added any readers. But, no, the publisher was staring at Voyage Captain Jason as if he'd just come down from the mount with two stone tablets. Jason was still laying down the law. "Furthermore, in order to increase profit potential, the paper needs to reduce costs the only way possible: by reducing staff, first through attrition and then through agreements with the union." He meant union-busting and forcing older employees into early retirement or, in the case of Monahan, early death. Well, the *Gazette* was already sailing into that swamp. I could see by the smile on the publisher's face that Jason was speaking his language.

"I'd like your input, people, before we go any further," Jason said.

Tolbart the money man spoke up first. He looked extremely pleased with himself. "The *Gazette* is already implementing some of the steps you mentioned to maximize profit potential. We are giving our people strong incentives to retire. . . ."

Like rotten hours and transfers to wretched assignments.

"And we will be bringing in a strong team of negotiators for the next Guild contract, a Sun Belt law firm that specializes in negotiating pro-publisher newspaper contracts."

Translation: They break unions.

"Excellent," Jason said, sending Tolbart to the head of the class. The publisher gave a small nod of approval, like a Roman emperor sparing a gladiator's life. That nod was all it took. Everyone jumped in, eager to agree with Jason. No one questioned anything he said. The Steel Magnolia talked about how the *Gazette* was sponsoring certain Gen-X concerts coming to town, being careful to avoid any lesbians or controversial (i.e., interesting) musicians. Also, the paper was easing out of sponsoring the mammogram education program at the local hospitals, because the *Gazette* name should not be associated with disease. She named six or seven other ways to offend or bore those coveted female readers, then sat down to general approval.

Charlie said prototypes of the new Go Away section the *Gazette* planned to launch were being shown to focus groups and advertisers and had received high rates of approval.

Roberto quickly slipped in, "One of my newer reporters has just announced she's pregnant, so maybe she could do a freelance column on motherhood for our women readers."

Charlie grabbed the floor back. "Good idea, Roberto," he said, the way you'd pat a dog for retrieving a Frisbee. "I'm sure we can find some freelance money in the budget for a project like that. Have her write some sample columns." Then Charlie smiled at me, always a bad sign. "And what about you, Francesca? You dress better than any other woman at the *Gazette*. Maybe you could write a fashion column. I bet Wendy could scrape another thirty-five dollars a week out of the Family budget for you. And it would be no trouble at all for you to write about clothes since you wear them so well."

Thirty-five bucks for another day's work. What an insult. It made me angry. "That's my qualification, huh, Charlie? I'm a woman and I wear clothes?"

Georgia began coughing loudly, her way of warning me not to fall into Charlie's trap. She was right. Her coughing fit gave me a moment to cool down and think. While Roberto fetched Georgia a glass of water, I considered the situation. I doubted if Charlie was really interested in a fashion column from me. He just wanted to get me to shoot off my mouth in front of the publisher. He'd forget the idea after the meeting. If he didn't, all I had to do was turn in some really bad samples. The important thing was not to make this into a major confrontation.

"Charlie, that's an interesting idea," I said, and smiled sweetly. The remark about being a woman and wearing clothes was just a joke, folks. I'm a humorist, remember? "Naturally, I'd like to take some time to consider it so I can turn in the best possible column for our Family section."

Georgia beamed at me. A good answer. So I kept going. "I think any women's coverage should be well thought out," I said. "I'm really concerned we think the only way to get women readers is to give them fashion and child care. That's 1950s thinking. Women are interested in more than these tired, traditional topics. Frankly, if they want fashion news, they buy *Vogue,* and if they want child care information, they can read a parenting magazine or buy a book by an expert. If the *Gazette* wants more women readers, the paper needs more women leaders who know what interests their gender."

I could hear Georgia making choking noises, but this time everyone ignored her. Everyone, including the publisher, was listening to me intently. That was good. The publisher surrounded himself with yes-people. He needed to hear someone tell him what's really happening. If he knew, I was sure he'd want to fix it.

"We have never had a woman managing editor. No woman has ever headed up an important department on the news side." (I didn't mention the women who'd slept with Charlie and been promoted. Everyone knew who they were and what talents they'd used for those jobs.) "We have men in charge of the financial page, the news side, editorial page, sports, the art department, the photography department, the Sunday roto magazine, and the copy desk. The only place where the *Gazette* has women editors are the female ghettos, features and food. If you want more women readers, hire more women editors and reporters. Women know what women want to read. It's that simple."

Georgia, my mentor, was signaling frantically for me to shut up. I couldn't see why. I wasn't angry or ranting. I was listing some well-thought-out reasons. Sorry, Georgia, the publisher needed to hear this.

"What's wrong with our readers being fifty?" I asked. "Most of the male management in this room is fifty and older—so is our Voyage Captain Jason—and I'm sure none of you consider yourselves over the hill. Why say that about your readers? The boomers are turning fifty now. They have plenty of dough and they spend it. They're different from previous generations this way. They like to spend their money as they age. There are surveys that back up what I'm saying. We need to make advertisers understand this change.

"Anyway, just because readers are young doesn't mean they're stupid or they want junk. If they want to read about celebrities and music, there are magazines devoted to those topics that do it better than the *Gazette* ever will—or they can look the subjects up on the Internet. Heck, they can download music and see great movie promos on the Net. We can't compete with that. We don't have to. Young and old readers want the same thing from their paper: interesting, well-written news stories, features that are entertaining, and think pieces with an original point of view. Instead, we're giving them warmed-over wire service.

"Another thing. We've gone crazy on this local news stuff. Look at today's front-page story: three kids who died in a car accident in Macon, Missouri. That's terribly sad, and it's news, but it's not front-page news. It doesn't give our readers much of a world view. St. Louis is a sophisticated city. The people here travel, they read, they watch CNN, and more and more, as they get disaffected with the *Gazette*, they subscribe to the *New York Times*. They want to know what's going on in the world, and we barely tell them. We treat them like a bunch of isolated Ozark mountaineers who haven't been down from the hills in fifty years."

"Are you saying we shouldn't cover local news?" Charlie asked, an expression of horror on his face.

"Of course we should do local news, but we should make our coverage hard hitting. It takes time and money to get good local stories. We need to let people know what city hall is trying to pull, what's happening behind the scenes at the county council, and why our downtown is practically a ghost town. Readers love local stories with bite."

The whole audience was staring at me. They must be fascinated. What the heck, why not go for broke?

"But we need more writers to do that, and right now we have more editors per reporter than any newspaper our size in the country. If successful newspapers don't need that many editors, why do we? Besides, some of these editors are good reporters, but they are not trained to manage. Now, they write memos. They could write stories. Why not give them a raise and a title and put them to work writing well-researched local stories? We need more writers, not less. Think of the money we could have spent on staff if we hadn't hired these consultants."

Oops. Maybe I went a little far with that remark. But I was pleased I got that speech off my chest. My mentor, Georgia, had quit signaling frantically. Now she was staring at the conference table. I sat down, feeling good about myself, as Voyage Captain Jason would say. It must have been a thought-provoking speech. There was a long silence, until Voyage Captain Jason took the helm again.

"Thank you for sharing, Francesca," the consultant said. "We appreciate another point of view, which you certainly advocate with enthusiasm. It is important for our corporate culture to reflect the diversity of the community we serve and we hope to engender enthusiasm and purpose to sustain the excellence the *Gazette* name stands for. We think at our next meeting we will have an exercise that will help build a corporate consensus while fostering communication at all levels. Until then . . ."

"What's he saying?" I asked Georgia, who can translate corporate-ese. Something was not quite right. The meeting was breaking up in a quiet that now seemed ominous. Everyone slipped out without saying anything. Georgia grabbed my elbow and steered me out the door and across the hall to the women's lounge. There was nobody sitting on the pale-green couches and the stalls were empty. Georgia hissed through clenched teeth, "They're going to try to recover your damage at the next meeting. That's what they're saying. Here's what I'm saying: When are you going to keep your big mouth shut?" Her eyes were narrowed and her skin was drawn tight across her small, elfin face. Uh-oh. She was too angry even to yell at me. She turned and walked out, leaving me standing there alone.

"Why did they ask for my opinion if they didn't want it?" I said to the empty room. Jeez. Now my mentor was mad at me, too. I went off to cover a story. The only people I got along with lately were my readers.

9

A man was following me in the park. I could hear his shoes on the blacktop path. I knew it was a man, even though I couldn't see him. I wasn't going to turn around and confront him. Not yet. It could be a neighbor out for a morning walk. The man wasn't running fast enough to be a jogger. But he was walking briskly. Was it to keep up with me? Or was I just being paranoid? Tower Grove Park was fairly safe by day, but still, there had been problems.

I was being ridiculous. The whole reason I took this walk this morning was that I needed to relax, and now I was finding more reasons to worry. I definitely needed more exercise. I speeded up. So did the man behind me. I walked even faster, as if I could walk away from all my problems, at home and at work.

After the Voyage Committee fiasco—that's what Georgia told me it was—I put in a long night. I interviewed a man who had a beer can collection. He was a true fanatic, and under the right circumstances his devotion to thousands of metal cylinders would have been charming and eccentric. But I couldn't make the column work. My words stumbled onto the computer screen, clumsy and graceless, and I was afraid I made the poor man look like a boring nutcase. Finally I gave up and sent the column in by modem after midnight, but I wasn't happy with it. I was a failure, personally and professionally.

I decided the best thing to do was stay away from the paper this morning. I didn't want to face an angry Georgia or a gloating Charlie. So I had breakfast at Uncle Bob's—another reason I needed exercise—then called the office and said I was working on a story. I was, but not until around eleven. Scarlette wasn't answering the phones and Wendy wasn't at her desk. Good. I didn't want to talk to either one. I left a message on the department answering machine.

It was a warm sunny day in late fall, with just a hint of chill underneath. It was the kind of day that made me sad because I knew there wouldn't be many more like it this year. Soon the cold would close in for months and the days would be short and gray. But walking in the old Victorian park calmed me. The lily ponds and prettily painted gazebos had been there for more than a hundred years. The people who'd walked in the park a century ago had survived problems worse than mine. Their lives went on. Mine would, too.

I could still hear the man walking behind me, but I refused to turn around. This part of the winding path was edged with tall bushes and seemed deserted. I was out of sight of the street. I walked a little faster. So did the walker. If he was going to give me trouble, this spot was ideal. As I topped the next hill, I felt better. The path was less curvy. Now it ran alongside Arsenal Street. I could see cars going by. A tired African American woman in a white uniform was waiting for a bus. A jogger passed me, a balding guy in his fifties who had either a big beer gut or the first case of male pregnancy. He was sweating earnestly. The flat-bellies ran between six and seven in the morning. I preferred the overweight joggers who struggled along later. I was never impressed by the early birds. They acted as if they were naturally virtuous because they woke up before the rest of us.

The man was still following me. I could hear his shoes scraping the walkway. Then I came into the park entrance off Arsenal and forgot all about him. The morning sun had turned the yellow-leaved gingko trees lining the drive a glorious gold. The sky was a pure blue. The colors were so lovely, I stopped dead. That's when he caught me, the man who hurt me before and wanted to hurt me again. It was that no-good louse Lyle.

"Hi," he said. "I've been trying to catch up with you for blocks. I even called your name, but you ignored me. I figured you were in one of your funks."

He smiled his special smile. Crooked but cute. That was Lyle all right. His smile must have charmed that woman—no, that girl, that child—when she pawed him in O'Connell's Pub, a place where he used to take me for lunch. How could Lyle neck with a blonde, right in front of my editor, Charlie? He knew Charlie was always looking for ways to knife me.

Naturally, Charlie picked the middle of the news-room to announce Lyle had a little lunchmate. I was never so humiliated in my life. I was never less recep-tive to Lyle's smile.

I smiled, too, but it wasn't a very nice smile. "It's chilly, Lyle. You might catch cold. You should have a warm student wrapped around your neck," I said sarcastically.

"Francesca," he said, "please don't be this way. I've spent all morning looking for you. I went to Uncle Bob's, and Marlene said you'd already left. I stopped by your place, and Mrs. Indelicato said she thought you were walking in the park."

We were at the center drive, near a small gray ga-zebo. We must have looked like a Victorian painting, if you didn't count my jeans and leather jacket. Lyle took one of my hands and clasped it tenderly. I didn't take it back. I was angry, but I had to admit he looked good. He was wearing my favorite blue sweater, the same color as that heartbreaking sky.

"I missed you so much," he said, his voice soften-ing, and he took a step toward me. I missed him, too, but I didn't let him get any closer.

"You missed me so much you were seen consol-ing yourself with a nineteen-year-old blonde at O'Connell's," I snapped. He stepped back, as if I might bite. Maybe I would.

"What was I supposed to do?" he said. "I asked you to marry me and you didn't want me. You walked out on me. You left me." He gave me a hurt look, like a puppy dog who had his paw stepped on.

"You didn't waste any time finding someone else," I said, yanking my hand back.

"So I took a student out to lunch." He shrugged, as if he'd forgotten it and I should, too. It was one of his most irritating habits. He continued to explain away the nineteen-year-old blonde, as if words could erase her. "She's not my student, anyway. She's not in my class. But she is interested in writing. She's nothing to me, although I admit it was nice to have someone hanging on my words, as if they meant something to her."

"That isn't all she was hanging on," I said. "Charlie was there at the restaurant. He saw you. He told me about it in front of the entire newsroom."

"That's all you care about," Lyle said, and now he was angry. "You don't care about me. You aren't upset that we broke up. All you care about is how it looked to Charlie. We're back to your job again, aren't we? It always comes back to that."

We no longer looked like a charming Victorian painting. We looked like two angry people screaming at each other. "At least I can count on my job," I yelled. "It's there. It's not running around with empty-headed young blondes."

"Ashley isn't empty-headed," Lyle said firmly.

"Oh, it's Ashley, is it?" I said. There was acid in my voice. "Every airhead I ever knew was named Ashley. I bet she has her own horse, and her daddy bought it for her."

That stopped him. "How did you know that?" he said, sounding puzzled. Then he went back to being angry. His fair skin was starting to flush. "You know what I like about Ashley?"

"Her big tits?" I said sweetly.

That did it. Lyle was spitting mad. The cords in his

neck stood out. "You have a vulgar mind," he said contemptuously. I knew he was furious because he lowered his voice to a deadly tone.

"It's the secret of my success," I said.

Lyle ignored me. "I like to go out with Ashley because it's refreshing to be with someone who has no problems. I don't have to listen to her agonize at three A.M. about her terrible childhood and her unfaithful father and her crazy mother. If I ask Ashley to marry me, she'll give me an answer based on how much she loves me, not how much she hates her parents. She's only nineteen, and she's refreshing. She doesn't follow me around, telling me the latest thing she did to Charlie and Charlie did to her. She doesn't ask me what I think Charlie will do next, or badger me with endless questions about those wackos who run the *Gazette*. She doesn't know anyone at the *Gazette*. She doesn't even read the *Gazette*."

"She's probably too young," I said, and lowered my voice to a matching snarl. I said each word distinctly, as if I were pounding it into his thick skull. "I am sorry for what I said about Ashley. I'm sure she doesn't have any problems. How could she? She hasn't had a life yet. But you do have problems. Ashley is thirty years younger than you. You're not dating. You're child-molesting. That must be why you're hanging around the park: You're waiting to pick up more children."

I left him standing there. He shouted something at me, but I wasn't listening. Head high, I turned around and walked briskly out of the park. By the time I got home, I was sweating. Yep, that was sweat in my eyes. I wasn't going to waste my tears on the likes of Lyle.

Having confronted one male rat, I set off to find another. I was in just the right mood to deal with Hudson Vander Venter. That man had used his secretary to avoid me long enough. I was going to track him down and corner him in his parking garage until I had some answers. Hudson's office was in one of the gleaming mirrored glass cubes that infested downtown Clayton. They made the suburban business district look like it was wearing mirrored sunglasses. I wondered about 1980s architecture. All those mirrored business towers, reflecting other people's work. Couldn't the architects come up with anything creative?

The lobby of Vander Venter's office building had enough beige marble to build a small Roman amphitheater. The tropical plants could restock a rain forest. The brass elevator doors looked like they opened onto bank vaults—or maybe burial vaults. How warm and friendly. Just like Hudson. I found a pay phone back by the door to the parking garage. I fished a quarter out of my wallet and called Hudson's office. His secretary said he was in a meeting until noon. Good. He was at the office. I hung up without leaving a message. I checked my watch. It was eleven-forty. I figured he would go to lunch somewhere around twelve. I walked into the parking garage and wandered up and down the ramps until I found the reserved spaces for Vander Venter and Associates on the orange level. There H. VANDER VENTER was stenciled in black on the wall. The sign was right over the hood of a huge black BMW, the kind of car that Darth Vader would drive if he wore business suits. It had been hand-polished to a frightening gloss. I could see my face in this dark mirror. I fixed my hair and then leaned against a concrete pillar to wait for Hudson.

I waited about half an hour. Security never came around once. At twelve-twelve, Hudson stepped out of the parking garage elevator. He was smaller than he looked in his pictures, and his skin was tanned the rich bronze of club-car leather. His quiet gray suit shouted money. It was a beautiful match with his steel-gray hair. His steely eyes were mean and hard. His shoes were as black and polished as his car. A black nylon gym bag completed the ensemble. He looked powerful and bored. He seemed to walk inside a capsule of dead air.

"Mr. Vander Venter?" I said quietly, walking toward him.

His eyes flicked over me briefly, then dismissed me as someone who was not important. He looked around the parking garage, possibly for a minion to remove me. We could hear doors slamming and cars starting up in other areas. But no one was near us. Hudson ignored me and kept walking toward his car. I blocked his path.

"I'm Francesca Vierling with the *City Gazette*," I said. "I'm very sorry about your wife's death."

He nudged me out of his way and kept walking to his car. I followed. "I hate to bother you here, but I couldn't get through to you at your office. I need to ask you a few questions about your late wife. Do you have any theories about who might have killed her?"

Still no answer. Now he was at the trunk, and I was right behind him.

"Do you think it was a biker? Or someone from your own social circle?"

He pinched his thin lips together as if he were zipping them. Then he opened the trunk. Wow, those cars had huge trunks. I moved closer to see inside. Since he wasn't answering my questions anyway, I decided to ask a really rude one, just to see if I'd get any reaction.

"Mr. Vander Venter, the police say there are fifteen minutes you cannot account for at the cigar smokers' dinner the night your wife was murdered," I said. "Can you tell me what you were doing during that time?"

He turned on me. He didn't bother to get angry. I wasn't important enough. He just spit out the words while he stared at me with his flat gray eyes. "Whom do you think you are badgering, young woman?" he said. "I'll have your job."

I was impressed. This was a man so controlled he even said "whom" when he was angry. He threw his gym bag into the trunk. It snagged on a cardboard box. The box flap came open. Inside were about half a dozen plastic quarts of motor oil—and room for six more in the half-empty Exxon oil box. What was Hudson doing with motor oil in his car? If he changed his own oil, I'd drink it. Was that oil left over after he killed Jack? Was he so sure he wouldn't be caught that he didn't bother to remove it from his car? Wait till Mark Mayhew heard about this.

"What about that oil in your trunk?" I said. "It looks like you had a dozen quarts in the box, and six are missing. Can you tell me what happened to them?"

He didn't answer. He walked purposefully to the driver's door, as if I were invisible. He opened it and got in. I kept peppering him with questions: "Are you aware that the man your estranged wife lived with was murdered Friday night? And his death involved motor oil? Can you tell me where you were at midnight Friday?"

He refused to answer. I refused to move, hoping I could goad him into saying something I could use. Instead, he started up the car and began backing it out of his spot. If I hadn't jumped out of the way, he would have run over my foot. As he pulled out, the front bumper hit my knee. Well, okay, it bumped my knee slightly. But I could have been seriously hurt if I hadn't jumped out of the way. He didn't care. He didn't even stop to look back. A man who could coldly run me down could just as coldly kill. I didn't get any answers to my questions, but I got a demonstration of what Hudson Vander Venter could do. As far as I was concerned, he was capable of murder.

I stopped at a nearby yuppie soup and sandwich shop for a quick lunch. The soups were six bucks a bowl and they all came from exotic places. It wasn't bean soup, it was Tuscan bean soup, Italian plum tomato with basil, and Yukon gold potato soup. I ordered a turkey sandwich from nowhere special. It came with a huge gob of those hairlike sprouts. I ate them, too, hoping they might absorb some of the grease in my system.

By one-thirty I was in the office, chuckling at my mail. Howard Ohlendorf had sent me another joke.

Howard was president of a dental supply company and the father of nine. He had an eye-glazing list of civic honors and achievements, and ran for the U.S. Congress twice. But Howard had something I never saw on any résumé—a sense of humor. He loved jokes, even at his expense. When he lost the bid for Congress, he said he received a twenty-five-thousand vote mandate to stay home. Howard kept me supplied with jokes, quips, and witticisms. I appreciated all the laughs. The letter contained his current one, called "What Does the Graduate Ask?"

The graduate with a science degree asks, "Why does it work?"

The graduate with an engineering degree asks, "How does it work?"

The graduate with an economics degree asks, "How much will it cost?"

The graduate with a liberal arts degree asks, "Would you like fries with that?"

I laughed out loud. This one was a keeper. I tossed it into my bulging Jokes folder, which was filled with funny lines, letters, and stories from readers. I never knew when I was going to be in serious need of a good laugh. There was no author credit with Howard's joke. I wondered who wrote the original. Jokes seemed to arise spontaneously and move around the country by snail mail and e-mail on some migration pattern I couldn't figure out. A shrill voice interrupted these pleasant thoughts.

"There you are!" said Wendy the Whiner, as if I were a two-year-old who had wandered out of the yard. She stood at my desk, hands on her hips. "Charlie's looking for you. He wants to see you immediately." Wendy didn't bother to conceal her satisfaction. I was in trouble, and she was delighted. I needed to give her something else to think about.

"Interesting outfit, Wendy. You must tell me where you buy your things."

That way I could avoid the place. Wendy was wearing a gathered brown skirt that looked like it was made out of burlap. It sagged on one side, as if she had rocks in her pocket. Her white blouse had a matching brown stain on the pointed collar. There were three long mouse-colored hairs on her wrinkled brown jacket lapel.

Wendy knew when she was being made fun of. "I don't have time for your foolishness, Francesca," she whined. "I'm swamped with work. Go see Charlie now." As she turned and walked off, I saw a hunk of dingy slip hanging below her skirt.

Charlie's secretary wasn't there. I knocked on his half-open door. "Come in, Francesca," he said sharply. Charlie had completely redecorated the office after he took over from his predecessor. He cleared out the newspaper museum the old managing editor maintained in that office. He had workers rip up yards of perfectly good beige carpeting and throw out expensive beige curtains. Then he put in pale-gray carpeting, black vertical blinds to cover up the view of the *Gazette* parking lot, and a black Lucite desk big enough to seat twelve people—or one Charlie-size ego. Rumor had it that his black-leather-and-chrome chair was specially built to make him look taller, but none of us could prove it and his secretary wouldn't tell. He had two computer terminals on a black credenza, Dell Pentiums with twenty-one-inch color monitors, bigger, better, and faster than anything the staff had. One wall was covered with pictures of Charlie with celebrities: Charlie grinning at the publisher. Charlie and Dan Quayle grinning at each other—a meeting of the minds. Charlie and the mayor solemnly shaking hands. Charlie staring open-mouthed at a stunning Vanessa Williams, while she maintained a dignified distance from him.

The rest of the walls were covered with awards. The *Gazette* hadn't won a major newspaper contest in three decades. But we had won the American Pre-Treated Materials Association's Good Media Citizen Award for a business feature called "No Quality Ceiling on Pre-Treated Flooring." Professional associations thanked the *Gazette* for portraying them in a positive light. Small-time newspaper associations gave us plaques that said:

THIRD PLACE FOR BEST FEATURE PAGE LAYOUT
PAPERS WITH 50,000 CIRCULATION OR OVER
MID-MISSISSIPPI VALLEY BEST NEWSPAPER CONTEST

The award plaques were cheap wood covered with fanciful gold seals and ugly knobs of bronze. Woodward and Bernstein wouldn't have touched them with tongs, but Charlie went to every rubber-chicken lunch and two-day newspaper conference, and accepted each useless award as if it were a huge honor. He always made sure a *Gazette* photographer captured the moment, and he always looked proud.

Now he looked stern. Charlie, the great leader, was

putting down an employee rebellion. He sat up straight behind his desk, trying to appear taller. I stayed standing. He knew I was looking down on his bald spot. He cleared his throat and began his speech, solemnly listing my sins. "Francesca, Mr. Hudson Vander Venter, a respected businessman and a recent widower, says that you followed him to his car in a private parking garage and accosted him with questions about his wife's unfortunate end. Then you had the temerity to mention the biker who lived off that sad woman. How could you do that? How could you embarrass poor Mr. Vander Venter that way? Obviously his wife was off her head to take up with such a person. He says she was probably menopausal. But you didn't have the decency to ignore her mental problems. You mentioned that biker person to Hudson Vander Venter. You had to remind him of his wife's public shame. And if that wasn't bad enough, you virtually accused him of murdering the man. Accused Hudson Vander Venter, a community leader, of murder. Even for you, Francesca, that is too much.

"Mr. Vander Venter was absolutely shocked and appalled by your unprofessional behavior. He called me. He called the publisher—the *publisher*, Francesca, the man who runs this newspaper. The man who saw your revolting display yesterday at the Voyage Committee meeting. And now, one day later, you are badgering his griefstricken friend with improper and unprofessional questions." Charlie was sputtering with rage, and probably fear. The publisher must have been really pissed if he bothered to chew out Charlie. If Charlie lost this job, no other newspaper would hire the untalented little stump. The best he could do was teach journalism at some godforsaken hole.

"Fortunately for you, Mr. Hudson is a personal friend of the publisher. So he will not be bringing legal action against this paper. But I have promised the publisher that you will be disciplined for your pushy behavior."

"That's called reporting, Charlie," I said mildly.

"Shut up, Francesca! I don't want any more of your smart mouth. You are insubordinate. A written warning will be put in your file. Here is one copy. Another copy goes to the publisher, so he knows you have been disciplined. This is your second written warning in a month. Let me remind you, according to the Newspaper Guild contract, you can be fired after three written warnings. And I'm telling you now. You *will* be fired. You will have nothing to do with Hudson Vander Venter or his son, Hudson Junior. You will not write, you will not call, you will not accost those grieving people again. You will have the decency to leave them alone. Any contact whatsoever, and you will be fired. That will be your third transgression, and you're out—out—out! Fired, fired, fired!"

Even his bald spot was beet red. He was pounding on the desktop like our other wimpy managing editor used to do. Yelling this way couldn't be good for Charlie's blood pressure. If he kept it up, I stood a good chance of outliving the little twerp. Who did he think he was, lecturing me about proper professional behavior, a man who promoted his girlfriends? His idea of good reporting was when the reporter who copied the press release spelled all the names right. As for labeling poor Sydney crazy, wasn't that just like a certain kind of power-mad man? When Sydney got herself a lover, she had to be crazy—crazy to want anything besides the great Hudson Vander Venter. She was supposed to mope around in whatever house he let his castoff wife live in. Funny, nobody called Hudson crazy because he took up with Brenda the lawyer.

I grabbed the warning notice and stuffed it in my purse. Then I left his office and walked through an unnaturally quiet newsroom, straight for the elevator, without telling anyone where I was going. It was two-ten and I was feeling insubordinate. I was supposed to meet Mark at three. I made it back to my place in record time—fifteen minutes. I parked Ralph around back in the alley and ran upstairs. I needed to wash away that encounter with Charlie. I had just enough time to take a shower. No point in wearing old underwear after a fresh shower. I rummaged in my drawer until I found the fancy stuff I bought at Neiman Marcus: a lacy bra and those expensive trashy-looking panties. Then I put on my black jeans, a black cashmere turtleneck sweater, and an absolutely killer pair of square-toed Calvin Klein boots. Finally, I pulled on my black leather jacket and fished around in the pocket for my leather gloves.

Mark was in front of the store at exactly three o'clock, motorcycle rumbling softly. I didn't invite him inside. I pulled my front door shut and went outside. He was wearing the same thing I was: black leather jacket, black cashmere sweater, black jeans, and black square-toed boots, and they looked even better on him. He had a black-and-chrome Harley to complete his outfit. He was also wearing a black helmet. He handed me one, too.

"Here," he said. "You'll need this."

I'd forgotten how heavy helmets are. They feel like you're wearing a hollowed-out bowling ball on your head.

"Hold on tight," he said. When we first took off, I was scared. We were only going thirty-five, but it felt faster. I held on even tighter when we hit the highway and started going sixty-five. Cars and trucks screamed past us, and I felt naked without a car's protective metal shield. When you're on a motorcycle, the big lug nuts on a semi's wheels look like the blades on a war chariot. I thought about trucks hitting my unprotected legs and turning them into ground chuck. When a van cut us off, I imagined the cycle flipping, or sliding, and I saw myself flying through the air and then through a windshield. Or bouncing off the hood of a Toyota and landing under its wheels. I remembered that Cutup Katie called motorcycles donor cycles.

Then I decided if I was going to die, I might as well enjoy it. And I quit worrying. Just like that. I'd either die or I wouldn't. If I didn't, then there was a lot to enjoy. Mark's Harley felt sexy between my legs. The ads don't mention that interesting little vibration. We hit a bump, and I hung on tighter to Mark. He smelled good. Different from Lyle, but definitely masculine: coffee and peppermint and a hint of spice shaving lotion. I missed having a man around. We couldn't talk during most of the trip, except for a few shouted phrases. The last few miles of Missouri before we crossed the Mississippi River into Illinois were a dismal stretch of flat land, fireworks stands, and cheap cinderblock businesses, including the Discount Barn. No one wasted money on architectural niceties. This was flood plain, and it still showed the ravages of the Great Flood of 1993. We passed lonesome stands of drowned, blackened trees killed by the rising water.

Just as suddenly, the landscape became beautiful. The last thing I saw in Missouri was the Riverlands Environmental Demonstration Area. I caught a glimpse of graceful long-necked water birds feeding in the marshes. I forgot about them when I saw the Clark Bridge. It made the Golden Gate Bridge look like a clumsy hunk of orange iron. The Clark Bridge was twin golden fans of cables suspended from concrete poles. The gleaming golden bridge looked as delicate as a spiderweb, yet it was eighty-one-hundred tons of structural steel. As we crossed over to Illinois, I gave an inarticulate shout of awe. The great sparkling river spread out below us, the golden cables soared overhead, and the sunlight dazzled my eyes. Then we were in the old brick river town of Alton, riding through the antiques district. The little shops, with their frilly curtains and cute names, were clustered near the Alton casino boats. I wondered how many people walked off the gambling boats with their winnings, then lost them in those innocent little lace-lined antiques shops.

When we passed the ConAgra grain elevators, the Great River Road opened onto another stunning view: On one side were soaring white limestone bluffs. On the other side was the Mississippi River, wide, smooth, and silver in the sunlight. It was a sight you expected to see in California, not the Midwest. I selfishly hoped its beauty would stay undiscovered.

Right before we got to the little gingerbread village of Elsah, Mark turned off on Dorfmann Road. We passed ranch houses and mobile homes with carports and satellite dishes. We saw flocks of plastic lawn ducks, chickens, and deer. Then the homes and lawns vanished. The road grew more deserted and hilly. There were long stretches of woods and a few fields. Fat round hay bales were rolled against the barbed-wire fences. The fences were covered with bright red vines that were probably poison ivy. Tough, bug-bitten flowers and yellowing weeds grew along the road. I spotted a dead possum that had been run over, its guts red and glistening on the center line, and I shuddered and tightened my helmet strap, thinking of Jack. There was a sharp curve around a cornfield, then a steep rollercoaster drop. Mark took it fast—at least sixty. My stomach fell into my boots, then lurched up again when we hit a bump and another curve. After the curve, Mark braked the motorcycle and pulled off the road. We had reached the scene of Jack's death. If Jack came roaring drunk down that hill and swerved to avoid the box at the bottom, he didn't have a chance. He'd slide into the oil and gravel on the curve, go straight into the dense trees and down into a ditch.

I didn't get any special evil feeling about the place. There wasn't much to see. The oil on the blacktop road had been cleaned up. Mark pointed out the ugly skid marks. He showed me the thick old maple with the cycle-scarred bark on the curve. I saw the tread going down into the muddy ditch. We walked up the road a little way, and Mark showed me where the accident reconstruction team thought the killer's car might have been parked.

"Seen enough?" he said. I nodded. Then we walked back to his motorcycle and rode a little farther to a fruit-and-vegetable stand with a hand-lettered sign: CLOSED FOR THE SEASON. SEE U NEXT YEAR. The stand was a weathered white that probably would get another coat of paint next summer when it reopened, and it had four tiers of boards, like steps, for displaying produce. I sat down, while Mark rummaged in his saddlebags and came out with a metal Thermos, a foam cup, paper napkins, and a bag of muffins.

"Thirsty?" he said.

I was, after that ride. He poured his coffee into the foam cup and gave me my coffee in the top to the Thermos. I reached in the bag and took out a big gooey raspberry muffin, the kind that looks virtuous and isn't. It was good. Food is always extra good after a ride, maybe because part of you never expects to eat again. Hoping to keep the subject on business, I told Mark about seeing the motor oil in the trunk of Hudson's car.

"Why isn't a rich guy like him going to the Jiffy Lube?" he asked.

"I didn't get to ask Hudson if he changed his own oil," I said. "He called up and complained to Charlie and the publisher and now I'm under orders to stay away from him and Hud Junior."

Mark grinned. "I can ask Hudson, though," he

said. "Not that I expect he'll give me a straight answer. He'll probably have his lawyer call the mayor, who will remind me it's not illegal for a man to have motor oil in his trunk. But it's damn strange for someone like Hudson."

Mark smiled, and I didn't feel so much like an outsider. "The son has been behaving oddly, too. Hud Junior was stopped by a city patrol car near the Casa Loma the night of his mother's murder. He was buying drugs in an alley off Cherokee and California. The dealer ran off. The officer ran Hud Junior's plates and decided a rich kid like him would have Daddy hire an expensive lawyer and bail him out before he even finished the paperwork. The officer was tired and it was almost the end of his shift. He let the kid go with a warning to keep his drug-buying Ladue ass out of the Third District. Said if he ever saw him in the neighborhood again, he'd run him in. The kid looked scared and took off. But when the officer heard that Mrs. Vander Venter was murdered that night, he mentioned the incident to me. We've got it on tape. The officer radioed in a 27 car check, with Hud Junior's car make and license number. The kid was stopped a block or so from the Casa Loma, half an hour before his mother was killed."

"Interesting," I said. We sipped coffee in a companionable silence. I thought about what Mark told me.

Now father and son both had reason to avoid me. What if Hud Junior didn't leave the Third District? What if he stayed around and killed his mother? If he was buying drugs, he needed more money than he could make working at a coffeehouse. His mother's trust fund was instant cash. He was furious at her. Was he mad enough to kill her? I needed to find out more about him.

I finished my coffee and Mark finished his. When we got to his motorcycle, I handed him the muffin wrapper and my Thermos cup. Our hands brushed, by accident or design, I have no idea, but then we were kissing on the back of his motorcycle and un-zipping zippers, when a beat-up old pickup truck came by and the driver honked and whistled and I straightened up. "We can't do this here," I said.

"We can't go to my place. How about yours?" he said, and then added, "You know I'm married. I won't leave my wife and kids."

"Good!" I said, with a force that surprised us both.

We rode back to my place without saying another word. I held Mark tightly. I liked everything about this man: his hair, his smell, his smile, and the fact that unlike Lyle, he'd never pressure me to marry him. The high speeds and road noise blew any sensi-ble thoughts out of my head, and that's how I wanted it. The hour-long trip back seemed shorter. When we got to my place, he parked his Harley in front. I pulled off my helmet, and he put it away in his sad-dlebag and took off his. We peeled off our gloves and stuck them in our jacket pockets. I unlocked my door while Mrs. Indelicato stared out her confectionary window at us. Her glare could remove the paint from my door. I knew she disapproved if I was bringing home another man. Mrs. I is a great fan of Lyle's. Good thing she didn't know Mark was a married cop.

My front door opened into a typical South Side

arrangement: a long, dark flight of steps with a bend near the top. Three green-and-pink art-glass windows were set in the staircase wall. The steps were steep and painted with flat brown deck enamel. They started in a narrow entranceway with just enough room for a throw rug and a radiator. Over the radiator I had a framed poster of St. Louis artist Ernest Trova's "Falling Man." It should have been Falling Woman. I barely shut the door against Mrs. I's soul-stripping glare before Mayhew took up where he stopped on the roadside. He leaned me up against the opposite wall, kissed me hard and then softer and then harder, and ground his pelvis into mine. I ground right back and wrapped my arms around his neck and kissed him just as hard. A long motorcycle ride is a great aphrodisiac. Holding him tightly for miles had melted any awkwardness between us. I felt like I already knew him and we fit together. Mark didn't talk a lot, but he made appreciative little moans and groans while he kissed me. I hoped Mrs. I didn't hear them. I could feel his hands under my sweater. They were warm and slightly callused. Mmmm. I started to move up the steps and he followed, but we only got about three steps up when we stopped for more kisses. I was half lying, half sitting on the steps, with my head on a stair tread, and he was on top of me, French kissing me with an interesting rhythm while one of his hands unzipped my killer Calvin Klein boot. It dropped on the stairs with a loud *thunk!*

I felt his other hand down the back of my black jeans, and if Mrs. I didn't hear that boot *thunk!* I was pretty sure she heard that last moan from me. Or was it Mark making those noises? I came up for air long enough to say "We really should go upstairs."

"Mmmmunh," he said, which I took for yes. We made it four more steps and then we stopped again and I lost the other boot and my sweater, and he took off his leather jacket to pillow my head and kiss me some more, and he unbuckled his shoulder harness and hung it on the banister, and I helped him out of his sweater, but he had a shirt on underneath. Three steps later he'd unzipped my jeans, although I still had them on. I'd lost my socks and he'd lost his boots and his belt was unbuckled. The stairs looked like the last hour at the parish rummage sale, when all the clothes are marked down to twenty-five cents and people start flinging them everywhere. We were moaning and smooching like a couple of teenagers making out on a car seat, and let me tell you, a stair tread is even more uncomfortable than a gear shift knob. I was dizzy with lust and my lips were swollen from his kisses by the time we got to the bend near the top of the stairs. Three more steps and we'd be in my apartment. The bend formed a triangular landing and gave us more room to maneuver. I got a few buttons undone on his shirt, and he got me out of my black jeans. I could hear them sliding down the stairs and I could feel myself sliding back on the landing and I could feel him on top of me, and we needed a bed. If we didn't make it to the bed, the living-room carpet would be more comfortable. I could handle rug burn better than stair-tread marks.

"Upstairs," I said between kissed-bruised lips.

"Yes," he said, his warm breath in my ear. "Oh, baby, yes."

I managed to stand up, even though I was a bit shaky. I stood at the top of the steps, down to my new underwear.

10

If you're going to have an affair with a married man, don't do it at your grandparents' house. The first thing I saw, when I was standing at the top of the stairs in my sexy underwear, was my grandma's TV shrine: the picture of Christ over the Magnavox television set. The TV was one of those big dark old cabinet jobs from the early 1960s, with skinny brass-tipped legs. On top the TV, as if it was an altar, Grandma had two white candles in glass candle-sticks. Christ's picture was wreathed in white plastic roses. Christ's eyes follow you around the room. They followed me around in my underwear, watching half my ass hanging out the back.

Suddenly I felt foolish, standing half naked in Grandma's living room with someone else's husband. I also felt chilly. Did I turn down the heat? Or did the temperature suddenly drop? It was cold in here. I had goose bumps, and they weren't from pleasure. Before I found the thermostat, I better find a condom. Did I even have one? Lyle and I had been faithful to each other for so long, we quit using them a couple of years ago. I hated condoms. But I'd hate AIDS a lot more. I remembered a diagram I saw in the *Gazette* showing what it was like when you had unprotected sex with someone. The diagram showed you and the guy holding hands, since the *Gazette* did not put unmarried people in bed in a family newspaper. Behind your man were all the women he'd slept with, standing in a ghostly line, and you sure hoped it was only women he'd had for lovers. Then there were all the men you'd slept with forming another ghostly line. My line would be pretty short, not much longer than the line at an ATM on a Tuesday night. But if the gossip was true about the way Mark Mayhew was behaving since he broke that last big case, he'd need red velvet ropes like a ticket counter line at the airport. Heck, the diagram would look like one of those "Where's Waldo?" drawings, with zillions of people swarming all over the place.

Somewhere in that picture would be Charlie and the guys at the *Gazette*. And my father. I'd have joined the crowd. I'd be one of the destroyers, one of the people who ruined lives, wrecked other people's marriages, and hurt their own children and spouses with their careless adulteries. Now I was going to be in that picture. I'd be just as bad as my philandering father, who drove my mother crazy with his infidelities. I'd be just like Charlie, who screwed staffers and then promoted them in kingly fashion after they'd been touched by the royal scepter. Soon I'd be promoting my squeeze, writing funny little features about the noble police detective who'd been in my pants. A fine future awaited me. My virtue, or whatever you called it, was thinner than my fancy underwear at this point. I'd just about lost it, step by step. But I still had a few scraps covering me. I didn't want to lose them.

If Mark had come up to me at that moment, put his arms around me, and whispered the right words, I might have gotten over my case of the other woman jitters and we could have fallen happily into my grandparents' big oak bed. But he came up the steps and said the exact wrong—or right—thing.

"Jesus Christ!" he said, and I knew he wasn't talking about Grandma's holy picture. "Who's your decorator? Goodwill? Look at that ancient TV. And those bowling trophies. You still have the original cellophane on those lampshades. Francesca, you dress like a million bucks and you're living in this dump. Where did you get this crap—a Cherokee Street rummage sale?"

"It was my grandparents' furniture," I said, with as much dignity as I could muster in my current condition. "They brought me up. When they died, I kept everything the same, I guess so I could keep them. Because I admire them."

Mark looked stricken. He really was a nice guy. "I am sorry, Francesca. It was a stupid thing to say and I apologize. Will you forgive me?"

I turned my head away. He turned it back. "Look at me," he said.

So I did. Another mistake. He'd shed his shirt and pants. It was the first time I'd seen Mark without his exquisite clothes. He looked ridiculous in blue boxer shorts, which were ironed, probably by his wife. That made me feel even more guilty. He had the beginning of a paunch, which his tailoring hid. He was hairy as a hibernating bear. He had black hair on his legs, his chest, his stomach, his back, even his shoulders. The man should shave his shoulders. The man should braid his shoulders. I put my arm around him and my amethyst birthstone ring snagged on his back hair. That was the final straw—or hair. I wasn't hot for Mark. I was in love with his clothes. When I saw the real Mark, I didn't want him. I should stick with his wardrobe and his fine mind.

"I really like you, Mayhew," I said, "but not this way. I can always find a lover. I need a friend."

He shrugged. "As you wish," he said. Maybe he was as turned off as I was. I went into the bedroom and put on my full-length black terry robe. I stayed in the room long enough to give Mayhew the chance to put on his clothes. When I came out of the bedroom, I saw that he was dressed and he had gathered my clothes off the stairs. He had my boots in his hand and my jeans and sweater neatly folded over his arm. He handed them to me like a valet, and bowed. We both started laughing nervously, and I gave him a sisterly hug and stepped back pretty quickly. I didn't want to ignite any lingering sparks. "Good-bye, Mark. Thanks. I'm sorry."

"Too bad, Francesca, you got a great body," he said. He kissed me on the nose and left. Mayhew had class.

If someone could do a full-body blush, it was me. I was embarrassed. I'd probably never be able to sleep with another man as long as I lived. I'd probably never be able to walk down the front steps again.

Every time I did, I'd see Mayhew and me groping each other. God, this was mortifying. He'd been so nice about it, too. I couldn't even hate the man. All I could do was hate myself, for being so weak. And hate Lyle, for pushing me into this life of degradation. If he hadn't tried to force me to marry him, I wouldn't have wrapped myself around Mayhew like some cycle slut. I felt my face grow hot again when I thought about this afternoon. I picked up my jeans to put them on and saw the seat was dusty. Those stairs needed to be cleaned. I came from a long line of Scrubby Dutch, people who cleaned house for recreation. To them, steps as dusty as mine were more shameful than sex with a married man. And a lot easier to undo. I got a dustpan and brush and a damp rag and wiped the steps down from the top to the bottom, a South Side penance. But no matter how much dirt I swept up, I couldn't wipe away my embarrassment. Even house cleaning didn't make the time pass. It was now a little after six o'clock. I'd managed to mess up my life in three hours. How could I have done that with Mayhew? Why had I done that? Why did I start it? Why did I stop it? My brain kept chasing the same ideas again and again, like a kitten chasing its tail. I needed to think about something else. So I did what I always do when I don't want to think about my messed up life. I went to work.

I went down the back steps, which had only memories of taking out the garbage and bringing up the groceries, and got in Ralph. Then I drove over to Eric's apartment in Richmond Heights, the place where Hud Junior was living temporarily. Charlie had ordered me not to talk to Hudson or his son, but he didn't say anything about Eric, Hud's roommate. Maybe he could tell me something useful. Highway 40 had what passed for a traffic jam in St. Louis, which means the cars slowed down for a few exits, and drivers complained as if they were in a Manhattan gridlock. We don't like to wait, especially not on Highway 40, the road to the rich suburbs. A few years ago that road was renamed Interstate 64, but no true St. Louisan ever called anything by its new name. It was still Highway 40 to us. This makes it tough for outsiders to get around our town, because we don't give directions. We give history. No matter what the signs said, it would always be Highway 40. We still called one of the main routes through downtown Twelfth Street, even though it became Tucker Boulevard in 1979. Which meant that any tourists who went downtown on local directions wandered around helplessly for days, living on roots and canned beer, until they figured it out.

Eric and Hud lived in a hulking brown brick apartment building right off Highway 40. I could see it from the road. I found a parking place on the street and knocked on the door. Eric came to the door. He could have been a clone of Hud, from his blond hair to his black T-shirt, except he didn't have the dark circles under his eyes. I asked if Hud was home. "Hud isn't here right now," Eric said civilly.

"That's okay," I said. "I can talk to you. I'm Francesca Vierling with the *City Gazette*."

"You!" he snarled, as if I'd just announced the IRS would be giving him a free audit. "We've both been warned about you. Hud's not supposed to talk to you and neither am I. If you don't get away from my door I'll . . . I'll . . . call the police." Eric slammed the door in my face, and I could hear two locks click and a chain rattle, which I thought was excessive. I wasn't a mugger, just a mild-mannered reporter.

Well, that trip was a dead end. Hud and Hudson were out as sources. Mayhew could check them out. But Charlie didn't say anything about staying away from the grandmother, Elizabeth. Maybe she could explain where her grandson was the night her daughter-in-law was killed. Maybe she knew what her son was doing during those missing fifteen minutes at the cigar smokers' dinner. Maybe she could tell me why Hudson was carrying motor oil in the trunk of a new car. Maybe I could give her a call.

I don't have a car phone. I know it's inconvenient, but every jerk in the Western world has a car phone. I refuse to put one in. Which means that the drug dealers and I are constantly driving around, looking for an unvandalized pay phone. I stopped at a supermarket to make my calls and do some shopping. I couldn't face picking up anything at Mrs. Indelicato's confectionery for a while after . . . well, you know why.

I don't know if you've ever been in a St. Louis supermarket, but they are cathedrals of canned goods and produce. The one in my neighborhood plays Vivaldi tapes and has a coffee bar. The produce section is an invitation to an exotic banquet: Asian pears and persimmons. White asparagus and purple potatoes. Passion fruit and pine nuts. Portobello mushrooms, Vidalia onions, and edible flowers. In the seafood section, I could choose from five kinds of fresh shrimp, frog legs, smoked scallops, shark, squid, turtle meat, periwinkles, oysters, and Cajun crawfish. There were live lobsters in a tank and escargot and green-lipped mussels in the freezer. I didn't feel like cooking, so I threw an asparagus quiche and two vegetable burritos in my cart. I bypassed the bakery and the liquor department as more temptation that I didn't need. Then I bought myself some fresh flowers, since no one else would. I loved wandering around St. Louis supermarkets. A New York friend who came here on a visit compared them to the food hall at Harrod's. If a neighborhood supermarket could sell such exotic fare in St. Louis, you'd think the editors of the *Gazette* would quit feeding readers the same old pabulum.

A guy came over to me with a pack of fresh tuna steaks. "Do you know how to fix these?" he said, and smiled fetchingly. That fishy question was the male pickup ploy. Rather than hit on you at a bar, the smart guys tried to meet women at the supermarket. The subtle ones avoided the produce department. This guy was a cute blond in his thirties, a little on the bland side, with no visible tattoos, scars, or zits. He was wearing a pinstriped suit and polished shoes, so he probably had a job. But helpless men just don't appeal to me. I picked a three-pack of canned tuna out of my cart and said, "This is probably more your speed. Just open the can and it's ready."

He looked hurt and left. Just as well. I didn't want to tell anyone I'd picked that little something up at the supermarket. After today, I was through with men. I'd probably give them up permanently. Maybe I could spend my weekends doing good works at a homeless shelter or a children's home. Heck, their lives were miserable enough without having me around. Maybe I could spend my time alphabetizing my spices and sorting my socks. I checked out my groceries, got two dollars in quarters, and started making calls. I had an idea on how to break the case without talking to Hudson or Hud. This was St. Louis, where everyone knows everyone else. This city is the world's biggest small town. I was betting that there was some connection between Hudson and the dead biker Jack besides Jack's affair with Sydney. I was even beginning to wonder about that "chance" meeting Sydney and Jack had in Uncle Bob's. Suppose it was a setup? Suppose Hudson paid Jack to get rid of his troublesome wife? Suppose Hudson killed off Jack when the biker tried blackmail? That made a whole lot of sense. In fact, it was the only theory that fit all the facts. If I could establish a link between Jack and Hudson before Jack moved in with Sydney, I was on my way to solving this murder. And I had an idea how to do it. First, I needed to know just how far the Vander Venter roots went in this area. Some of the old families also had a country home, farm, or hunting lodge near St. Louis. Did Hudson? I didn't know, but I knew who did. I called my friend Jinny Peterson. The woman was better than five computer databases. She was intrigued by my question. "I don't know, either," she said, "But I can find out. Call me back in five minutes."

Perfect. That gave me enough time to talk to Elizabeth. I wondered if Hud's mother would shut me out the way her son did. Cordelia answered the phone. She came back after a short wait and said that Elizabeth would speak to me. Perhaps Hudson hadn't called her yet to warn her of my interfering ways. Maybe I better start asking questions now, in case he put the clamps on his mother talking to me, too.

"Thank you for talking to me," I said, and I meant it. "I know you are a great bargain hunter. Do you know where I can get any bargains in motor oil?"

Okay, it was clumsy. But she went for it. Elizabeth even laughed, a sound like ice cracking. I knew where her son got his warm personality. She said, "My reputation has caught up with me, I see. I'm not really the bargain hunter everyone thinks I am. I just can't stand to waste money. I was a recycler before it was fashionable. I believe our precious resources must be saved."

Especially those Vander Venter eagles.

"I don't know anything about motor oil," Elizabeth said, "but I did get a good price on Lapsang souchong. Would you like to come for tea tomorrow afternoon? It's Cordelia's day off, so we'll have to rough it, I'm afraid. It will just be you and me."

I was stunned. Elizabeth was actually inviting me to take tea with her. She was oozing charm for a Vander Venter. Of course, I said yes. "Four o'clock tomorrow afternoon then," she said, and hung up.

Still awed by my success, I dropped another quarter and called Jinny Peterson back. "The Mister is home from his evening bicycle ride, so I have to go," she said, "but the Vander Venters have a country place—they call it a farm—near Washington, Missouri." She hung up, too.

Two hits in a row. I tried for three. Sonny was the third part of my plan. I got the biker's answering machine: "This is Sonny and Debbie, gone out to play, we'll call you later in the day," his voice chanted.

"Hi, Sonny, it's Francesca, I wanted to . . ." I heard the sound of someone picking up the phone.

"Francesca, is that you?" Sonny said. "What can I do you for? Debbie and I were heading out the door. We're getting her cousin from Wisconsin some brains."

"You're not going to do that to an innocent stranger."

"Hey, he says he thinks he'll like 'em. We'll find out." Sonny laughed wickedly. "You called me. What do you need?"

"I want to ask you a couple of questions about Jack."

"The poor bastard," Sonny said. "We gave him a real biker's funeral. About forty of us rode in the funeral procession and then we went to one of his favorite bars. Listen, how soon do you need your questions answered?"

"Uhh," I said.

"That means right now. Debbie and I really are ready to run out the door with Arnold. Why don't you meet us there and we can talk? We're taking the kid to Dieckmeyer's. I don't have to tell you where that is. If nothing else, it's worth the trip to see Arnold's face."

I wondered if Arnold knew what he was in for. In St. Louis, going to get some brains didn't mean you went to school or the bookstore or the library. It meant you went out for deep-fried brain sandwiches. Brains are not beautiful. Slathered with ketchup and onion, which is the way we eat them, they look like a lab experiment. And if you think looking at a brain is bad, try eating one. It's a death-defying act. Brain sandwiches have the highest concentration of cholesterol on the planet. A dietitian once gave me these horrifying figures: Brains have 3,392 milligrams of cholesterol, 30 grams of fat, and 500 calories. And that's if you don't order the fries.

If you came from a German family, like I did, then you ate brain sandwiches. You didn't think about what they were, if you'll pardon the pun. They were dinner. They were lunch. They were cheap—or at least they used to be. Germans never wasted anything, not even organ meats. St. Louis Germans figured if you could fry something or cover it with sugar, you probably could get it down. Brains were fried. My grandma made some dandy ones. Cleaned them and fried them into little patties and put a big slab of Bermuda onion on top of each one and served them on hamburger buns. She made a few hamburgers for the squeamish who wouldn't try brains, but most everyone ate brains then, except for one Irish relative who didn't know any better.

Nowadays very few people made brains at home, but you could still get them at a handful of bars. Dieckmeyer's was an old family restaurant that was famous for its brains. It was decorated like your living room, if your living room had tables for four and a long bar, and it was probably cleaner than your house. Bud Dieckmeyer had died a few years ago, but his wife, Lorraine, and their children, Nancy and John, ran the place in the old tradition. Now poor Arnold from Ohio was going to eat his first brain, and because he didn't get them as a kid, he was going to have to think about what he was doing.

Arnold turned out to be a nice lad in his mid-twenties who had his head shaved and an earring in one ear. He'd convinced himself that he was tough. He was going to eat a brain sandwich, and so what? No big deal. He downed a beer to keep up his courage. Debbie and Sonny had matching grins on their faces. They were enjoying this. They both wore black Harley T-shirts and drank beer out of the bottle, biker style. Bikers don't like draft beer.

Finally the sandwich arrived. Plopped on two pieces of rye bread was something that looked like a brain, except it was covered with golden breading. You could see all the furrows and ridges. You could practically hear that sandwich think. Arnold turned a delicate shade of green.

"Er," he said. "It sure looks fried."

"Taste it," we said, sitting there like a pack of ghouls, waiting for him to take a bite.

"Sure. Sure. Let's let it cool off a bit first," Arnold said.

"Oh, you don't want to eat cold brains," said Sonny.

"That's not smart," Debbie said, laughing.

Arnold turned even greener. With the ketchup bottle in one hand, he was starting to look like a Christmas display, except he wasn't very festive. He poured ketchup on the sandwich until it looked like an accident scene. "Right," he said. "Bite. Just don't think about it."

"Its thinking days are done," said Sonny, who was enjoying this hugely. "Brains are food for thought."

Arnold couldn't stomach any more of Sonny's awful puns. He closed his eyes and took a big bite, then chewed slowly. "Not bad," he said, his voice quavering.

"What's it taste like?" we asked. Everyone has a different description.

"Sort of like a liver soufflé," the kid replied.

"Here, gimme that," Sonny said, putting Arnold out of his misery. "Brains are scarce these days. They shouldn't be wasted on someone who doesn't appreciate them." He smiled. "You're all right, Arnold. Most people aren't as brave as you. We'll take it from here. Get yourself something else."

Sonny and Debbie divided up the sandwich. Arnold, manhood confirmed, happily ordered a hamburger, which came from a cow, too, but wasn't so obvious about it. I had Lorraine's chicken and dumplings. While we ate, Sonny and Debbie told us stories about some of the one-percenters, the outlaw bikers, that were making the rounds.

"One of these guys was going with the ex-girlfriend of a Saddle Tramp," Sonny began.

"That's a biker gang, like the Hell's Angels," Debbie explained to Arnold.

"The ex-boyfriend put out a contract on the new one," Sonny continued. "The new boyfriend started carrying two or three guns in his saddlebags. Then he realized he might not be able to get to them in time. So he started wearing three sticks of dynamite on his chest. He figured if they got him, he was going to take them with him. So far as I know, he's still riding around with the dynamite strapped to himself."

"What's his bike look like?" I asked. "There are a lot of potholes on the streets these days. My luck, I'll be the car behind him."

"You don't have anything to worry about in your Jag," he said. "That car is built like a tank."

By the time we ordered apple pie, Sonny was telling us "All these one-percenters got girlfriends, along with the wife. I know one who leaves his wife at home and takes his girlfriend along on long trips. She sleeps in the weeds on the side of the road with him. These are not rich guys. They don't have money for hotels."

"Was the girlfriend hot-looking?" Arnold asked. If he expected a romantic biker babe, Sonny took care of that notion.

"Skinny as a drowned rat," he said. "That beer bottle's got a lot of meat on it compared to her calves." Arnold looked respectfully at the beer bottle, as if it were one of the players in this drama.

"Didn't his wife ride?" I asked.

"She used to," Sonny said. "Then a couple of friends got in a bad accident and she got scared. But this girlfriend and wife business gets interesting. I heard about the biker woman whose husband roughed her up once too often. She called her boyfriend and told him, 'You get over here and do something.' Then she took a shower. While she was in the shower, her boyfriend came over. When her husband answered the door, the boyfriend blew him away."

"That's doing something, all right," Debbie said. "Tell her about the Saddle Tramp's funeral."

"One of the Saddle Tramps got killed," Sonny said. "It was a foggy night, and he and his girlfriend were out riding on one of those country highways. His bike quit, just like that, in the middle of the road, and he was rear-ended by a car. He got killed and his girlfriend wound up in a wheelchair. We went to the funeral. It was weird. There was his wife, talking about what a fine Christian man he was, and there was his girlfriend in the wheelchair, sitting right there. About half the funeral was outside. Those were the local biker crowd. Inside were all his wife's churchgoing friends. It was like two funerals in one."

"I'll tell you, if my husband died with his girlfriend, you'd have to send me pictures of the funeral, because I wouldn't be there," Debbie said, but the way she looked at Sonny you knew there was no chance of that. They'd ridden thousands of miles together and got along fine. They'd even been to Sturgis, the wild summer party of the biker world. "Biggest danger there at Sturgis is getting drunk and passing out and getting run over, or having a drunken biker run over you when you're asleep. I know guys who got their arms and legs broken that way."

"You ever ride anything but a Harley?" I asked.

"I had a Jap cycle before I knew better," Sonny said. "Now I don't ride anything but Harleys. It's almost like I'd be committing adultery if I rode anything else. Except that adultery might be fun, and riding anything but a Harley wouldn't."

Debbie threw him a glare that should have peeled the Harley emblem off his black shirt, but he just laughed at her and rubbed her shoulders. "You know I'm just talking, baby."

"You better be," she said.

He grinned his rabid chipmunk grin. Then he got

serious. "The working man is getting priced out of the Harley world. It's getting to be a real issue for us. Harley approached money people like Malcolm Forbes about riding Harleys, and it set the stage for people of means to buy them. Harleys are a good investment. You can't lose—the price always goes up. When the money people got involved, the prices really went up. Now the waiting list for a new Harley is one year, and regular working guys have trouble affording them. If you have three kids to feed, it's hard to justify twenty thousand dollars for something for yourself."

Sonny's speech gave me the opening I needed. "I think that's why Jack tried to sell me the name of Sydney's killer—he wanted to pay his bills before he lost his motorcycle," I said.

Sonny looked surprised. "He tried to sell you the name? Jack? He must have been really hard up."

"He never was too bright," Debbie said, "but I didn't think he'd do something like that."

I told them the whole story, and how I didn't believe him and how he was found dead on a back road in Illinois and why I thought he might have been doing some dirty work for Hudson Vander Venter.

"How's he going to meet Hudson Vander Venter?" Sonny said. "Show up at one of their black-tie parties? Invest with his firm? No way they'd know each other."

"This is St. Louis, Sonny," I said. "Everybody knows everybody else if you dig deep enough."

"Get out your shovel then," Sonny said. "But I don't think there's a connection."

"Let's start with the son, who's now living in Richmond Heights," I said. "Do you think Jack would know Hud?"

"I don't think so. How would he know Hud?"

"The kid has—or had—a drug problem," I said. "Jack ever sell anything?"

"A little," Sonny said. "Only to friends. He wouldn't sell to a Ladue kid. That's asking for trouble."

"Did he ever work for the father, Hudson?"

"At the investment house?" Sonny said. "Are you kidding?"

"Did Jack ever do any handyman work, carpentry, lawn mowing, leaf raking, brush cutting?"

"Not if he could help it," Sonny said. "And not in Ladue. They wouldn't let someone like Jack ride around in Ladue. The police would chase him out, the way he looked. He couldn't go near the Vander Venters on a Harley."

"What about a pickup truck?" I said.

"He might," Sonny said. "Except Jack didn't have one. Might have borrowed his brother's pickup."

"I didn't know he had a brother in St. Louis," I said.

"He doesn't. He has a brother in Washington, Missouri. You'd never guess him and Jack came from the same gene pool. His brother Eddie is a good Christian man. He never drinks, never smokes, works hard. He has steady habits and he's very trustworthy. Eddie does a lot of work for the rich St. Louisans who have farms and weekend places around there. Those rich folks guard his name and phone number like it was the family jewels. Keep him loaded with work. Sometimes, if he got really busy, he'd ask Jack to come down and help him out. Offer him good money, too. Jack did it a few times and then he stopped."

"Why?"

"I'm not sure," Sonny said. "There may have been some kind of trouble like something missing at one of the houses, or clearing brush may have been more work than Jack wanted to do. I just know he did it for a while, and then he quit."

We were close. I knew it. I just had to ask the right question. "The Vander Venters have a farm out that way," I said. "Did Eddie work for them? Did he ever have Jack help out around their farm?"

"Might have," Sonny said. "Wait a minute. I remember something. Yes, yes, Jack did some work for his brother on the Vander Venter farm. I remember now. I don't think it lasted very long, but Jack sure bragged about it."

"He bragged about working for the Vander Venters?" This didn't sound like the Jack I knew.

"Nope," Sonny said. "He bragged about *not* working. About how he took the money, sat around and drank beer, and did next to nothing. Got eight dollars an hour for it. He didn't talk about it until after he took up with Sydney. Then he told us about it. I remembered what he said, too: Now he'd screwed both Vander Venters."

■

Finally I had the information I wanted. I'd established the first connection. Jack knew Hudson. Tomorrow, when I saw Hudson's mother, I'd try to find out just how well Hudson knew him and what other work Jack did for him. And if they were in contact during that fifteen minutes Hudson couldn't account for the night of his wife's death.

I thanked Sonny and Debbie and congratulated Arnold on his successful introduction to St. Louis brains. I was so elated, I picked up the whole check, which wasn't that big, anyway, even for a *Gazette* expense account. It was nine-thirty when I got home. There were no spots in front, so I parked Ralph in back and went up the back stairs. I'd barely dropped my briefcase by the door when I heard the doorbell ring.

I wondered if it was Mayhew, returning. I wondered if I could look him in the eye. I blushed again just thinking about our encounter. What would it do to our friendship? My front door was a big panel of beveled glass, set in a wooden door. Like all proper South Side households, it was covered with a sheer white curtain. If we South Siders stood at the top of the steps and didn't turn on the stairway light, we could get a pretty good idea who was standing at our door.

I studied the form. It was a man, taller than I, and he had a bunch of flowers in one hand. It wasn't Mayhew. It was Lyle. I was in no mood for him right now. I ran down the steps, prepared to send him and his flowers packing.

"What are you doing here?" I said. "I'm too old for you."

"Shhh. Shhhh," he said, as if he were quieting a child. Lyle folded me in his arms. "I'm sorry. So sorry this ever happened. It was so unnecessary. I know how much you love your grandparents. I'd never want you to give up their place. I just want you with me as much as possible."

I started to cry, but I didn't want him to see me. "What happened to Ashley?" I said, sniffing.

"She talks about her horse Pumpkin and her cat Pookie and she complains constantly about how her roommate doesn't clean up," he said. "She spent thirty minutes telling me how her roommate hung a wet towel over the shower curtain and it will mildew if she keeps that up. She also said my wardrobe was too old and I dressed like her dad. There's a good reason why I dress like her dad. I found out I'm three years older than her dad."

I snickered. I couldn't help it. I don't think Lyle heard. He kept talking and stroking my hair. "She wanted me to wear an Armani suit. I told her I'd look like a gunsel. She didn't know what a gunsel was. Every morning she read me my horoscope and actually believed it. It was the only thing she read in the *Gazette*. She said Bosnia was boring.

"When I mentioned Woodstock, she thought it was the bird in the Snoopy cartoon. I was wrong about her not having problems. She has lots of problems and they aren't nearly as interesting as yours. Francesca, could we please try again? I love you so much. I don't want to be without you."

He kissed me softly, as if I were very fragile and valuable. I kissed him back. I smelled the familiar Lyle smells of coffee and sandalwood soap. I unbuttoned a button on his shirt and saw his nice hairy chest. He didn't look like a bear. In fact, he looked just right. He leaned me up against the wall in the entrance hall and kissed me softly and then harder and I kissed him back and realized it had been a long time. . . .

"Do I need to wait for the results of a blood test?" I said, between kisses. I was *not* getting into bed with Ashley and all her boyfriends and her horse, too.

"Francesca, you don't have to believe me, but we didn't get much further than some heavy necking," he said, kissing me again. "But if you want to wait . . . I'll leave right now and get tested in the morning."

"No, I believe you," I said. "I can imagine exactly how that's possible."

"You can?" he said happily, kissing me harder.

"Oh, yes," I said. I let out a long sigh. It looked like the poor and the orphaned were off the hook. I wasn't going to give up sex and devote my life to good works. I'd overcome the trauma of the Mayhew disaster in less than four hours. An amazing recovery.

Lyle was frenching me with an interesting rhythm. He started to lower me to the stairs when I stopped him. Oh, no. Not the stair treads again.

"Upstairs," I said. He didn't hesitate or argue. We ran up the steps without stopping. We didn't even notice the holy picture on the wall over the TV, and if the eyes of Christ followed me into my bedroom, I didn't know it.

11

The next morning I woke up and smelled the coffee.

Lyle was standing beside my bed with a large latte and an Asiago cheese bagel from the St. Louis Bread Company. "Good morning," he said, and smiled. "I went for a walk. I thought you might like these."

I smiled back, stretched, and drew him down for a good-morning kiss. Then I sat up and took the bagel and latte. Last night had been wonderful. How could we have wasted so much time being angry at each other? He sat down on the bed to drink his own latte, and I tickled his ear.

"So it's decided," he said. "You'll move in with me but keep this place."

"And if it works out," I said, "we'll think about getting married."

"We *will* get married," he said, kissing me firmly.

"We will," I repeated. I hadn't said when. I'd just said I would. Someday.

He looked at his watch. "It's eight o'clock. I have to be at the university for my eight-forty class. I'll call you this afternoon. Maybe we can have dinner if you're not tied up at work." He said it without a trace of sarcasm. He meant it.

"I'd like that," I said. "I love you. After last night, this day will only get better."

Boy, was I wrong. If I knew what was in store for me, I'd have never gotten out of bed. But I was in a rush to greet this day. I got up and dressed, taking time only to admire the flowers Lyle had brought last night, a big bunch of fragrant white lilies with deep pink throats. Star Gazer lilies, he said they were.

Now it was eight-thirty in the morning, and I was heading down the back steps to get Ralph. I had a Voyage meeting at ten-thirty. This time I wasn't going to be late. I was going to listen and keep my big mouth shut . . . I screamed. Someone had attacked Ralph. They'd hurt my beautiful blue Jaguar, the love of my life, after Lyle, of course. All Ralph's windows were broken. Every single one. Both windshields, front and back, plus all four passenger windows. Glass sparkled on the concrete parking pad like pieces of ice. It crunched underfoot when I went over for a closer look. I didn't have to go far to see what had broken Ralph's windows. Lying by the right rear tire was a concrete cinder block. It had glass on it, too, and one corner was chipped. But the block didn't make those deep scratches in Ralph's blue paint. That had to be a key or some sort of knife. Probably a pocketknife, a sharp one. Sharp enough to cut through the leather on the front seats. Even under the drifts of bluish ice-glass, I could see stuffing poking out of both seats. I had no idea Ralph had so much glass. It was safety glass, so most of it broke into pellets. There were huge sparkling mounds of glass on the backseat and in the window wells. There were smaller mounds on the floor, the stick-shift console and the dash. Glass had scratched the burled walnut trim and filled the map pouch on the doors. Glass pellets sparkled like jewels on the handle. Heaps of glass glittered on the trunk and the bumper. There was even glass in the treads on the Pirelli tires. I didn't touch anything, because I didn't want to disturb it for the police. But I looked in through the empty front windows at the front seats. The damage was worse than I thought. Someone had used the knife to carve three words in the driver's seat. The person had a hard time making the Bs, but I still got the message. BEAT IT BITCH, it said, in the Isis blue leather.

And then, for one final, nasty touch, the vandal had opened the glove compartment, where I kept an ice scraper for the windows I no longer had, a pair of extra pantyhose, a box of emergency Tampax, tapes, and other junk. The vandal dumped them all on the floor, except the pantyhose and the Tampax. The pantyhose were slashed, but that was no great loss. They had a hole in the toe that I'd fixed with nail polish. I only kept them in the car in case I got a bad run in my nylons and couldn't go home to change. All the Tampax had the paper covers stripped off. The vandal made a hole in the car seat with the knife and stuck one stripped Tampax right in the hole. It looked violent, malicious, and personal. I felt hot, angry tears in my eyes. Ralph was a beautiful car, a sculpture on wheels. Who did this? And when? It had to be last night, after I got home from seeing Sonny and Debbie. Lyle came over about ten, and we were making enough noise of our own that we didn't hear anything out back. Then we fell into a sound sleep.

Maybe Mrs. Indelicato heard something. She lived in three rooms behind the store. I knocked on her back door, but she didn't answer. She must be in front, in the store. I ran through the concrete gangway and threw open the door, nearly knocking over a rack of Lay's potato chips. No customers were in the store. Mrs. I, a thin, gray woman, was stocking soup on the crowded shelves. Campbell's Cream of Mushroom was one of the great white sauces in this neighborhood. Today the usually friendly Mrs. I wore a starched shirtwaist dress and a look of disapproval.

"Mrs. I, Mrs. I, someone attacked my car. Did you hear anything last night?" I said.

"I heard a lot of things last night," she said. "And in the afternoon, too. Things no decent widow woman should have to hear. You are my landlady, and you own this building, but I'll have you know I run a respectable store. I cannot have you bringing bikers back to your grandparents' home. What if children had come in here when you were on those steps with that man? The moans, the groans. I never heard such things in my life."

She probably hadn't. Not even when Mr. Indelicato was alive. He was a pallid-looking creature, about as exciting as the mushroom soup. Same color, too. But it was mean to make fun of Mr. In-

delicato. His wife didn't deserve that. I was going to
have to apologize to her sometime. I might as well do
it now. I found some humility that I usually kept
hidden away and said, "Mrs. Indelicato, I am so
sorry if I disturbed you. I promise, as God is my witness"—that I will never go hungry again? What was I
doing quoting Scarlett O'Hara? Mrs. Indelicato
needed an apology—"that it will never happen again.
I will never have that man here. I am back with Lyle."

She smiled a little. "Lyle is a good, decent man
with a steady job," she said.

South Siders Mrs. I's age did not call desirable
men hunks. Here's how they drool over guys: "He has
a steady job." True South Siders would pass up marriage to John Travolta because he's out of work several months of the year.

"Lyle is cultured, too." This was lavish praise.
South Siders have an almost religious veneration of
education. Mrs. I pursed her thin lips again and
disapproved. "Not like that other one who rides
motorcycles. A biker hoodlum, that one. A bum." Not
exactly. But if I explained Mayhew was a St. Louis
homicide detective, I'd only make it worse. Her generation did not believe that Malcolm Forbes had
changed Harley's image. And she'd never believe the
biker was really Officer Friendly.

"I have a problem, Mrs. I," I said, finally getting
around to the real reason I was there. "Someone vandalized Ralph last night. Broke out all his windows
and tore up his seats."

"But that is a terrible thing," said Mrs. I, sincerely
shocked and upset. Right now she wasn't too sure
about me, but she loved Ralph almost as much as I

did. She said he was "good for property values," the highest accolade on the South Side. "What is this neighborhood coming to? More and more of the wrong element"—she meant color—"are moving in. People with no respect for property. People only interested in what they can steal and sell to buy more drugs."

"Nothing was taken, Mrs. I. Not even the radio." Jaguar radios are designed so they don't work outside the car without a code, and street smart thieves know this. Occasionally you got a really young or dumb thief who hacked away at the dash, trying to get out the worthless coded radio. He could do three or four thousand dollars' worth of damage to your dashboard.

"So who do you think did this terrible thing to Ralph?" Mrs. I. asked, as if a friend had been beaten up instead of a car. That's how I felt, too. My friend Ralph had been hurt.

"I don't know."

I didn't know. But I had a pretty good idea. That malicious destruction was a warning from either Hudson Vander Venter or his druggie son, Hud. It was pure meanness to break Ralph's windows and rip his leather, and that tampon in the seat was a particularly ugly touch. It could have been the kid. Drugs can bring out a strange, mean streak in some people. But Hudson Senior seemed more likely. The man was a bully. Look how he called the publisher and threw his weight around when I tried to question him. He was ruthless to Sydney, even though he was at fault, dumping a faithful wife because he was faithless. He tried to run me down when I got in his way. I must be on the right track. I just wished I knew what it was.

Mrs. I had not heard anything unusual, except for the sound of glass breaking about two-thirty that morning. But she only heard one crash. "I thought someone dropped a beer bottle in the alley," she said. "I went back to sleep." She let me call the police from her store, and by the time the squad car arrived thirty minutes later, we were back on our usual good terms.

There were two uniformed officers, both black, one in his forties and one in his twenties. The older one was built like an athlete going to seed. The younger one was slender. Both were equally uninterested in the destruction of my car. I showed them the shocking scene. They looked around a little and shrugged. The older one said, "You got boyfriend trouble?"

"Do I have what? What's that got to do with my car being attacked?"

"I don't know," the older cop said. "Maybe you had a fight with your boyfriend. Did you? See, I can tell by your face you broke up with him. Don't ever play poker, lady. He got mad and got back at you, didn't he? Man must know you love this fancy car, even if you don't love him."

"We made up last night, thank you. There is no longer any problem between us."

"What about the lady he was seeing when you weren't seeing him? Maybe she's unhappy he went back to you. Maybe she did this."

"Not a chance," I said. Ashley wouldn't risk her manicure.

The older cop stopped and suddenly stared dramatically at the sky, as if he had a divine inspiration. "I got an idea," he said, hamming it up for his partner. "Maybe a certain police detective's wife didn't like you fooling around with her hubby."

"I don't know what you mean," I lied.

"You don't?" the older one said. "The whole Third District knew where Detective Mayhew's motorcycle was parked yesterday around five o'clock. He was inside a good long time. Then a patrol car saw the great detective coming out of your place buttoning up his jacket and wiping dust off his knees."

"Must have been down on those knees praying, huh?" the younger cop said.

I blushed. I had nothing to be ashamed of with Mayhew (okay, not too much), but my stairs had been a South Side disgrace.

"Happens to me all the time," the older cop said. "I gotta get on my knees and beg my wife for sex."

"I'm not married," the younger cop said. "I just pray I'll get lucky."

While the two of them laughed at their own jokes, I pulled out my pad of paper and started writing down their comments. "Get serious, officers, or I'll report you," I said. I was angry. I was the victim of vandalism and I was getting this treatment.

"For what?" the older cop asked. He sounded surly and indifferent. He didn't like me and I suspected he didn't like Mayhew much, either. The department was rife with black-white resentment. "You going to complain to our superiors? You going to tell them we said you were having some afternoon delight with a homicide detective? Or maybe you're going to write us up in your column? What are you going to say in a family newspaper about this situation, newspaper lady? I'd love to read it. Maybe you can offer your readers a prize for guessing how the great detective got his knees dirty."

"Probably scrubbing floors," the younger cop said. "Don't they call these people around here the Scrubby Dutch?"

I'd had enough. I opened my briefcase, which was still sitting on the parking pad where I'd dropped it when I first saw Ralph. I pulled out my hand-held tape recorder, which for once had working batteries, and clicked the red button. "Maybe I should just tape record this conversation, officers, and your superiors can decide for themselves what they think at the citizen's complaint hearing. A little more publicity won't bother me," I bluffed. "And the press is on my side because I'm one of them." Another lie, but they seemed to buy it. "Now, are you going to do your job and call for an evidence van to take some prints off this car?"

"You can't take prints off this metal," the young cop said. "It's too damp."

I didn't know if they were telling the truth or they didn't want to bother.

"We will write up a report for your insurance," the older cop said, sounding halfway polite. "If you get any leads, please call us." It would sound good on the tape, but he didn't even bother giving me his phone number or card. He didn't mean a word. I knew exactly how much effort he'd put into this case. If I had any leads, please call. Yeah, right. I could imagine the fun he'd have if I told him I suspected Hudson

Vander Venter or his son had vandalized my car. He wouldn't believe me. He wouldn't even believe Hudson was in this neighborhood. And come to think of it, why hadn't anyone seen Hudson? A huge, expensive car like his would be noticed here. The old-timers drove modest, respectable Plymouths, Fords, and Chevys, American cars that were scrupulously maintained. The yuppie newcomers drove beat-up Hondas, Toyotas, and Volvos, plus an occasional Jeep Cherokee. The rehabbers had pickups, and the poorest people on the South Side drove big old avocado-green or mustard-color junkers with coat-hanger antennas. Neighbors would comment if an expensive car like Hudson's was parked nearby, even for a short time. They'd see it as another sign that the neighborhood was looking up. If nobody mentioned the car to Mrs. Indelicato in the next few days, I could be pretty sure he didn't drive it. Maybe he drove Sydney's Jeep. That might be less noticeable. Did he even have Sydney's car now that she was dead? Mayhew would know. If I ever got up the nerve, I'd call him and ask. Maybe I'd wait until I talked with Sydney's mother-in-law today. Elizabeth might give me more information on the Jack connection, or tell me how all the motor oil got in Hudson's car. Mayhew would be glad to talk to me then.

Meanwhile, I needed some wheels. I called my insurance agent. Carl was properly sympathetic and promised to have an insurance adjustor look at Ralph today, so I could arrange to have him towed and start the repairs. "That car's not fit to drive," Carl said. "You have it towed. You can't sit on that seat with all that glass and it will blow around the car.

Don't worry about the cost. It's covered. Your insurance will provide a loaner car. We have a special deal with a company on Morganford Road. You can walk there. Nice folks. Their cars are nothing fancy, but they're reliable. They always run. You tell Jimmy I sent you."

Retread Rentals had a collection of ancient, anonymous clunkers in tan, gray, and brown. They looked like the cars undercover police used for surveillance. They were so anonymous, they might as well have had UNMARKED GOVERNMENT CARPOOL stenciled on their sides. Jimmy, a skinny guy with an acne-scarred face, gave me a dented gray Ford that looked like a filing cabinet lying on its side. Drove like one, too. The car actually had four square corners and swayed when I made a turn. It was at least twenty years old. The File Cabinet rattled and shook and idled so roughly, I was queasy by the time I drove it three blocks. The steering was mushy and the radio was permanently stuck on a shock jock radio station. After I heard the morning show DJ talk about how he masturbated because "ya don't have to send Mrs. Palm and her five lovely daughters flowers, and your hand never has a headache" I decided silence was better than that. I entertained myself by watching my Dunhill briefcase bounce up and down on the red leatherette seat. A big tear on the passenger side was repaired with gray duct tape that matched the car's exterior. Spiffy touch, that.

Why joke about it? After Ralph, driving the File Cabinet was a depressing experience. No guys flirted with me when I was in this ugly, square car or gunned their engines and challenged me to a street race. They probably thought I was a narc. But I didn't have time to concentrate on my misery. I had to nurse the car at every red light, slowly feeding it gas, so it wouldn't die on me. And I had to get to Frontenac as fast as the File Cabinet could waddle. It was now five after ten, and the Voyage Committee meeting started at ten-thirty, this time in a conference room at the West County Inn. The high-priced hotel smelled of bayberry. I followed the six-foot-tall silk flower arrangements and crystal chandeliers to a peach-colored conference room. Once again, I was the last one to arrive. Even Voyage Captain Jason was there, fiddling around at the podium, getting ready to set sail on another sea of psychobabble. The publisher looked at me like I was a bug in his bathtub. Georgia frowned. Vonnie the Steel Magnolia and Charlie the Mendacious Managing Editor both smiled. They were thrilled that I was in trouble. Roberto started to give me a polite nod, then caught a look at Charlie and made a split-second decision to support the boss. He bared his teeth in an unpleasant grin. The two business guys, Simpson Tolbart and Tucker Gravois, were busy discussing golf. That meant Brittany, Courtney, Scott, and Jeremy, the four business office clones, hadn't been told how to think, so they kept their faces in their natural expression—absolutely blank.

Voyage Captain Jason tapped the microphone. "Good morning, people," he said. "Good morning, Francesca."

Evidently, I wasn't a person this morning. Our captain had singled me out for special attention, so I knew the name of the creek I was up, and I didn't have a paddle, either. He leaned forward and smiled at the publisher with his most engaging smile. The publisher smiled back, like the class homely guy who's finally been noticed by the cutest teacher in school. Voyage Captain Jason addressed his remarks to this class of one.

"We are not here to build circulation but to build teamwork, which will in turn build circulation once we learn where we want to go on our Voyage of Discovery," he said, profoundly serious. Based on that conversation, I figured we were going in circles. I wanted to go out the door and get some work done. I hadn't been able to go trolling for columns at Uncle Bob's this morning and I desperately needed a topic.

"Today we must learn to face our deepest divisions," he said, and looked me squarely in the eye, "and heal them so we can go forward into the future. We want our efforts to prove fruitworthy—"

Fruitworthy? Was that a word?

"Ahoy, Francesca, are you home?" Captain Jason said. The guy was sticking to me like a barnacle today. He must have been really ticked at my display last time, and this was his way of getting back at me. But I'd resolved to behave myself, so I answered ever so politely. "I was lost in admiration at your unique use of the language, Captain, sir," I said. Georgia's frown cut a deeper furrow in her forehead. She knew I was making fun of Jason. Good thing the captain didn't recognize bilge. He seemed to swallow it.

"Before we can sail into our new future, we must face death," our captain said. "On this voyage, death must not only be met. Death must be conquered."

The publisher straightened his shoulders, as if preparing for the struggle. Charlie straightened his tie. Vonnie crossed her legs. Each member of management prepared to fight the Conqueror Worm in his or her own way.

"But in our case, death is not the end of our journey. It is the beginning. We shall rise from this death and begin a bold, shining, successful new day at the *Gazette*. Ladies and gentlemen, are you ready to meet death?"

We all nodded. This was sounding suspiciously like a sermon. No one but me seemed uneasy with the semireligious tone. Maybe it was the devil in me. Voyage Captain Jason clapped his hands. The conference room door swung open. Six men dressed like undertakers in black suits, white shirts, and dead black neckties carried a coffin into the meeting room and set it on the conference table. It took up almost the whole table. Everyone hurried to move notebooks and coffee cups, so Death wouldn't touch anything of ours. An empty foam coffee cup went skittering over the edge, but no one picked it up. We were too stunned. Besides, no one wanted to bow to death. I'd never been eye level with a coffin before. It was a real one, too, the cheap gray kind used for cremations. I'd done a story about coffins once and inspected several models. This one had shiny silver metal handles that didn't melt when you burned the coffin. The lid was closed.

It was a little too authentic for one of the business office quadruplets. "Eeeuwww," squealed either Brittany, Courtney, Scott, or Jeremy. All four looked disgusted, as if Voyage Captain Jason had exposed himself in the country club dining room.

"Some of you might find this shocking," he said. "That's good. We need to shock ourselves out of our old ways. The sands are running out on the old *Gazette*. But before we set sail into the future, we must sing our swan song."

Then he gave each one of us a two-pocket black vinyl ring binder with THE VOYAGE COMMITTEE printed on the cover in gold. "In the future, this will be a place to store your committee reports and notes," he said. "A free gift before we embark on our journey into the future."

The publisher beamed. He loved free gifts, even if he was paying for them. He started to open his present.

"Don't do that," Jason said, like a mother cautioning an overeager child. "Don't open it yet. It has a surprise inside—our swan song, which I wrote specially for the *Gazette*. Don't open it now," he said, rapping Roberto coyly on the head. Roberto had been caught trying to sneak a peek. "First let me pass out these."

He gave each one of us several black-bordered white cards, engraved with one word, "Regrets."

"These cards are to write down our regrets about the *Gazette*," he said. "We can regret many things: our impatience with readers, our dissension with our colleagues"—once again he gave me a look—"our hesitation to take bold new steps. Let me give you a few moments to think about your regrets and write them down."

Charlie and Vonnie were busy scribbling. Roberto peeked at Charlie's card and then wrote something.

Georgia thoughtfully chewed her ballpoint pen tip and then wrote. The publisher pulled out a four-hundred-dollar gold-banded Waterman fountain pen and wrote with such seriousness, you'd have thought he was signing the Constitution. Tucker Gravois and Simpson Tolbart both exposed their own expensive pens and wrote with a flourish, as if they were signing checks. Brittany, Courtney, Scott, and Jeremy looked like four students working on a tough term paper. Everyone wrote with surprising speed. I think they all wanted to go forward into the future—and get that blasted coffin off the table. Only I sat there. I had a lot of regrets about the *Gazette,* but I wasn't going to write them down for this bunch. I regretted that I was stupid enough to ever think that runtlike rat, Charlie, was my friend. Lyle had warned me about him, but I didn't listen. For almost ten years, I was one of his admirers. I think he reminded me of my father, another man who was good at betrayals. Dad was handsomer than Charlie, and a good foot taller, but they had a lot in common, and I knew it. I called myself a trained observer. I'd observed Charlie's constant infidelities. I knew he pimped his girl-friends to the managing editor to advance his career. I knew he sold pot to his friends and jacked up the price. I knew he betrayed his male friends, sometimes to get ahead and sometimes just for the fun of it. I'd observed all of that. But I never thought he'd betray me. Until Georgia showed me the famous not-so-secret memo, where Charlie tried to ruin my career the way he'd destroyed so many others. After that, I avoided the little creep like *E. coli.*

Now I regretted the day he was born. I regretted

the day he took over the *Gazette*, because no matter what Voyage Captain Jason said or did, with Charlie at the helm, we were rearranging the deck chairs on the *Titanic*. But I regretted most of all that I couldn't say any of this. The publisher was crazy about the little toady and thought he was the greatest advance in the newspaper business since the invention of movable type. So with no regrets at all, I left my "regrets" card blank.

"Do we all have our regrets, people?" Voyage Captain Jason asked, as if he were talking to a class of low achievers. I nodded along with everyone else. After all, I had major regrets. I just didn't write them down.

"Here's what I'd like you to do. I want you to take all those regrets that you have written down and throw them into the coffin. I want us to bury our regrets and animosities. We will read them aloud first. And while we do this, we will sing this special song that I wrote for the *Gazette*. This is an important ceremony," he said. "It is a rite of passage, a grave undertaking"—he gave a little laugh to let us know it was a pun—"so we can pass into the new bright future." He tapped on the podium like a conductor and said, "I will begin singing the special hymn to the *Gazette*. Please join in. I know you know the tune. You may now open your books so that you can sing along with me. Our special song is called"— and he paused to smile at the publisher—" 'Amazing *Gazette*.' " And then, to the tune of that beautiful old Protestant hymn, he began singing these words, in a surprisingly good tenor:

Amazing *Gazette*, how great thou art,
To employ a wretch like me
I once was lost but now I'm found
I was blind but now I see.

I did see. It was blasphemy, pure and simple. I was
about as religious as a rattlesnake. I hadn't attended
Sunday Mass since my grandparents died, and Catholics didn't sing that hymn. But I had Baptist friends
who did, who loved those words and reverently used
them to praise their God. They would be shocked
and horrified to know it had been put to this godless
use.

"Okay, people, let's sing it from the top, one more
time," Jason said, looking smug and pleased.

I waited for the publisher or Charlie to say that
this display was in poor taste. Surely, after all the
lectures I'd had on what was tasteless and what
wasn't, what was suitable for a family newspaper
and what wasn't, they knew when something was
over the top. Even someone like me, who had most
of her taste in her mouth, knew that comparing the
Gazette to the Almighty was definitely tasteless, not
to mention inaccurate. But the publisher was smiling
benevolently, and Charlie looked impressed. I realized why they weren't shocked. Most newspaper editors thought they were God, so a hymn to them was
in order.

Everyone but me dutifully picked up their ring
binders as if they were hymnals and sang the first
verse again. The group had strong voices and they all
stayed on key. I noticed that Jason had skipped the
verse beginning, " 'Twas Grace that taught my heart

to fear . . ." probably because if he substituted the
word *Gazette* for Grace, he'd get something a little
too close to God's honest truth. Instead, the group
launched into a verse where he had to change only
one word—"God's praise" became "your praise." I
hung my head in shame for the whole newspaper
when I heard the committee sing:

> When we've been here
> Ten thousand years
> Bright shining as the sun
> We've no less days to sing your praise
> Than when we first begun.

When they finished, they applauded themselves. I
waited for lightning bolts to blast the room. Nothing
happened, except that almost everyone looked
pleased with themselves. The publisher was so
happy, he vibrated like a tuning fork. Only Georgia
wouldn't look at me. I think only she had the saving
grace to be ashamed. Even for a penthouse overlooking Forest Park, I wouldn't sing that wretched song
in praise of the *Gazette*. But I had promised her—and
myself—that I'd keep my mouth shut. That's all I had
to do. Shut up. Shut up. Shut up. I repeated it to
myself over and over like a mantra.

When the applause died down, Jason took a little
bow, then gave two sharp claps. The six undertakers
appeared again and opened the coffin. It was lined
with white satin. Inside was a wreath with black silk
flowers and a big black satin bow. I wondered if the
thrifty Jason used silk flowers so he could reuse the
wreath at other papers' mock funerals. I wondered if

"Amazing *Gazette*" ever became "Amazing *Times*" or "Amazing *Tribune*."

"Thanks, people," our captain said modestly. "Now, to complete the ceremony, I'd like us to once and for all bury our regrets about the old *Gazette*, so we can sail off into the future. Please read your regrets aloud before you put them in the coffin. The publisher will of course go first."

The publisher took out his card, put on his reading glasses, and said, "I greatly regret that I occasionally have not shown more firmness of leadership."

Amen, brother, I thought. The publisher tucked his regret gently under a black silk rose. He had publicly admitted a fault. An admirable fault, perhaps, the fault of compassion, but still it was a fault. After he said that, everyone piled more faults upon themselves, and some of those sounded oddly like praise for themselves. Of course, all the leaders admitted that they too lacked firmness of leadership, to identify with the boss. Charlie also regretted his impatience with readers and "their stupid phone calls." The publisher smiled down on Charlie. This was just the right thing to say. The publisher, too, suffered from the outrageous stupidity of readers. Absolute nobodies called him because someone had misspelled their name or the paper dropped a comic they liked. But now the publisher would manage the paper more forcefully. He would tell his secretary he was too busy to take calls from those halfwits who read the paper. That's why he paid editors. Let them talk to the idiot readers.

"Georgia?" Jason said, raising one eyebrow.

Georgia was sly. "I regret any time I spent at the

Gazette that wasn't spent working," she said. I knew she meant regretting any time she spent in meetings like these.

But the publisher graciously said he couldn't imagine any time when she didn't have her nose to the grindstone, and everyone laughed because he was the publisher. Then Tolbart said she had such a small nose she must have spent a lot of time grinding it down to that size, and everyone laughed but Vonnie, because she didn't like to see any other woman get attention.

Roberto couldn't wait to list all his faults. He said he too lacked leadership, and also regretted his impatience with the morons who complained that the newspaper ink came off on their hands—that got a big laugh—and then he added a new fault. He regretted he sometimes got angry at his underlings, although he felt forceful leadership called for anger at times, and therefore he managed sneakily to erase his fault, although I don't think anyone but me noticed. Tolbart also regretted his lack of leadership, although he felt he had enough to lead us into fiscal stability. But now he wanted to make oceans of profit—that sentiment was thoroughly applauded—and he regretted being too lenient with the office supply distribution to the various departments. These supplies needed to be monitored. I regretted his regrets, because it meant we'd have to account for every paper clip.

After Tucker Gravois regretted his lack of leadership he also said he regretted he was too lenient with the papers' unions, and if he was indeed a leader then the *Gazette* should not have another set of managers boring from within, and he would be firmer with them in the future. This sentiment was cheered by everyone but Georgia and me. I thought the *Gazette* was pretty boring inside and out. But that's not what Tucker meant. He wanted to destroy the unions, and after our last limp contract, he was well on the way. After the cheers, someone made a joke about being totally at sea, and we all had a good laugh. It was turning into a jolly party. Brittany, Courtney, Scott, and Jeremy didn't have any leadership to regret, but they said they were sorry for the times when they weren't team players. I couldn't imagine when that was, but the publisher smiled on them like a doting grandfather.

They were the last of the group, except for me. I was hidden behind the open coffin lid and hoped Voyage Captain Jason wouldn't notice me. I even hummed the tune while everyone put their regrets in the coffin, hoping I could blend in. But this was not my lucky day. Jason singled me out. "Do you have any regrets to bury, Francesca?" he asked.

I looked at the coffin. All I had to do was say something, anything. I didn't even have to write it down. No one would know my regrets cards were blank. But I couldn't do it. I couldn't join the ranks of slimy sucks like Charlie and Roberto. Then I had a flash of brilliance and saw a way out of this tunnel.

"I haven't any regrets that I can say," I said. I thought that was remarkably tactful and truthful at the same time. Shows what I know. As they say, the light at the end of the tunnel is the headlight of the oncoming train. The publisher did not look pleased by my statement. He looked angry. *Very* angry. Then

I realized what I did wrong. He'd confessed to a public fault, and I wasn't admitting one. I wasn't playing the game. I wasn't abasing myself properly like the rest of the committee.

"Young woman, our captain asked you a question," he said in his first attempt at firmer management. "You owe him the courtesy of a serious reply."

Charlie took the helm with his own effort at new, firm management. "Francesca, you must name a regret. That is a direct order. Under the Guild contract, you cannot refuse a direct order." He smiled his weasely smile, and I felt his trap closing on me. Time seemed to stop. The room grew silent. The laughter died. Everyone watched the showdown. I could see Georgia, pleading with me with her big brown eyes. I could almost hear her thoughts, unless they were my thoughts: "Tell him something, anything. Tell him you regret not being a team player." Except I didn't. I didn't want to be on this team. "Tell him you regret your anger at your editors." But I didn't. They deserved it. "Tell him you regret impatience with your stupid readers." But I didn't think my readers were stupid. I thought they were smarter and funnier than the editors who sneered at them.

"I'm waiting," Charlie said.

"We're all waiting," the publisher said impatiently.

"Please, Francesca, we need your contribution so we can continue our voyage into the future," said Jason, in a pleading tone. "Please help set the *Gazette* on course."

But that was the problem. The *Gazette* was so far off course, it would never get back. We were playing silly games when we should have been running the paper. My job was to interview people and dig up stories, not play office politics. But I could go back to doing what I was good at, if I could just say something.

I tried, I really tried to open my mouth and come up with a regret. But the words stuck in my throat. Maybe I'd been chanting "shut up, shut up" too often. Now I couldn't talk. And if I didn't, I would be fired on the spot. This was strike three, and I was out. I couldn't refuse a direct order. I must be crazy. I made good money. I had a good job. I had readers I loved. I was respected in this community. Was I going to throw it all away for false pride? I'd lied before. Why couldn't I lie now?

"Now, Francesca, or you're fired," Charlie said. "You have two warnings in your file. This is the third. Everyone in the room is a witness to your recalcitrance. Tell me your regret or you are fired."

Then I felt the paralysis loosening in my throat. Thank God. I could say something. I said, "I regret . . ."

The whole room was literally waiting on my next words. I looked at them all, except Georgia. I couldn't bear to look at her. But I saw the publisher, and Charlie, Roberto, Tolbart, Tucker, Vonnie, and the quads. Why was I kowtowing to these soulless creatures, who were destroying a once-great newspaper? These people couldn't save the *Gazette*. They couldn't save string. I couldn't save the *Gazette* by myself, either. My career at this mediocre paper wasn't worth saving. All I could do was save the few shreds of dignity I had left.

So I took a deep breath and put a nail in my own coffin.

"I deeply regret that I ever got involved in this foolishness," I said.

12

"**T**hat's it, Francesca. You're fired," Charlie screamed. "You're out of here!" I figured I was, too, but I kept that to myself.

"She refused a direct order," Charlie snarled to the Voyage Committee. "She's insubordinate. She's fired." He couldn't quite keep the satisfaction out of his voice. He'd waited a long time to say those last two words.

Everyone else sat there stunned and silent, except Georgia. "Francesca didn't refuse," she said. "You asked for her regret and she told you."

"It wasn't a proper answer," Charlie snapped, glaring at me. He was so angry his bald spot glowed red through his carefully combed hair.

"Legally, her answer satisfied your request," Tolbart answered levelly. Charlie took a deep breath but didn't reply. He recognized that word "legally" for what it was, a warning. Tolbart had touched on the *Gazette*'s unspeakable little secret. The paper had a slew of EEOC suits filed against it by angry employees. The paper settled the suits out of court. It couldn't risk being judged by a jury of disgruntled readers, who had been insulted when they called the *Gazette* with a complaint or had their paper thrown in the bushes that morning.

Voyage Captain Jason, now that he knew which way the wind was blowing, weighed in with his opinion. "I fear Georgia is correct," he said. "Francesca was perhaps not in tune with the spirit of this voyage, but she did comply with her editor's command."

At this, the publisher managed a weak smile, the first one since my outburst. He'd reacted to my anger as if he'd been singed. The publisher hated any strong emotion. He loathed disagreement. He had an intense dislike for loud voices. He spent his days in a museumlike hush, as if he were one of the art treasures he collected. That's why he had surrounded himself with soft-spoken flunkies, toadies, and attorneys. They were supposed to protect him from anything unpleasant. He did not appreciate this mutiny during his Voyage of Discovery. The whole table waited for his pronouncement. As if to compensate for my noise, the publisher spoke in almost a whisper. "Charlie has handled the situation with commendable firmness and has elicited a proper response," he said.

Charlie relaxed, and his angry red bald spot faded to a soothing rose pink. Charlie knew he was not going to take the blame for my scene. The rest of the table gazed expectantly at the publisher, waiting for him to say more. Instead, he fumbled with his four-hundred-dollar pen. He seemed totally at sea on this voyage.

But Voyage Captain Jason knew exactly what to do—throw me overboard. "There is a difference between discussion and dissension," he said. "I think perhaps Francesca would be happier if we found someone else to take her place on our voyage."

The others nodded happily. They were eager to be rid of me, too. Vonnie the Steel Magnolia preened, anxious to assume her accustomed role as the most decorative woman in the room. Even Georgia secretly agreed that I was a pain in the ass and better off out of the committee. But she didn't say anything. The room erupted into an animated discussion of who should be chosen to replace me. I used the time to slip out the door and find my miserable excuse for a car. Georgia followed me, running across acres of flowered carpet until she finally caught up with me on the parking lot. I hadn't gone anywhere yet because I couldn't find my car. I was still standing there, in aisle T, trying to remember where I parked the File Cabinet. How could anything that big be so anonymous? Maybe I could put a flower on the antenna to help locate it. Somehow I couldn't picture a perky fake flower on the gray File Cabinet. I wondered how duct tape would look on the antenna.

"There you are," I heard Georgia yell. "What in the hell did you think you're doing?" She scolded me like a mother whose toddler had wandered off in the mall. Her small blond person seemed overwhelmed by her heavy gray suit. She should have looked ridiculous. But she didn't. Georgia looked formidable.

She folded her arms and stared at me. "Well," she said. "I'm waiting."

"There was no point in hanging around watching Charlie gloat."

"I don't know what you mean. Charlie was as close to eating crow as I've ever seen him. But you didn't even stay to enjoy it."

"I'm sorry, Georgia," I said, and I meant it, at least a little. "But I couldn't stand what that idiot Jason was doing to that fine old hymn. 'Amazing *Gazette*,' indeed."

"Why do you care?" Georgia said. For a small person she could be surprisingly forceful. "You haven't been in a church in years. You don't even believe in God."

"That's not true."

"Whatever," Georgia said. "That hymn doesn't mean a rat's ass to you, and you know it, so don't go all noble on me. Why did you make a scene?"

"Because it means something to other people."

"You're hopeless," she said. "Now let's get back there. With any luck the committee will have chosen your successor and I'll have missed listening to more of their bullshit."

"How can you stand it?" I said. I was really puzzled.

"Because it's hot air," she said. "Your problem is you take it seriously. It doesn't mean anything, Francesca. I can't make you understand that."

"But why do it, if it doesn't mean anything?" I said to her gray wool-covered back. She was already walking toward the building.

"Because my fuckin' building is going condo," she

said, nearly hitting me in the face with the door. When we got to the conference room, she went in first and left me to face the committee on my own. It was a lot harder going back into the room than slipping out of it. I could feel the committee's dislike and see their distaste as I stood at the door of the conference room. The publisher looked at me like I was a hair in his mashed potatoes. I tried a smile. Everyone looked at the publisher to see how he liked it. Not very well. He didn't smile back. He looked like one of those animatronics figures you see at Disneyland: lifelike, but not really alive.

Voyage Captain Jason let me know I'd sunk myself for good. "Francesca, your hostility is in danger of shipwrecking our Voyage of Discovery," he said. "We must have a calm and peaceful journey. I am sorry to say that you are a disruptive influence. You are a talented individual, but I believe you will be happier if you set your own course and sail alone, without us." In other words, I was not a team player, the most damning insult in any corporation.

"In your absence we have chosen a compatible crew member, thanks to Charlie. He has suggested Wendy, the Family editor, and the committee has wholeheartedly approved his choice. Wendy will join us for the duration of the voyage, starting with our next meeting."

Wendy the Whiner? This was getting better and better. If she was on the Voyage Committee, she wouldn't be bothering the Family section staff. But this was no time to let my glee show. Instead, I nodded slowly, as if I'd just had my rank stripped off my uniform. I was afraid to say anything, in case Charlie

figured out how happy I was to be out of this boondoggle. I heard Voyage Captain Jason say something
about "a more appropriate choice." It sounded like
my court-martial was almost over. I couldn't wait to
escape this room and get back to writing. I needed a
column and I needed some lunch. I could get both at
Uncle Bob's. Grease, here I come. I could see a plate
with my name on it. I could see a column with my
name on it, too. I knew I'd have something if I went
to Uncle Bob's—probably an extra five pounds of fat.
But it was going to be a nice day after all. Later that
afternoon, I'd take tea with Queen Elizabeth Vander
Venter at her Ladue mansion. After that, I'd call Mayhew, because I was too chicken to face him in person, and tell him everything I'd been able to pump
out of Elizabeth. I'd also tell him about the destruction of Ralph, because I was sure that was done by a
Vander Venter, too. Then I'd casually mention that I
was back with Lyle, and could we just be friends,
huh, and forget we'd ever seen each other in our underwear? I mean, it wasn't that big a deal. I'd seen
smaller swim suits. Not on me, maybe, but they existed.

Charlie must have sensed my delight. He put an
end to my plans for a pleasant day. "Oh, Francesca,"
he said. "Since you're free right now, and I know
you're always looking for a column, I want you to
cover a noontime GEEP class at Chesterfield Mall."

"GEEP?" I must have looked puzzled.

"Geriatric Excellence Exercise Program. This one
meets at Chesterfield Mall. All those sweet old people
in their sweat suits. I know exactly what you'd want
to do with a story like that," the little twerp said, and

gave his most insincere smile. Of course he knew what I'd want to do with a story like that—and where I'd like to shove it. This was more than just a dull assignment. It was an insult. It was the kind of fluff piece usually given to a junior reporter and buried on page 26G in the Metro section.

"But . . ." I said.

"You don't have to thank me," Charlie said. "You don't have time, anyway. The GEEP class starts in"— he glanced at his watch—"twenty minutes. You can get to Chesterfield in time if you leave now."

So I left. All the way there, I devised curses for Charlie. I wished that all his hair would fall out and the only places it would grow were his ears. I tried to imagine Charlie totally bald. I wondered if his head came to a point, or was it round like a bowling ball? When he got angry, the bare patch on his head glowed red. If he was completely bald, his head would look like the bulb on a thermometer. This image cheered me up so much I was smiling by the time I got to Chesterfield Mall.

The GEEP program was in a storefront on the lower level. It was a white rectangle of a room with hardwood floors and three walls of mirrors. A white door opened into a back area that must contain dressing rooms, because the exercisers were coming out now. One was a cute, cuddly, elderly woman with a figure like a melting ice cream cone. Her baby-pink sweat suit matched her round pink cheeks. She looked like the ideal grandma. The woman following her did not. She had made titanic efforts to look younger, which somehow made her look older than Grandma. Her hair was dyed black and sprayed so stiff it would stay in place in a tornado. Several face-lifts had pulled her skin so tight I bet she had to bikini wax her lip. Her makeup was artfully applied, right down to the false eyelashes. Her nails were bright red—the same color as her red leotard and tights with flame designs on the legs and hips. Thirty years ago, this woman must have had a hot body. Now, as Gypsy Rose Lee used to say, she still had everything, it was just a little lower.

Another woman followed her out of the dressing-room door. This one looked like a stick figure: stick arms, spindly legs, and springy steel-colored curls. She was talking to a tall, stately woman who was a symphony in gray: dark-gray exercise togs, lighter gray tights and straight silver-gray hair. Ms. Silver made gray hair seem like something you wanted to achieve. After her came a couple of gnarled old guys with baggy exercise shorts and hairy legs. Behind them was the class teacher. She was a permanently perky blonde in her mid-twenties named Janni. I introduced myself to Janni, while other elderly exercisers streamed out. "Oh, you must join our class!" Janni said, jumping up and down with enthusiasm.

"Er, sorry, I didn't bring any exercise clothes," I said. I wasn't sorry at all.

"That's all right," the instructor said. "You look about my size. You can wear an extra pair of my shorts and a T-shirt. Working out with us will give you a real appreciation for what we do. Don't you agree, class?"

"Yes! Yes!" said the class. I was being smothered with senior vim and vigor. Oh, heck, I might as well try it. How tough could it be? The youngest person in

the class was sixty-five years old. Janni found me
some navy shorts and a white GEEP T-shirt. By the
time I'd changed and come back out, the class of
about fifteen people had arranged itself in three long
rows. Black exercise mats, like giant mousepads,
stood in front of each person. Lined up on the mats
were hand weights and stretchy rubber exercise
tubes and long rubber-coated exercise bars. Someone had set up a place for me. I was grateful to see it
was in the back row of the class. Janni put some
bouncy music on the boombox and started her patter
over the music:

"Okay, now, class, let's start with our warm-up.
Reach straight up. Up, up, up, put those arms in the
sky, but don't raise your shoulders, keep those shoulders down and bend your knees for support." I
looked around the class. These directions seemed to
make sense to them. They were smiling and stretching their arms. By the time I figured out what everyone was doing, Janni was on to the next exercise.

"We're going to march to warm up our legs!
March, march, march!" she said. "March left, left,
left!" The class began taking giant steps to the left,
except for me. I went right and ran into Ms. Silver.
She smiled and shrugged, letting me know it didn't
matter.

"Now, right, right, right!" Janni said. I went left
and ran into Ms. Silver again. She still smiled. I tried
to smile back, but I was breathing like I'd just run the
four-minute mile. Only fifty-five more minutes to go,
and we weren't even through the warm-up exercises.
This was going to be the most humiliating hour of
my life. By now, I realized I was a dyslexic exerciser.

When the class went left, I went right. When they were up, I was down.

Janni had the class pick up their weights. She was yelling "Biceps, triceps, biceps, triceps," like it was some weird mantra. Ms. Silver was swinging her five-pound weights like a couple of Q-Tips, while I struggled to lift a pair of three-pounders. Even more embarrassing, the plump, pink-suited grandma was hefting two three-pound weights in each hand. The woman in the flaming suit had ten-pounders and hadn't even broken a sweat. She hadn't even broken a fingernail. The woman was a Fitness Fashion Plate. I'd seen younger versions of her at the kind of gyms where people like to show off their bodies. It looked like the FFP could be any age, from eighteen to eighty. A true Fitness Fashion Plate works out in full makeup, including false eyelashes, and she always wears the latest gym togs. She never has a hair out of place. Of course, it was pretty heavily shellacked.

While I struggled to keep up with the seniors, I sneaked a peak at the two men. They turned out to be Gaper Twins. They were sweating—but not from the exercise. Every time Janni said "Move those glutes" and showed us her bouncing bottom, the Gaper Twins' eyes bulged. Ditto her demonstration of this command: "Lie on your back, bend your knees, and lift those hips—Up! Down! Up!" They nearly hyperventilated when she said, "Push those chests out. Push!"

When the Gaper Twins weren't watching Janni, they were studying the rest of us with awed delight. But we couldn't get mad at the Gaper Twins. They never said anything sexist, or even stared at the

women too long. The Twins looked like teenage boys
who accidentally walked into the cheerleaders' dressing room. They couldn't believe their luck and they
hoped no one noticed them. This was probably the
one time when exercise was bad for the heart.

My elegant Ms. Silver belonged to a different category of exerciser. She was a Sweater. She grunted.
She groaned. She flogged herself during a workout
until she was sweating like she'd been stoking steel-
mill furnaces. Sweaters wear gray gym clothes, to
show off their sweat to the best advantage. Naturally,
they always wear sweat bands.

At first, the whole class seemed to be working
equally hard. Then I noticed some people didn't complete the exercise sets. They started out vigorously,
but then these Slackers would quietly lie down on
the job. The Stick Woman was the worst offender.
She would do three pushups and spend seven resting
on the floor. She lifted the body bar over her head
four times, then rested it for six counts. She was an
expert at not drawing attention to herself, so she was
rarely reprimanded by Janni the instructor. The
Stick Woman would fit in well at the *Gazette*. I bet
she could sleep in front of the computer with her
eyes open, so she looked awake.

I tried to be a Slacker during the stomach
crunches, but Janni caught me. "Now, Francesca, no
lying down on the job. Only six more crunches, I
promise. You can do it. You're so much younger than
our other exercisers." The whole class turned around
and smiled. They were clearly enjoying watching me
sweat.

Finally, the hands of the clock neared 1:00 P.M.

"Now, bend over so your ribs are on your thighs," said Janni. The exercisers folded themselves neatly in half, with their rear ends in the air. I tried to do that, but I seemed to be lacking a couple of hinges. Then everyone but me gracefully straightened up. This class was not just strong, they were limber, too. "Now stretch toward the sky," said Janni, and they did. At precisely one o'clock, Janni said, "Good job, everybody." She applauded them, then the class applauded themselves.

I was impressed. My South Side grandparents would never have gone to an exercise class. I thought of Grandma as frail and old, but she could shove a mahogany dining table across a room to wax the floor. But I still clung to my stereotypes about older people. I would have a good column after all, which would certainly upset Charlie. By the time I interviewed Janni and some of the GEEP exercisers and checked my answering machine for messages, I barely had time to make it to tea with Queen Elizabeth. Now, after an hour of being shamed by senior fitness buffs, I was looking forward to an afternoon with an old woman who didn't lift anything heavier than a teacup.

I hoped this would be a useful visit. I wanted to find out more about Hudson's missing fifteen minutes and her grandson's drug buy. I wanted her to tell me how Hudson wound up with a trunk full of oil. I wanted to know what Hudson Senior and Junior were doing last night, and if it included trashing my car.

The Vander Venter mansion was still impressive. So was Elizabeth. But she seemed different. She caught me off guard when she answered the door herself. The woman had definitely defrosted. In fact, she was almost human. "Come in, come in," she said. "I admire your column so much. When I had an opportunity to invite you again, I just had to take it."

She did? What caused the big change?

"When I told my friends that Francesca Vierling was in my home, they were so impressed." Ah. That explained it. She wanted to impress her friends by hobnobbing with a local celebrity.

"And they heard how you solved those other murders. Fascinating."

"I didn't solve anything," I said. "I was just in the wrong place at the wrong time."

"You South Siders are so modest," she said, taking my coat and steering me out of the hall. "I want to ask you all about your detecting methods. But first, let me get the tea. It's Cordelia's day off, so you're stuck with me."

"Can I help?" I said, then realized the proper thing to say was "May I help?"

"No, no, you make yourself comfortable in the living room," she said. "Too many cooks, you know. I'll be right out." I heard a teakettle whistle, and then a few minutes later, she returned. She brought out a huge silver tray loaded with a silver teapot, a plate of crustless cress sandwiches, cream and sugar, and fragile porcelain cups. She carried it all into the living room without spilling a drop. The grossly ornamented silver was covered with flowers, fruit, and scrolls.

"That's an amazing silver service," I said. It was, too. It looked like it had a disease.

"Early nineteenth century," she said. "From my husband's family. Philadelphia silver in the French style."

She had wrists an Uncle Bob's waitress would envy. For an older woman, Elizabeth was certainly strong. Once again I thought how we underestimate older women. Some of the ones in that exercise class could lift twice the weight I could. Queen Elizabeth poured the smoky-tasting Lapsang souchong tea and chatted about her garden. She was considering a shade garden near the pool. She was fond of caladiums, but they were so difficult to find. I tried to steer the talk to the night of Sydney's murder, but it was hard to lead the conversation back to her bludgeoned daughter-in-law when Elizabeth was rattling on about herbaceous borders.

"I'm thinking of putting in an orchid greenhouse and I want my son to help me with the plans, but he's so busy these days," she said.

Ah hah! Here was the opening. Maybe I could find out what his alibi was for last night, when Ralph was being pounded into rubble. "He does seem to have many important dinners and events," I said. "I know he was at the big cigar smokers' dinner. My friends say it was a huge success." Of course, his wife's murder might have put a damper on his evening, or maybe not. Elizabeth said nothing.

"Our paths seem to cross a lot," I said. Unless I jumped out of the way.

"Wasn't your son at some other major event just last night? I can't remember the name." Because I don't know it. I was just fishing. But I'd finally hooked the old trout.

She said, "Oh, yes. He was at the Bar Association dinner last night."

Must have gone with his lawyer love, Brenda, I thought.

"Where was that?" I said.

"At Windows on Washington in downtown St. Louis," she said. "They've renovated the old International Shoe Company building on Washington Avenue, and they now hold dinners and other events there. Hudson told me the views from the upper windows are magnificent, but I don't approve of him going downtown. It's so dangerous. He assured me that the area is secure. He must have had a super time because he stayed until two o'clock in the morning, and Hudson is not a late-night person."

"You were with him last night?" I said, wondering how she knew when he left the event.

"Certainly not," Elizabeth said a trifle sharply. "I haven't been in the city since the Women's Exchange moved out of the Central West End. If the city isn't safe for them, it's no place for me. My son called me to talk about the evening. He often calls in the morning." I could hear the maternal pride in that last sentence. If she kept it up, I might actually come to like Queen Elizabeth. I'd like her even better if she gave me another important piece of information. Windows on Washington was not far from my place. If her son left there at two o'clock, he was less than twenty minutes away from my apartment. He could have easily been bashing Ralph's windshield by the time Mrs. Indelicato woke up and heard glass breaking at two-thirty. Maybe he had Brenda with him, and they made wrecking Ralph their shared delight.

Maybe they went there in her car, and that's why no one in my neighborhood saw Hudson's large and luxurious vehicle. Now I knew the senior Hudson Vander Venter was definitely a possibility. I wanted to find out about the junior one.

"Windows on Washington is just as safe as my neighborhood, near Tower Grove Park," I said. "I think I've seen your grandson in the coffeehouses on South Grand."

"Recently?" she said sharply. "Did you see him there this week?"

"No, I don't think so," I said. "I'm sure it was some weeks before that." I hadn't seen the kid there ever. I'd been trying to find out if he hung around in my neighborhood, because the cops caught him buying drugs nearby. Lots of twenty-somethings went to the South Grand area, for the restaurants, offbeat shops, and coffeehouses. There was even a body-piercing parlor.

Elizabeth relaxed a bit and smiled. "I don't want my grandson in that area. I know it's bohemian and you enjoy it, Francesca, but it's not a proper environment for my grandson. He needs to be with his own kind. South Grand is not safe. There are young people there who use drugs. I don't want him with drug users."

It would be hard to keep the kid away from himself, I thought. He was one of the drug users blighting my neighborhood. I wished the kids with too much money would stay in the burbs, where they belonged.

"Can I tell you something in confidence?" she asked, patting my hand. "I'm paying him an allowance to stay away from that neighborhood. I hope you won't tell his father. I thought the money was a bargain if it would keep him away out of an unsuitable area."

I wondered if the crafty kid took her money and went there, anyway, but I didn't think about that for long. Elizabeth had given me the opening I needed.

"Speaking of bargains," I said. "I hear you are the ultimate bargain hunter. One of my friends spotted you at the Discount Barn, of all places. She said you scored quite a bit of motor oil."

"Your friend is mistaken," she said tartly.

"I don't think so," I said. "You're a very striking person."

"I said she is mistaken," she said, giving me a glare like I hadn't seen since Sister Fulgencia Joseph nailed me for talking in class. Then she rearranged her face into something that resembled a smile. "Not that it makes any difference if she did. But it's easy to be mistaken. One old woman looks like another."

Bingo. I'd definitely hit a nerve. Maybe I should probe a little more and find out why. "No, no, she was sure it was you. She recognized your car, too."

I smiled. She smiled. Or rather, she tried to turn her lips up. The rest of her face was frozen. She said through clenched teeth, "I . . . would . . . never . . . shop . . . there."

"Oh, I can understand why you'd deny being there. I mean, it's not exactly Neiman Marcus, but really, bargain hunting is an art. I admire someone who is successful at it and doesn't confine herself to those boring luxury shops. What a bargain hunter you are. And generous, too. You must have shared some of your bargain bounty with your son. I saw he had a good half-dozen quarts of oil in his car. Did you give them to him?"

She smiled primly. "Surely you have more important things to worry about than where I shop?" She reached out and grabbed the teapot. Her hand trembled slightly. She squeezed the silver handle so hard I thought she was going to bend it into a new shape.

"Will you have more tea?" she said. Every time there was a pause in the conversation, the Queen pushed more tea on me. You'd have thought her quarterly dividends depended on how much tea I drank. I'd downed four cups now, and I definitely needed a bathroom. The interrogation would have to hold. I couldn't. Damn. Just when I was getting somewhere. Columbo didn't have these problems. You'd think if you'd designed someone as big as me, you'd put in larger kidneys. At least make them as big as my feet. The doorbell rang as Elizabeth was in the middle of telling me "It's upstairs and to the right. I have to answer the door. Cordelia isn't here."

"It's Dudley, here to pick up your clothing donations for St. Peter's Episcopal Church bazaar," I heard. This Dudley had a strangely feminine voice. I tiptoed down the upstairs hall and peeked out the window, which looked down on the front of the house. Dudley was a woman. I could see the top of her blond head. I couldn't see her face, which was too bad. She sounded interesting.

"I have these sweaters for you. They're cashmere," Elizabeth said, sounding as if she was giving away her firstborn. She handed out a stack.

"They're so . . . vintage," Dudley said tactfully.

If Elizabeth was donating items that met her usual lousy standard, those sweaters were so worn I wouldn't use them for dust rags.

Then I heard a different tone. Dudley sounded pleasantly surprised.

"Oooh, these shoes hardly look worn," she told Elizabeth. "They're a sensible style. They should sell. And so will this big, black purse. It looks new."

"It's not my taste. But it's been used only once," said Elizabeth.

Suddenly I knew exactly when the purse and shoes had been used—the one night Elizabeth murdered her daughter-in-law, Sydney. She carried the drive chain in the big black purse. *She* was the old lady seen in the alley, wearing a dark coat.

I remembered what Cutup Katie had said: "A small strong person could have killed her if very angry," and Elizabeth was strong and extremely angry. And now I knew why. Parts of my conversation with Sydney's Chicago friend Jane floated into my mind and rearranged themselves so I saw a pattern. Jane had talked with Sydney the day she died. Sydney seemed happy. She was on the paper trail to uncover her husband's hidden assets. She was sure she would get the money due her in the divorce. Sydney said she had a breakthrough thanks to her boyfriend, Jack. He found some papers that would change everything in the divorce. She wouldn't tell Jane how she got them. "Don't ask," Sydney told her friend. After Sydney's death, Jack had papers that he wanted to sell me. Papers with the murderer's name, he said. Papers that he stole for Sydney. She didn't need them now and Jack needed the money to save his Harley.

But he had a little honor. Before he used them to blackmail Sydney's murderer, he tried to sell them to me. When I wouldn't buy them, he sold them back to the killer. Who was that—Hudson? He was my first choice. But Jane said Hudson didn't have "the guts to murder anyone." Hudson would have given Sydney everything she wanted to prevent her lawyer from serving those papers on his business partners. He couldn't take the embarrassment. Hudson wasn't strong enough.

But Elizabeth was strong. Mentally and physically. I saw her carry in that heavy tray. Sydney was after the family money, and that hit Elizabeth where she lived—literally. The subpoenas were going to be served the next day, and Hudson would have caved in to save face with his partners. Elizabeth knew her son Hudson wouldn't kill his wife. But Elizabeth could. Elizabeth didn't approve of her daughter-in-law living in the city, but she used it to her advantage. She killed Sydney and made it look like a biker murder. Elizabeth's expensive clothes would be out of place in South St. Louis. So she stole Cordelia's coat—Cordelia told me herself that her coat was missing. It would stay missing, too. The coat was probably drenched in blood. Elizabeth was smart enough to toss it somewhere far from the scene. So why didn't she throw out the purse and shoes, too? The answer floated up from the front door.

"I'd like a tax letter for one thousand dollars," Elizabeth crisply told Dudley.

That was it. Greed. Elizabeth's motive for the murder. The strong killer's weakness. Elizabeth was so tight she squeaked. She wanted that charity deduction. If the purse and shoes had any blood on them, Elizabeth wiped it off. I knew she was cold. Could she calmly clean off her daughter-in-law's blood to get a tax deduction? Of course she could.

"We'd have to have them appraised," said Dudley, who was shrewd enough to know Elizabeth's donation wasn't worth that much.

I didn't listen to any more of the conversation. I felt sick. I headed for the bathroom, flipped on the light, and saw myself, pale and shaken, and greener than the old-fashioned bathroom tile. I wanted out of this house of horrors. I would grab my briefcase and leave. I'd tell Mark Mayhew everything I'd found out—if he was still speaking to me—and let him handle Elizabeth. She was too much for me. I don't know how long I was in the bathroom, but I was still shaky when I started down the stairs.

That's why I was clutching the stair rail tightly, and that's what saved my life. When my foot caught on the clear plastic fishing line stretched across the third step from the top, I plunged forward but managed to hold on to the rail.

"My dear, you almost had a very nasty fall," said Elizabeth, standing at the bottom of the steps. She guided me toward my seat by the tea tray, and I was too shaky to resist. "You could have been killed."

"I thought you usually used bike chains," I said.

"I have no idea what you are talking about," she said. But her eyes were colder than the winter sky.

"You killed your daughter-in-law. You killed her biker boyfriend when he tried to blackmail you. You tried to kill me because I figured it out."

"You are distraught, Francesca. Would you like more tea?"

She was the coolest woman I ever met. She was going to pour me more tea when I'd just accused her of murder. I watched her pick up the heavy silver pot. She took a swing at me with it. I ducked and knocked over the little table covering the hole in the rug, then held the table in front of me like a shield. It shattered with one blow of the silver teapot. Luke-warm tea splattered across the Kirman rug. I rolled forward to the mantel and reached up for an ugly green vase I saw there. The thing was acid green trimmed with gold and looked like the vase my aunt Gracie won at a carnival.

Elizabeth froze. "Put that down, you idiot," she commanded. "It's Meissen. It's worth a fortune. Seventy thousand dollars for a matched pair."

As long as I held on to the vase, I was safe. I could back out the door with the vase and run for my car.

But I didn't get a chance. She came running for me, like a springing lioness I'd seen on a *National Geographic* special. I made a run for the front door, but she blocked my way, swinging the heavy silver teapot. I had to run, either back into the living room or upstairs. I chose the stairs, remembering to step over the fishing line on the third step from the top. I managed to hang on to the vase, too. Elizabeth ran right after me and leaped the line like a spring lamb.

About then I realized I'd made a dumb decision. I was trapped upstairs. I had to get back down those steps again so I could get out the door. I ran into the bathroom and locked the door behind me. Elizabeth pounded on it. "Come out, Francesca, come out. We can get you help," she said.

Wonderful. Now I was the crazy one. Well, I was sitting on the commode, holding a vase worth more than my annual salary. No doubt Charlie the managing editor would believe Elizabeth before he believed me. If it were up to him, I'd be wearing a jacket with wraparound sleeves. After about ten minutes, Elizabeth quit pounding and pleading for me to come out. I could hear her go into the bedroom across from the bath and quietly pick up the phone. Who was she going to call? Her son? Charlie the managing editor? The police?

I didn't wait to find out. I opened the bathroom door and started down the steps. Very carefully, I stepped over the fishing line again. Then I moved faster. But she heard me. I could hear her drop the phone and then I saw her at the top of the steps. I was still a long way from the bottom and the escape to the outside.

"Come any further, and I'll drop this over the side," I said. I plastered myself to the banister and held the vase out over the slates in the entry hall.

"Francesca, I'm sure the newspaper will get you the best care," she said. "I won't file any charges, if you'll just put down the vase."

The vase wobbled in my hands. "I'm putting it down all right, unless you tell me how you killed your daughter-in-law."

"People in my position don't murder," she said. "You're the one who comes from murderers and suicides. With your past, who'd believe anything you'd say about me? Especially when . . ."

Was that an admission? I didn't find out. She made a lunge for me in midsentence, trying to grab her precious vase. She forgot about the fishing line she'd tied across the third step. It caught her by the foot and flipped her right over, headfirst. Her head bounced on the steps going down. Then she landed on the foyer slates with a sound like a watermelon falling out of a window. I hope I never hear that sound again. A pool of very dark blood began spreading around her head. She never moved. She would never move again. Elizabeth was dead.

I was numb, but I could feel a cold raw fear starting in the pit of my stomach and spreading outward. She'd never admitted that she had committed the murders, and she couldn't confess now. What if she didn't murder Sydney and Jack? I'd been wrong before. Was I wrong again? Had I killed an innocent woman?

I realized I was still on the stairs and still clutching the vase. I tried to walk downstairs. I made it, wobbly and sweaty, to the last step when the doorbell rang. I guess the sound startled me, and the sweat made my hands slippery. The ugly green vase slipped out of my hands and crashed to the floor. It lay there broken and ruined, like its owner.

Epilogue

"**G**ood God, you've killed Mother!" Hudson Vander Venter said. He'd rung the doorbell and used his key to let himself in for an afternoon visit with Elizabeth. Now he stood in the slate-floored foyer, staring at her broken body. Even from where he stood, it was obvious she was dead. He did not run over and touch his mother. Probably didn't want to get blood on his good suit. But he did take a step or two closer. Bits of the acid-green vase crunched under his feet. After three crunches, he realized what was making that noise: the vase I broke when he rang the doorbell.

"Good God," he said again. "You've destroyed a matched pair of Meissen." I couldn't tell which disaster left him more shattered—the loss of his mother, or the Meissen.

"It was an accident. I didn't mean to," I said, sounding like Dorothy when she threw the pail of water on the Wicked Witch of the West.

"You killed her, you wretched woman. You'll pay
for this." He grabbed his cell phone from his briefcase and dialed 911. I grabbed the phone by the
couch and called Mayhew's office. He wasn't in, but I
left an urgent message. My voice shook as I said,
"Tell him that there has been a major break in the
Vander Venter case. He should get to Elizabeth Vander Venter's house in Ladue immediately."

Then I called the *Gazette* to tell Georgia what happened. I was halfway through my explanation when
Hudson grabbed the phone out of my hand and hung
it up. "You may NOT use Mother's phone," he said,
peevishly. I tried to wrestle it back to call Lyle, but
gave up. I could hear the sirens of the approaching
police cars. After that, it was nothing but confusion,
accusations, and explanations. Mayhew arrived
about twenty minutes later, and Georgia blew in half
an hour after Mayhew with a matched pair of *Gazette*
lawyers, who promptly told me to shut up, the same
advice that Georgia always gave me, except she
didn't charge to say that. I was done talking for a
while, anyway. I'd already told my story half a dozen
times, and now the police were checking it. There
was plenty of evidence to support my version, from
the shattered table to the fishing line on the stairs.
Only Elizabeth's fingerprints were found on and
around the fishing line, so Hudson couldn't say I'd
used it to kill his mother. Hudson wasn't saying anything at the moment. His lawyers had arrived, and
they told him to shut up, too.

I wished Lyle was there, but I was also glad he
wasn't. Shock was setting in. My teeth were chat-
tering and I felt cold. Someone offered me a cup of

hot tea, but I didn't think I could ever drink tea again. Georgia gave me her jacket to wear, but I couldn't stop shivering. I'd killed Elizabeth. Maybe not on purpose, but my intentions didn't matter. I told myself that she'd tried to kill me. If I wasn't such a klutz, if I hadn't held on to the stair rail, she might have succeeded. But knowing that didn't help. I wished I could feel sorry that she was dead. I wished I could feel sad. I wished I could feel anything but what I did feel: cold. I was so cold I didn't think I'd ever be warm. For months afterward, I would dream that Elizabeth was chasing me through the house and down the stairs. I could see her foot catch in the fishing line. I would watch her fall down the steps and I would hear once again those dreadful thumps. Suddenly it was me who was falling. I was trying to grab on to something, but I couldn't stop falling. I always woke up before I hit the bottom. I would be shivering and sweating, but so cold.

It was hours before I got out of that house. Hudson was making threats when I left and his lawyers were trying to muzzle him. But he couldn't do anything. The power of the Vander Venters was as broken as the vase.

The police found plenty of proof that Elizabeth was the killer. Sydney's blood was on the shoes and purse that Elizabeth donated to the church bazaar. One of Sydney's hairs was in the purse. Elizabeth's skin fragments were in the drive chain used to beat Sydney to death. The cast of the tire matched the front tire on Elizabeth's car. In the trunk of her car were smears of motor oil. Police found credit card receipts for three cases of Exxon motor oil (twelve quarts to a case, eighty-nine cents a quart) and a motorcycle drive chain from the West Alton Discount Barn. The site of Jack's murder was a few miles across the river.

But the best evidence was in the can, just like Sydney told her friend, Jane. Elizabeth used a coffee can safe to hide the papers that showed all the devious ways she and her son were defrauding Sydney. She put the can on a shelf in her refrigerator. Too bad Jack missed the ruby necklace Elizabeth kept in the vegetable bin in a fake head of lettuce when he went through her refrigerator—that would have been enough lettuce to get him out of town. Jack wouldn't have had to blackmail the lethal Elizabeth. The crafty old woman devised a perfect way to take out a big, mean biker. After she murdered Jack, Elizabeth didn't destroy the papers. She returned them to her coffee can safe in the refrigerator. It was a stupid move by a smart woman.

"I can't believe she kept a ruby necklace in the icebox," I said to Mayhew. Elizabeth's death took care of any awkwardness between us. When he showed up at her house, the last thing I worried about was what he thought of me after our afternoon together. Now we were back to being old friends. Mayhew gave me an update over breakfast at Uncle Bob's, while Marlene sedately brought our food and didn't say a single snotty word.

"You'd be surprised what rich people do," Mayhew said. "I know one guy with an incredible art collection—Monets, Cézannes, Picassos, the works. He has it guarded with the cheapest possible alarm system. I wouldn't have it at my house to protect my CD player."

No one is exactly sure how Elizabeth found out the papers were missing, but I liked Mayhew's theory. Here's what he thinks happened: "Cordelia complained to Elizabeth about those muddy footprints on her kitchen floor," he said. "At least, Cordelia says she made a fuss."

"I know she did," I said. "Cordelia even complained to me about the footprints."

"I think Elizabeth saw the footprints and knew someone had been in her kitchen," Mayhew said. "She waited until Cordelia left for the day, then checked the safes. The ruby necklace was untouched, but the coffee can safe was empty. She immediately suspected her daughter-in-law, or someone acting for her, took the papers. Who else but Sydney would benefit from them?"

"Did Sydney know about the coffee can safe?"

"Hud Junior told us she often joked about Elizabeth's cut-rate security system. Sydney thought the refrigerator was the first place a burglar would look for cold cash and valuables. It's probably the first place she had Jack check when she gave him the key to her mother-in-law's house."

"How did you know she gave Jack a key?"

"We found it on his key chain. We didn't know what door it matched until after Elizabeth's death. We think Elizabeth decided to kill Sydney before her daughter-in-law claimed her share of the family fortune in the divorce. Elizabeth found the perfect way to make herself invisible. She dressed like a dowdy, respectable old woman. Elizabeth stole Cordelia's coat. She bought the sensible black shoes, felt hat, and a big black purse at a store in Florissant, about as far away from Ladue as she could go—but conveniently on the way home from the Discount Barn. We found that credit card receipt, too, and the clerk definitely remembers Elizabeth."

Mayhew can't prove his theory, because nobody ever found Cordelia's coat. But it made sense to me. Why else would a tightwad like Elizabeth buy Cordelia a new coat?

"Did you ever find out what Hudson was doing in those missing fifteen minutes?" I said. That was the question I couldn't answer.

"He just might have been in the bathroom, like he said," Mayhew said. "We pressed him about it again after his mother died. This time he was scared enough to tell us he had diverticulitis—a bowel problem that could keep him in there for a while. The great financier said he was too embarrassed to admit he had this 'weakness.' Hudson even gave us permission to talk to his internist, who confirmed he had been treated for an inflammation of the large intestine."

Hudson also admitted his mother gave him six quarts of oil, but he swore he didn't know that she murdered Jack. Hudson said he never changed his own oil. He planned to give it to his handyman on the next visit to the farm.

Hudson still denied beating my car with a cinder block. So did his lawyer-lover, Brenda, when the police questioned her in connection with the case. Hud Junior said he didn't do it, and I believed him. Maybe it was Elizabeth, but crude vandalism didn't seem subtle enough for her clever mind. It could have been the neighborhood kids. But I didn't think so. The incident nagged at me.

But I had too many good things to think about. Lyle and I are getting along fine. I've moved in with him—almost. I still keep a few clothes and things at my grandparents' place, and I go there whenever I need a break from living with Lyle. I slop around in an old hairy pink bathrobe, order pizza, eat tuna out of the can, and sleep sideways in the bed. Single-mindedness dies hard. Besides, I have to go back to clean those steps.

But after a day or two, I go home to Lyle. I miss him. I still have the dreams about my parents, and I wake up with my heart pounding. But then I tell myself that Lyle is not like my father, and I am not like my mother. If I don't say that, Lyle does, which is another reason why I like him beside me. Often he'll kiss me to reassure me that everything is all right, and then my heart ends up pounding for another reason.

■

Sonny and the other bikers thanked me for clearing their names. I told them the truth: I didn't do anything. But they insisted on being grateful. Stephanie gave me a T-shirt that said BITCH WITH A BAD ATTITUDE. I appreciated the compliment. Crazy Jerry gave me a fifth of Jack Daniel's and a twelve-pack of Busch, so I could learn to drink like a biker. Streak solemnly gave me his card, which had only his street name— "Streak"—a PO box, and "Viet Nam Vets MC." That stood for Motorcycle Club. He signed his name on the back. "Show that if you're ever in trouble," Streak said. I put it in my wallet. I'm always in trouble.

I politely declined the new-looking CD player Gilly brought me, but I did accept two tickets from Sonny for the next Leather and Lace Ball. They were the hottest tickets in town. This time Lyle went with me. We danced to "Born to Be Wild" while the Harley roared around the room. We both enjoyed looking at the extreme outfits. But Stephanie and Crazy Jerry weren't the most outrageous couple this year. They'd split. Oddly enough, they both turned up wearing the same thing: black jeans, black boots, and faded black Harley shirts.

Nothing has changed at the *Gazette*. I like my readers and I like my job, and I consider myself lucky when the editors leave me alone. I suppose I owe that to the Voyage Committee. The committee commissioned a telephone survey of three thousand readers and nonreaders. The survey found that I was the most popular columnist at the *Gazette* with women readers—exactly the people the *Gazette* advertisers were eager to court. Nobody on the committee could figure out why readers liked me—they took it as more proof the folks who buy the paper weren't real bright—but the committee decided I should keep on doing whatever I was doing. Georgia slipped me the survey information and said, "With your readership, Francesca, they'd have to be morons to fire you." She seemed to think that sentence would reassure me, but I didn't see it as job security. I still had those two warning letters in my file, and I knew Charlie, that toad, was eager for another excuse to fire me.

Georgia also told me that Voyage Captain Jason gave me his blessing after he cast me off, so the publisher wasn't too unhappy with me. Jason told the committee, "Some creative types are happier if they sail alone. Francesca seems to be one of them." I thought Jason was all wet, but as long as I didn't have to go to meetings, I wasn't going to make waves.

When Wendy took my place on the Voyage Committee, the whole department enjoyed peace for six months. For once, we were one big happy Family section. The committee met more often as the end approached. They were busy writing white papers and confidential reports. Wendy, looking dumpy and self-important, would bustle into the office maybe two days a week. The other three days were like a vacation. We knew it couldn't last and finally, eight months after it had begun the Voyage of Discovery was over. The final report would be delivered at three o'clock Friday. Attendance was mandatory, which made the staff surlier than usual. Most Friday afternoons we were long gone by three o'clock. Paychecks were delivered at noon, and only the staff with Sunday deadlines hung around after that. Now we were all stuck at work, and we were about as happy as a class kept after school. We draped ourselves on desks and leaned against pillars, waiting sullenly for the announcement, so we could start the weekend. I found a place behind the fire extinguisher.

The entire Voyage Committee assembled in the newsroom, minus me, of course. Georgia hid her small self behind the tall Tolbart. The less she was associated with this boondoggle, the better. The publisher looked as tanned and relaxed as if he'd been on a real voyage. He stood proudly next to Voyage Captain Jason, who still wore his uniform of jeans and work boots. Jason looked like a Marin County poster boy. He did the talking. "Eight months ago, the Voyage Committee embarked on a journey of self-discovery," he said. "The voyage was not designed to fix what was wrong with the *Gazette*."

"Nobody could do that," I muttered under my breath.

"The purpose of the voyage was more important. We are preparing the *Gazette* to sail into a brilliant new future, and it gives me great pride to say that we have reached four major conclusions about the *Gazette*'s needs in the future," Jason said. He held up four fingers and then counted them off, one by one.

"Number one, the paper needs younger readers and more women readers.

"Number two, the *Gazette* needs more reader involvement.

"Number three, the *Gazette* needs lighter, brighter, shorter stories.

"Number four, the *Gazette* needs more local stories."

The publisher gave a stately nod to seal these conclusions. Voyage Captain Jason continued, "Therefore, the Voyage Committee recommends the following four policies be implemented to reach those objectives:

"First, a series of 'Tell Us What You Think' features will begin immediately, to promote reader involvement." The entire staff groaned.

"Second, the feature section will include one celebrity interview each day." The entire Family section groaned.

"Third, no story will be longer than thirty inches." The editorial page, famous for mind-numbing seventy-inch "think" pieces, groaned.

"Fourth, all stories must have a local angle. There will be no exceptions." The staff was struck speechless at this particular piece of stupidity.

"Any questions?" Jason asked.

There were lots. This was not a happy crew. The reporters were so upset, they didn't even care if the publisher was present. They peppered Jason with angry questions:

"Are we going to skip covering world events now? How on earth can we make a typhoon in Taiwan local?" Jasper demanded. For once, his vile temper was turned on the right person.

"You can localize that story. Write about the St. Louis relief effort to help the victims," Jason said brightly.

"What about stories covering the conflicts in Africa and Eastern Europe?" asked Clay, a serious cityside reporter. "How do we make international news local?"

"Interview the refugees who resettle in St. Louis," Jason said.

"How do we explain what these people are doing here in the first place, if we don't cover the wars that made them flee their countries?" Clay pressed.

"I know you'll find a way," said our captain, who obviously hadn't a clue about news gathering. This wasn't a Voyage of Discovery. It was a shakedown cruise. Captain Jason looked longingly at the door, as if he wanted to bolt for the exit before the crowd turned on him. "One more question," he said.

My hand shot up first, and the other reporters held back, waiting to see what I had to say. I wanted something cleared up before Voyage Captain Jason took off, and I wanted his answer in front of witnesses, so our esteemed Family editor couldn't waffle later and stick us with the blame.

"How can the Family section do stories about national celebrities if you want only local stories?"

Voyage Captain Jason had an answer ready: "We will localize the celebrity interviews by asking the person 'What do you think of St. Louis?' "

That was the last treasure from Captain Jason.

■

Charlie had his triumphs, too. The whole town talked about his new Go Away section for weeks. They hated it. Three thousand readers called up and complained about Go Away the first week it was launched. They hated the name, and they hated the tabloid format. I could have told the paper that tabloids work only in commuter cities, where people read the paper on the subway or the train. But I didn't charge half a mil and call myself a consultant. Hundreds of people canceled their subscriptions. But the new section was still considered a great success. Marketing had told the publisher to expect five thousand complaints. When the other two thousand complaints didn't materialize, Go Away was pronounced a hit. Still, there is talk of a graphics makeover to stimulate more circulation.

Charlie succeeded in getting rid of the old Family

office manager, Louise. After struggling through six miserable months of computer training, Louise was put on the 12:00 to 6:00 A.M. shift in the morgue. Nobody in their right mind worked at the *Gazette* at that hour. People who were crazy, or crazy mean, roamed the deserted streets around the paper after dark. The parking lot closest to the building was reserved for the bosses. Louise would have had to walk more than two blocks through some of the city's meanest streets. When Smiling Steve, Charlie's right hand, offered her a paltry five-thousand-dollar retirement incentive, she took it. "I know when I'm beat, sweetie," she told me, and she did look weary. "No job is worth dying for."

The staff chipped in and bought Louise and her husband a trip to Cancun. At her retirement party, she seemed happier than she had in years. But the party was still a sad event. Charlie had triumphed. Scarlette presides over the Family section now. The phones ring unanswered, the vacation checks are late, and the freelancers' payments are often screwed up. When Charlie canceled sixteen contracts with local freelancers, Scarlette forgot to stop their weekly payments. An audit caught the four-thousand-dollar overpayment six months later. The *Gazette* rudely demanded that the freelancers pay the money back. Only two bothered spending thirty-two cents on a stamp to tell the *Gazette* to go to hell. The rest just dropped the letters in the circular file. Charlie made up the shortfall by taking four thousand dollars from the Family department travel budget. He continues to stop by daily to stare down the front of Scarlette's sweater. I consider it pay-for-view.

It took a full month and five thousand dollars, but Ralph was restored to his former beauty. In fact, he never looked better. His body shone with six coats of lacquer. His chrome glowed like well-polished silver. All the little dings and chips that a working car accumulates were gone. So was the rust that had bubbled up around the windshield. Inside, his Iris-blue seats had the intoxicating smell of new leather. Thanks to the redone Ralph, I was getting more exercise. I parked him way in the back of the parking lots, far from other cars, to protect his new paint job.

The first day I had Ralph back, I took him to Uncle Bob's for breakfast. I was hiking in from the farthest corner of Uncle Bob's lot when I saw Mayhew leaving with a woman. Oh, please, God, don't let it be his wife, I thought. I felt bad enough about what happened without meeting her. The couple was heading in my direction, toward three cars parked near the Dumpsters. As they got closer, I saw this wasn't Mayhew's round soft little brunette wife but a skinny hard-faced blonde in tight jeans and high heels. She had to be Sheila, the girlfriend Mayhew sometimes brought to Uncle Bob's, the one the waitresses hated because they liked his wife. I'd get an earful from Marlene today.

Should I say anything? They were so close now, it would be awkward to ignore him. "Hi, Mayhew," I said and waved. Mayhew looked trapped and uneasy. When she saw me, Sheila clamped her hand on his arm like he was a felon about to escape. She gave me a glare that should have peeled off four layers of my skin. The woman was possessive. I continued talking anyway. "Look at Ralph. He's good as new."

"They fixed your car already?" Mayhew said, sounding genuinely pleased.

"Already? It took a month!" I said. "But everything is back where it should be."

"Even the Tampax?" Sheila sneered.

Mayhew blushed bright red. By the time I said "How did you know about that?" he had steered Sheila to her red Firebird. She locked the doors like I was a carjacker and drove off the lot with an angry screech of tires. He was running for his car by the Dumpster.

"You've got some explaining to do, Mayhew," I yelled, running after him.

"Can't stop to talk," he said. "My beeper just went off. Gotta run."

He did have to run. Because when I caught up with him, I was going to get an explanation of little Sheila's statement. Where did she get such intimate knowledge of my car? Not from me. I couldn't see Mayhew talking about Tampax with a girlfriend.

He evaded me for a week and a half, but finally, I found him at Uncle Bob's one morning, eating his waffle. I plopped down at his booth and said, "Okay, Mayhew. Confess. You know who attacked my car, and it wasn't any Vander Venter."

Mayhew turned the color of the Strawberry Dee-Lite Waffle. But he told the truth. "It was Sheila," he said. "She's . . . uh . . . a little possessive."

"I saw the way she grafted herself onto your arm," I said.

"She's insecure. You have to understand her position," he said.

"Missionary?" I said snidely.

He looked wounded. "Francesca, I was honest with her, just like I was honest with you. I said I loved my wife and could never marry her. Sheila said she understood, but I guess she really didn't. She gets a little jealous sometimes. She lives over on Hartford, and she recognized my Harley parked in front of your place that afternoon and thought I was in Mrs. Indelicato's store. She went in to see me. But Mrs. I said I wasn't in the store. Then Sheila heard some . . . sounds from us on the steps and . . . uh . . . thought she knew what they were. She left without making a scene in front of Mrs. I, but she brooded on it all day, and that night she took a cinder block to Ralph."

Jeez. I'd had all the disadvantages of a fallen woman and none of the fun. I didn't belong in the adultery game.

Mark was contrite about what Sheila did to Ralph. "I'm sorry, Francesca. I meant to tell you before this. It's my responsibility. I'll pay for the damage."

"Forget it, Mark," I said. "My insurance covered it." My insurance covered all but five hundred dollars. But I didn't want any man to pay for Ralph.

"I feel guilty," he said. "I've hurt your car."

"Ralph wasn't hurt. He came back better than ever. In fact, he's perfect."

Almost perfect. But I wouldn't find his one flaw until months later, on the first warm day of spring. Then I turned on Ralph's air conditioning and heard a rattle. It sounded like a small piece of window glass was trapped inside. I could have taken the car back and had the rattle removed, but I didn't. I keep it there. When I get too hot, the rattle reminds me to cool off. And keep my hands off other women's husbands.

■

That happened in March. Soon St. Louis was in a green and glorious spring. When the dogwoods were in bloom, I took the afternoon off and went to see Sydney. She was buried at Bellefontaine Cemetery, in North St. Louis. The *Gazette* liked to say that some of the city's oldest families were buried there, but I figured we all came from old families, or we wouldn't be here, right? Certainly some of the city's richest and most notorious families were planted in these hills. Thomas Hart Benton, Missouri's first senator, was with the silent majority at Bellefontaine. Adolphus Busch, the beer baron, did not bury his pride even in death. His mausoleum says VENI VIDI VICI. He came, he saw, and he conquered . . . what? The boss's daughter? Adolphus didn't found the Anheuser-Busch brewery. He married Eberhard Anheuser's daughter, Lilly.

The gloomy and arrogant monuments were softened by the white clouds of dogwood. They looked beautiful in the spring sunshine. Sydney was not buried with the family that killed her, but with her own people. A pink dogwood wept over her pink granite stone. In a vase was a single white rose. The rose was fresh. It rested just below her name and dates, against the inscription: "Beloved Mother." Her son must have done that.

I owe you an apology, Sydney, I thought. I misjudged you. I thought your life was silly and useless. I thought I was superior to you because I have a career and I am a local celebrity. But your son loves you. And you loved him. I could not put "Beloved Mother" on my mother's tombstone. I could not love her. And she could not love me. You have something that I will never have.

I stood by Sydney's grave for some time. I heard the birds singing, and the grass being mowed in a distant section of the cemetery, and a car going by. But from Sydney, there was nothing. No sign. No word. Beloved Mother was enough for her.

∎

Sydney's son continues to honor her memory. So far he's stayed off the drugs. I saw him recently at Has Beans, the Clayton coffeeshop, but this time he was a customer. The kid looked good. The dark shadows were gone from under his eyes. He seemed like another twenty-something, maybe a little more serious than most. Hud told me that the cop scared him into virtue when he picked him up in that South Side alley. "I was afraid my father wouldn't bail me out if I got caught," he told me. "My heart was pounding so badly I could hardly breathe. I knew a city cop would love to run in a rich kid like me. When he didn't, I went back to Eric's and collapsed. I locked the door and didn't move all night long. I couldn't believe I'd escaped."

One month after his mother's death, Hud went into drug rehab again. This time he made a serious effort to stay clean. He's back in school, on a scholarship, in the top 10 percent of his class.

Hud's going to need that degree. He won't have a job waiting for him in the family firm. Investigators

**THE MOST FAMOUS
BOOK IN AMERICA ON
THE RELATIONS
BETWEEN PARENTS AND
THEIR CHILDREN!**

**OVER 60 WEEKS
ON THE
BESTSELLER LIST!**

"Simply stated, with specific words
and ideas that parents can use in
child guidance . . . Combines good
science with good common sense."
                                    Family Life

"Time and again one comes on observations so true and so well put that there is an urge to copy them and hang them over the kitchen sink."

The Episcopalian

"Parents have been studying children-ese and putting it into practice. All those we interviewed found the method . . . infinitely rewarding."

The New York Times

"Dozens of extremely helpful ideas for achieving those goals which most parents hold . . . it is a great relief to hear from enlightened professionals who have practical, illustrated advice."

Christian Science Monitor

Between Parent & Child

New solutions to old problems

Dr. Haim G. Ginott

Graduate Department
of Psychology
NEW YORK UNIVERSITY

AVON
PUBLISHERS OF BARD, CAMELOT AND DISCUS BOOKS

Acknowledgment is gratefully made to the following
copyright holders for permission to reprint from
previously published materials:

McGraw-Hill Book Company for an excerpt from
Group Psychotherapy with Children by Dr. Haim G.
Ginott. Copyright © 1961 Haim G. Ginott. Used by
permission of McGraw-Hill Book Company.

The Viking Press Inc. for an excerpt from *East of Eden*
by John Steinbeck, Copyright 1952.

Harper and Row for an excerpt from *Child Behavior*
by Francis L. Ilg and Louis B. Ames, Copyright 1955.

AVON BOOKS
A division of
The Hearst Corporation
959 Eighth Avenue
New York, New York 10019

Copyright © 1956 by Dr. Haim G. Ginott.
Published by arrangement with The Macmillan Company.
Library of Congress Catalog Card Number: 65-20189.
ISBN: 0-380-45369-X

First Avon Printing, March, 1969.
Thirtieth Printing

AVON TRADEMARK REG. U.S. PAT. OFF. AND
FOREIGN COUNTRIES, REGISTERED TRADEMARK—
MARCA REGISTRADA, HECHO EN CHICAGO, U.S.A.

Printed in the U.S.A.

To the memory of my younger brother

Contents

Contents

Contents

Preface

No parent wakes up in the morning planning to make his child's life miserable. No mother says to herself, "Today I'll yell, nag, and humiliate my child whenever possible." On the contrary. In the morning many mothers resolve: "This is going to be a peaceful day. No yelling, no arguing, and no fighting." Yet, in spite of good intentions, the unwanted war breaks out again. Once more we find ourselves saying things we do not mean, in a tone we do not like.

All parents want their children to be secure and happy. No one deliberately tries to make his child fearful, shy, inconsiderate, or obnoxious. Yet in the process of growing up, many children acquire undesirable characteristics and fail to achieve a sense of security and an attitude of respect for themselves and for others. We want children to be polite and they are rude; we want them to be neat and they are messy; we want them to be self-confident and they are insecure; we want them to be happy and they are not.

The purpose of this book is to help parents identify their goals in relation to children and to suggest methods of achieving those goals. Parents are confronted with concrete problems that require specific solutions; they are not helped by cliché advice such as "Give the child more love," "Show him more attention," "Offer him more time."

For the last fifteen years, the author has worked with parents and children in individual, as well as in group, guidance and psychotherapy. The book is the fruit of this experience. It is a practical guide: it offers concrete suggestions and preferred solutions for dealing with daily situations and psychological problems faced by all parents. While the book gives specific advice, it also sets forth basic principles to guide parents in living with children in mutual respect and dignity.

Acknowledgments

I am grateful to my friends and colleagues who read the manuscript and contributed suggestions and criticism: Dr. Ralph Dreger, Sue Zohar Desheh, Bea Livingston, Dr. Arthur Orgel, Patricia and Howard Pearl, Angela Podkameni and Rosalind Wiener. Special thanks to Bette Kaufman for assistance and encouragement, and to Dr. Stanley Spiegel for his help in starting the book. Lastly, to the parents who shared with me their feelings and experience, I acknowledge my greatest debt.

HAIM G. GINOTT

Between
Parent
& Child

CHAPTER 1

Conversing
with children

CHILDREN'S QUESTIONS: THE HIDDEN MEANINGS

Conversing with children is a unique art with rules and meanings of its own. Children are rarely naive in their communications. Their messages are often in a code, that requires deciphering.

Andy, age ten, asked his father, "What is the number of abandoned children in Harlem?"

Father, a chemist and an intellectual, was glad to see his son take an interest in social problems. He gave a long lecture on the subject and then looked up the figure. But Andy was not satisfied and kept on asking questions on the same subject: "What is the number of abandoned children in New York City?" "in the United States?" "in Europe?" "in the world?"

Finally it occurred to father that his son was concerned, not about a social problem, but by a personal one. His questions stemmed not so

21

much from sympathy for abandoned children as from fear of being abandoned. He was looking, not for a figure representing the number of deserted children, but for reassurance that he would not be deserted.

On his first visit to kindergarten, while mother was still with him, Bruce, age five, looked over the paintings on the wall and asked loudly, "Who made these ugly pictures?"

Mother was embarrassed. She looked at her son disapprovingly, and hastened to tell him, "It's not nice to call the pictures ugly when they are so pretty."

The teacher, who understood the meaning of the question, smiled and said, "In here you don't have to paint pretty pictures. You can paint mean pictures if you feel like it." A big smile appeared on Bruce's face, for now he had the answer to his hidden question: "What happens to a boy who doesn't paint so well?"

Next Bruce picked up a broken fire engine and asked self-righteously, "Who broke this fire engine?" Mother answered, "What difference does it make to you who broke it? You don't know anyone here."

Bruce was not really interested in names. He wanted to find out what happened to boys who break toys. Understanding the question, the teacher gave an appropriate answer: "Toys are for playing. Sometimes they get broken. It happens."

Bruce seemed satisfied. His interviewing skill had netted him the necessary information:

Conversing with children

"This grownup is pretty nice. She does not get angry quickly, even when a picture comes out ugly or a toy is broken. I don't have to be afraid. It is safe to stay here." Bruce waved good-by to his mother and went over to the teacher to start his first day in kindergarten.

Carol, age twelve, was tense and tearful. Her favorite cousin was going home after staying with her during the summer.

CAROL (*with tears in her eyes*): Susie is going away. I'll be all alone again.

MOTHER: You'll find another friend.

CAROL: I'll be so lonely.

MOTHER: You'll get over it.

CAROL: Oh, mother! (*Sobs.*)

MOTHER: You are twelve years old and still such a crybaby.

Carol gave mother a deadly look and escaped to her room, closing the door behind her.

This episode should have had a happier ending. A child's feeling must be taken seriously, even though the situation itself is not very serious. In mother's eyes a summer separation may be too minor a crisis for tears, but her response need not have lacked sympathy. Mother might have said to herself, "Carol is distressed. I can help her best by showing that I understand what pains her." To her daughter she might have said any or all of the following:

"It will be lonely without Susie."

"You miss her already."

"It is hard to be apart when you are so used to being together."

23

"The house must seem kind of empty to you without Susie around."

Such responses create intimacy between parent and child. When the child feels understood, his loneliness and hurt diminish, because they are understood, and his love for mother is deepened because she understands. Mother's sympathy serves as an emotional band-aid for the bruised ego.

FRUITLESS DIALOGUES

Parents are frustrated by dialogues with children because they lead nowhere, as illustrated by the famous conversation: "Where did you go?" "Out." "What did you do?" "Nothing." Parents who try to be reasonable soon discover how exhausting this can be. As one mother said, "I try to reason with my child until I am blue in the face, but he doesn't listen to me. He only hears me when I scream."

Children often resist dialogues with parents. They resent being preached to, talked at, and criticized. They feel that parents talk too much. Says eight-year-old David to his mother, "When I ask you a small question, why do you give me such a long answer?" To his friends he confides, "I don't tell mother anything. If I start in with her, I have no time left to play."

An interested observer who overhears a conversation between a parent and a child will note with surprise how little each listens to the other. The conversation sounds like two monologues, one consisting of criticism and instructions, the other of denials and pleading. The tragedy of such "communication" lies, not in the lack of love, but in the lack of respect; not in the lack of intelligence, but in the lack of skill.

Our everyday language is not adequate for communicating meaningfully with children. To reach children and to reduce parental frustration, we need a new mode of relating to children, including new ways of conversing with them.

THE NEW CODE OF COMMUNICATION

The new code of communication with children is based on respect and on skill. It requires (*a*) that messages preserve the child's as well as the parent's self-respect; (*b*) that statements of understanding *precede* statements of advice or instruction.

Eric, age nine, came home full of anger. His class was scheduled to go for a picnic, but it was raining. Mother decided to use a new approach. She refrained from clichés that in the past had only made things worse: "There is no use crying over rained-out picnics." "There will be other days for fun." "I didn't make it rain, you know, so why are you angry at me?"

To herself she said, "My son has strong feel-

ings about missing the picnic. He is disappointed. He is sharing his disappointment with me
by showing me his anger. He is entitled to his
emotions. I can best help him by showing understanding and respect for his feelings." To
Eric she said:

MOTHER: You seem very disappointed.

ERIC: Yes.

MOTHER: You wanted very much to go to this
picnic.

ERIC: I sure did.

MOTHER: You had everything ready and then
the darn rain came.

ERIC: Yes, that's exactly right.

There was a moment of silence and then Eric
said, "Oh, well, there will be other days."

His anger seemed to have vanished and he
was quite cooperative the rest of the afternoon.
Usually when Eric came home angry, the whole
household would be upset. Sooner or later he
provoked every member of the family. Peace
would not return until he was finally asleep late
in the evening.

What is so special about this approach, and
what are its helpful components?

When a child is in the midst of strong emotions, he cannot listen to anyone. He cannot
accept advice or consolation or constructive
criticism. He wants *us* to understand him. He
wants us to understand what is going on inside
himself at that particular moment. Furthermore, he wants to be understood without having to disclose fully what he is experiencing. It

is a game in which he reveals only a little of what he feels needing to have us guess the rest.

When a child tells us, "The teacher spanked me," we do not have to ask him for more details. Nor do we need to say, "What did you do to deserve it? If your teacher spanked you, you must have done something. What did you do?" We don't even have to say, "Oh, I am so sorry." We need to show him that we understand his pain and embarrassment and feelings of revenge. How do we know what he feels? We look at him and listen to him, and we also draw on our own emotional experiences. We know what a child *must* feel when he is shamed in public in the presence of peers. We so phrase our words that the child knows we understand what he has gone through. Any of the following statements would serve well:

"It must have been terribly embarrassing."

"It must have made you furious."

"You must have hated the teacher at that moment."

"It must have hurt your feelings terribly."

"It was a bad day for you."

A child's strong feelings do not disappear when he is told, "It is not nice to feel that way," or when the parent tries to convince him that he "has no reason to feel that way." Strong feelings do not vanish by being banished; they do diminish in intensity and lose their sharp edges when the listener accepts them with sympathy and understanding.

This statement holds true not only for chil-

27

dren but also for adults, as illustrated by the following excerpt* from a parents' discussion group:

LEADER: Suppose it is one of those mornings when everything seems to go wrong. The telephone rings, the baby cries, and before you know it, the toast is burnt. Your husband looks over the toaster and says: "My God! When will you learn to make toast?!" What is your reaction?

MRS. A: I would throw the toast in his face!

MRS. B: I would say, "Fix your own damn toast!"

MRS. C: I would be so hurt I could only cry.

LEADER: What would your husband's words make you feel toward him?

PARENTS: Anger, hate, resentment.

LEADER: Would it be easy for you to fix another batch of toast?

MRS. A: Only if I could put some poison in it!

LEADER: And when he left for work, would it be easy to clean up the house?

MRS. A: No, the whole day would be ruined.

LEADER: Suppose that the situation is the same: the toast is burnt but your husband, looking over the situation, says, "Gee, honey, it's a rough morning for you—the baby, the phone, and now the toast."

* Haim G. Ginott, *Group Psychotherapy With Children* (New York: McGraw-Hill Book Co., 1961), pp. 180-182.

MRS. A: I would drop dead if my husband said that to me!

MRS. B: I would feel wonderful!

MRS. C: I would feel so good I would hug him and kiss him.

LEADER: Why?—that baby is still crying and the toast is still burnt?

PARENTS: That wouldn't matter.

LEADER: What would make the difference?

MRS. B: You feel kind of grateful that he didn't criticize you—that he was with you, not against you.

LEADER: And when your husband left for work, would it be difficult to clean up the house?

MRS. C: No! I'd do it with a song.

LEADER: Let me now tell you about a third kind of husband. He looks over the burnt toast and says to you calmly, "Let me show you, honey, how to make toast."

MRS. A: Oh, no. He is even worse than the first one. He makes you feel stupid.

LEADER: Let's see how these three different approaches to the toast incident apply to our handling of children.

MRS. A: I see what you're driving at. I always say to my child, "You are old enough to know this, you are old enough to know that." It must make him furious. It usually does.

MRS. B: I always say to my son, "Let me show you, dear, how to do this or that."

MRS. C: I'm so used to being criticized that it comes natural to me. I use exactly the same

words my mother used *against* me when I
was a child. And I hated her for it. I never
did anything right, and she always made me
do things over.

LEADER: And you now find yourself using the
same words with your daughter?

MRS. C: Yes. I don't like it at all—I don't like
myself when I do it.

LEADER: You are looking for better ways of
talking with your children.

MRS. C: Yes, I sure am!

LEADER: Let's see what we can learn from the
burnt toast story. What is it that helped
change the mean feelings to loving ones?

MRS. B: The fact that somebody understood you.

MRS. C: Without blaming you.

MRS. A: And without telling you how to improve.

This vignette illustrates the power of words
to engender hostility or happiness. The moral of
the story is that our responses (words and feelings) can make a decided difference in the atmosphere of our home.

SOME PRINCIPLES OF CONVERSATION

From event to relationship.—When a child
tells of, or asks about, an event, it is frequently
best to respond, not to the event, but to the
relationship implied.

Flora, age six, complained that "lately" she

had been receiving fewer presents than her brother. Mother did not deny the complaint. Neither did she explain that brother was older and so deserved more. Nor did she promise to right the wrong. She knew that children are more concerned about the depth of their relationships with parents than about the size and number of gifts. Mother said, "You, too, want more presents?" Without adding another sentence, mother embraced her daughter, who responded with a smile of surprise and pleasure. This was the end of a conversation that could have become an endless argument.

From event to feelings.—When a child tells of an event, it is sometimes helpful to respond, not to the event itself, but to the feelings around it. Gloria, age seven, came home upset. She told mother how her girl friend Dori was pushed off the sidewalk into a rain-filled gutter. Instead of asking for more details of the event, mother responded to her daughter's feelings. She said:

"That must have upset you."

"You were angry at the boys who did it."

"You are still mad at them."

To all these statements, Gloria responded with an emphatic "Yes!" When mother said, "You are afraid that they may do it to you, too?"—Gloria answered with determination, "Let them try, I'll drag them with me. That would make a splash!" And she started to laugh at the picture in her mind of the drag and splash. This was the happy ending of a conver-

31

sation that could have become a sermon of useless advice on methods of self-defense.

When a child comes home with a host of complaints about a friend or a teacher or about his life, it is best to respond to his feeling tone, instead of trying to ascertain facts or to verify incidents.

Ten-year-old Harold came home cranky and complaining.

HAROLD: What a miserable life! The teacher called me a liar, just because I told her that I forgot the homework. And she yelled. My goodness, did she yell! She said she'll write you a note.

MOTHER: You had a very rough day.

HAROLD: You can say that again.

MOTHER: It must have been terribly embarrassing to be called a liar in front of the whole class.

HAROLD: It sure was.

MOTHER: I bet inside yourself you wished her a few things!

HAROLD: Oh, yes! But how did you know?

MOTHER: That's what we usually do when someone hurts us.

HAROLD: That's a relief.

From general to specific.—When a child makes a statement about himself, it is often desirable to respond, not with agreement or disagreement, but with details that convey to the child an understanding beyond expectation.

When a child says, "I am not good in arithmetic," it is of little help to tell him, "Yes, you are pretty lousy with figures." Nor is it helpful to dispute his opinion or to offer him cheap advice: "If you studied more, you would be better." Such hasty help only hurts his self-respect and the instant lesson only decreases his confidence.

His statement, "I am not good in arithmetic," can be met with earnestness and understanding. Any of the following would do:

"Arithmetic is not an easy subject."

"Some of the problems are very hard to figure out."

"The teacher does not make it easier with his criticism."

"He makes you feel stupid."

"I bet you can't wait for the hour to pass."

"When it is over, you feel safer."

"Exam time must be extra tough."

"You must be worrying a lot about failing."

". . . worrying about what we will think."

". . . afraid we'll be disappointed in you."

"We know some subjects are not easy."

"We have faith that you'll do your best."

A twelve-year-old boy related that he almost "dropped dead" when father talked to him with such understanding after he brought home a failing report card. His inner reaction was: "I must live up to my father's faith in me."

Once in a blue moon, almost every parent hears his son or daughter declare, "I am stupid." Knowing that *his* child cannot be stupid, the parent sets out to convince him that he is bright.

SON: I am stupid.

FATHER: You are not stupid.

SON: Yes, I am.

FATHER: You are not. Remember how smart you were at camp? The counselor thought you were one of the brightest.

SON: How do you know what he thought?

FATHER: He told me so.

SON: Yah, how come he called me stupe all the time?

FATHER: He was just kidding.

SON: I am stupid, and I know it. Look at my grades in school.

FATHER: You just have to work harder.

SON: I already work harder and it doesn't help. I have no brains.

FATHER: You are smart, I know.

SON: I am stupid, *I* know.

FATHER (*loudly*): You are not stupid!

SON: Yes I am!

FATHER: You are not stupid, Stupid!

When a child declares that he is stupid or ugly or bad, nothing that we can say or do will change his self-image immediately. A person's ingrained opinion of himself resists direct attempts at alteration. As one child said to his father, "I know you mean well, Dad, but I am not *that* stupid to take your word that I am bright."

When a child expresses a negative view of himself, our denials and protests are of little

34

help to him. They only bring forth a stronger declaration of his convictions. The best help we can offer is to show him that we understand not only his general feeling, but its implications:

SON: I am stupid.

FATHER (*seriously*): You really feel that way, don't you? You don't think of yourself as smart?

SON: No.

FATHER: Then you suffer inside quite a lot?

SON: Yeah.

FATHER: In school, you must be afraid a great deal of the time

... afraid you'll fail.

... afraid you'll get low marks.

When the teacher calls on you, you get confused.

Even when you know the answer, it doesn't come out right.

You are afraid that your words will sound ridiculous

... and that the teacher will criticize you.

... and that the children will laugh at you.

So, many times you prefer to say nothing. I guess you can remember times when you said something and they laughed at you. It made you feel stupid in your own eyes. Hurt and angry, too. (Here the child may tell you of some of his experience.)

FATHER: Look, son! In my eyes you are a fine person. But you have a different opinion of yourself.

This conversation may not change the child's

image of himself right then and there, but it may plant in him a seed of doubt about his inadequacy. He may think to himself, "If my father understands me and considers me a fine person, perhaps I am not that worthless." The intimacy that such a conversation creates may lead the son to try to live up to his father's faith in him.

When a child says, "I never have good luck," no argument or explanation will change his belief. For every instance of good fortune that we mention, he will respond with two tales of misfortune. All we can do is to show him how intimately we understand the feelings that lead him to his belief:

SON: I never have good luck.

MOTHER: You really feel that way?

SON: Yes.

MOTHER: So when you play a game you think inside yourself, "I'm not going to win. I don't have luck."

SON: Yes, that's exactly what I think.

MOTHER: In school, if you know the answer you think, "Today the teacher is not going to call me."

SON: Yes.

MOTHER: But if you didn't do the homework, you think, "Today she *is* going to call on me."

SON: Yes.

MOTHER: I guess you can give me many more examples.

SON: Sure ... like for instance (*child gives examples*).

MOTHER: I am interested in what you think about luck. If something happens that you think is bad luck, or even good luck, come and tell me and we'll talk about it.

This conversation may not change the child's belief in his bad luck. It may, however, convey to him how lucky he is to have such an understanding mother.

VOICING OF AMBIVALENCE

Children love and resent us at the same time. They feel two ways about parents, teachers, and all persons who have authority over them. Parents find it difficult to accept ambivalence as a fact of life. They do not like it in themselves and cannot tolerate it in their children. They think that there is something inherently wrong in feeling two ways about people, especially about members of the family.

We can learn to accept the existence of ambivalent feelings in ourselves and in our children. To avoid unnecessary conflicts, children need to know that such feelings are normal and natural. We can spare a child much guilt and anxiety by acknowledging and voicing his ambivalent feelings:

"You seem to feel two ways about your teacher: you like him and you dislike him."

"You seem to have two feelings about your older brother: you admire him, but you also resent him."

"You have two thoughts on the subject; you would like to go to camp, but you also want to stay home."

A calm, noncritical statement of their ambivalence is helpful to children because it conveys to them that even their "mixed-up" feelings are not beyond comprehension. As one child said, "If my mixed-up feelings can be understood, they are not so mixed up." On the other hand, statements such as the following are definitely not helpful:

"Boy, are you mixed up! One minute you like your friend, then you resent him. Make up your mind, if you have one."

A sophisticated view of human reality takes account of the possibility that where there is love, there is also some hate; where there is admiration, there is also some envy; where there is devotion, there is also some hostility; where there is success, there is also apprehension. It takes great wisdom to realize that all feelings are legitimate: the positive, the negative, and the ambivalent.

It is not easy to accept such concepts inwardly. Our childhood training and adult education predispose us to a contrary view. We have been taught that negative feelings are "bad" and should not be felt or that we should be ashamed of them. The new and scientific approach states that only real acts can be judged as "bad" or "good," imaginary acts cannot be. Only conduct can be condemned or commended, feelings cannot and should not be. Judgment of feelings and censure of fantasy would do violence both to political freedom and to mental health.

Emotions are part of our genetic heritage. Fish swim, birds fly, and people feel. Sometimes we are happy, sometimes we are not; but sometimes in our life we are sure to feel anger and fear, sadness and joy, greed and guilt, lust and scorn, delight and disgust. While we are not free to choose the emotions that arise in us, we are free to choose how and when to express them, provided we know what they are. That is the crux of the problem. Many people have been educated out of knowing what their feelings are. When they hated, they were told it was only dislike. When they were afraid, they were told there was nothing to be afraid of. When they felt pain, they were advised to be brave and smile. Many of our popular songs tell us "Pretend you are happy when you are not."

What is suggested in the place of this pretense? Truth. Emotional education can help children to *know what they feel*. It is more important for a child to know what he feels than why he feels it. When he knows clearly what his feelings are, he is less likely to feel "all mixed-up" inside.

PROVIDING A MIRROR TO THE PERSONALITY

How can we help a child to know his feelings? We can do so by serving as a mirror to his emotions. A child learns about his physical likeness by seeing his image in a mirror. He learns about his emotional likeness by hearing his feelings reflected by us.

The function of a mirror is to reflect an image as it is, without adding flattery or faults. We do not want a mirror to tell us, "You look terrible. Your eyes are bloodshot and your face is puffy. Altogether you are a mess. You'd better do something about yourself." After a few exposures to such a magic mirror, we would avoid it like the plague. From a mirror we want an image, not a sermon. We may not like the image we see; still, we would rather decide for ourselves our next cosmetic move.

The function of an emotional mirror is to reflect feelings as they are, without distortion:

"It looks as though you are very angry."

"It sounds like you hate him very much."

"It seems that you are disgusted with the whole set-up."

To a child who has such feelings, these statements are most helpful. They show him clearly what his feelings are. Clarity of image, whether in a looking glass or in an emotional mirror, provides opportunity for self-initiated grooming and change.

40

CHAPTER 2

New ways of praise and criticism

THE CASE OF THE FLYING ASHTRAY:
A STORY WITH A MORAL

It was early in the morning, the Monday after Thanksgiving weekend. The woman on the telephone sounded frantic. "Figure this out," she said, "if you can. Here we are in the car, the whole family. We drove four hundred miles from Pittsburgh to New York. In the back of the car, Ivan behaved like an angel, quiet and deep in thought. I said to myself, 'He deserves some praise.' We were just entering the Lincoln Tunnel when I turned to him and said, 'You are such a good boy, Ivan. You behaved so well. I am proud of you.'

"A minute later the sky fell on us. Ivan pulled out an ashtray and spilled its contents all over us. The ashes, the cigarette butts, and the smoke kept coming, like atomic fallout. We were in the tunnel, in heavy traffic, and we were choking. I could have killed him. If it were not for the other cars around us, I would have murdered him on the spot. And what burned me up most was that I had just praised him so sincerely. Isn't praise good for children any more?"

Weeks later Ivan himself revealed the cause of the explosion. All the way home he had been wondering how he could get rid of his younger brother, who was snuggled up between mother and father in the front of the car. Finally the idea occurred to him that if their car were jackknifed in the middle, he and his parents would be safe, but the baby would be cut in two. Just then mother had congratulated him on his goodness. The praise made him feel guilty, and he wanted desperately to show that he did not deserve it. He looked around, saw the ashtray, and the rest had followed instantly.

PRAISING ACCOMPLISHMENTS OR PERSONALITY?

Most people believe that praise builds up a child's confidence and makes him feel secure. In actuality, praise may result in tension and misbehavior. Why? Many children have, from time to time, destructive wishes about members of their family. When parents tell a child, "You are such a good boy," he may not be able to accept it because his own picture of himself is

44

quite different. In his own eyes, he cannot be "good" when only recently he wished that his mother had a zipper on her mouth or that his brother would spend next weekend in the hospital. In fact, the more he is praised, the more he misbehaves in order to show his "true self." Parents frequently report that just after praising a child for good deportment, he starts to act wild, as though to disprove their compliment. It is possible that "acting-up" is the child's way of communicating his private reservations about his public image.

Desirable and undesirable praise.—Does this mean that praise is now "out"? Not at all. It does mean, however, that praise, like penicillin, must not be administered haphazardly. There are rules and cautions that govern the handling of potent medicines—rules about timing and dosage, cautions about possible allergic reactions. There are similar regulations about the administration of emotional medicine. The single most important rule is that praise deal only with the child's efforts and accomplishments, *not* with his character and personality.

When a boy cleans up the yard, it is only natural to comment on how hard he has worked, and on how good the yard looks. It is highly unrelated, and inappropriate, to tell him how good he is. Words of praise should mirror for the child a *realistic* picture of his *accomplishments*, not a Madison Avenue image of his personality.

The following example illustrates desirable praise: Jim, age eight, did a good job cleaning up the yard. He raked the leaves, removed the garbage, and rearranged the tools. Mother was impressed and expressed her appreciation of his efforts and achievements:

MOTHER: The yard was so dirty. I didn't believe it could be cleaned up in one day.

JIM: I did it!

MOTHER: It was full of leaves and garbage and things.

JIM: I cleaned it all up.

MOTHER: What a job!

JIM: Yeah, it sure was.

MOTHER: The yard is so clean now, it is a pleasure to look at it.

JIM: It's nice.

MOTHER: Thank you, son.

JIM (*with a mile-wide smile*): You are welcome.

Mother's words made Jim feel glad of his efforts and proud of his accomplishments. That evening he could not wait for his father to come home in order to show him the cleaned-up yard and again to feel within himself the pride of a task well done.

In contrast, the following words of praise addressed to the child's personality are unhelpful:

"You are such a wonderful child."

"You are truly mother's little helper."

"What would mother do without you?"

Such comments may threaten a child and

cause him anxiety.* He may feel that he is far from being wonderful and that he is unable to live up to this label. So, instead of fearfully waiting to be exposed as a fraud, he may decide to lessen his burden immediately by a confession of misbehavior.

Direct praise of personality, like direct sunlight, is uncomfortable and blinding. It is embarrassing for a person to be told that he is wonderful, angelic, generous, and humble. He feels called upon to deny at least part of the praise. Publicly, he cannot stand up and say, "Thank you, I accept your words that I am wonderful." Privately, too, he must reject such praise. He cannot honestly say to himself, "I am wonderful. I am good and strong and generous and humble."

He may not only reject the praise but may have some second thoughts about those who have praised him: "If they find me so great, they cannot be so smart."

OUR WORDS AND THE CHILD'S INFERENCES

Praise should deal, not with the child's personality attributes, but with his efforts and

* Praise may also be threatening to adults. In "Robert Frost Confronts Khrushchev," F. D. Reeve states: "The honors Frost received made him nervous, for honors . . . may be terrifying: it may mean you have to do something better next time, something which you fear will fail." *Atlantic Monthly* (September, 1963), p. 38.

achievements. Our comments should be so phrased that the child draws from them positive inferences about his personality. Kenny, age ten, helped his father fix up the basement. In the process he had to move heavy furniture.

FATHER: The workbench is so heavy. It is hard to move.

KENNY (*with pride*): But I did it.

FATHER: It takes a lot of strength.

KENNY (*flexing his muscles*): I am strong.

In this example, father commented on the difficulty of the task. It was the child himself who drew the inference about his personal power. Had his father said, "You are so strong, son," Kenny might have replied, "No, I am not. There are stronger boys than I in my class." A fruitless, if not bitter, argument might have followed.

SILENT STATEMENTS AND SELF-IMAGE

Praise has two parts: our words and the child's inferences. Our words should state clearly that we appreciate the child's effort, work, achievement, help, consideration, or creation. Our words should be so framed that the child will almost inevitably draw from them a realistic conclusion about his personality. Our words should be like a magic canvas upon which a child cannot help but paint a positive

48

picture of himself. The following examples illustrate this point:

Helpful praise: Thank you for washing the car, it looks new again.
Possible inference: I did a good job. My work is appreciated.
(Unhelpful praise: You are an angel.)

Helpful praise: I liked your get-well card. It was so pretty and witty.
Possible inference: I have good taste, I can rely on my choices.
(Unhelpful praise: You are *always* so considerate.)

Helpful praise: Your poem spoke to my heart.
Possible inference: I am glad I can write poems.
(Unhelpful praise: You are a good poet for your age.)

Helpful praise: The bookcase that you built looks beautiful.
Possible inference: I am capable.
(Unhelpful praise: You are such a good carpenter.)

Helpful praise: Your letter brought me a great joy.
Possible inference: I can bring happiness to others.

(Unhelpful praise: When it comes to letters, you are wonderful.)

Helpful praise: I appreciate greatly your washing the dishes today.
Possible inference: I am helpful.
(Unhelpful praise: You did a better job than the maid.)

Helpful praise: Thanks for telling me that I overpaid you. I appreciate it very much.
Possible inference: I'm glad I was honest.
(Unhelpful praise: You are such an honest child.)

Helpful praise: Your composition gave me several new ideas.
Possible inference: I can be original.
(Unhelpful praise: You write well for your grade. Of course, you still have a lot to learn.

Such descriptive statements and the child's positive conclusions are the building blocks of mental health. What he concludes about himself in response to our words, the child later restates silently to himself. Realistic positive statements repeated inwardly by the child determine to a large extent his good opinion of himself and the world around him.

CRITICISM: CONSTRUCTIVE AND DESTRUCTIVE

When is criticism constructive and when is it destructive? Constructive criticism confines itself to pointing out how to do what has to be done, entirely omitting negative remarks about the personality of the child.

Larry, age ten, inadvertently spilled a glass of milk on the breakfast table.

MOTHER: You are old enough to know how to hold a glass! How many times have I told you to be careful!

FATHER: He can't help it—he is clumsy. He always was and he always will be.

Larry spilled five cents' worth of milk, but the caustic ridicule that followed the accident may cost much more in terms of loss of confidence. When things go wrong is not the right time to teach an offender about his personality. When things go wrong, it is best to deal only with the event, not with the person.

How to behave when a child misbehaves.— When Martin, age eight, accidentally spilled his milk on the table, his mother commented calmly, "I see the milk is spilled. Here is another glass of milk, and here is a sponge." Mother got up and handed the milk and the sponge to her son. Martin looked up at her in relief and disbelief. He muttered, "Gee, thanks, Mom." He cleaned up the table while mother helped him.

51

She did not add cutting comments or useless admonitions. Mother related, "I was tempted to say, 'Next time be careful,' but when I saw how grateful he was for my benevolent silence, I said nothing. In the past, the cry over spilled milk would have spoiled the mood for the entire day."

HOW THINGS GO WRONG

In many homes, storms between parents and children develop in a regular and predictable sequence. The child does or says something "wrong." The parent reacts with something insulting. The child replies with something worse. The parent retorts with high-pitched threats or with high-handed punishment. And the free-for-all is on.

Nathaniel, age nine, was playing with an empty teacup.

MOTHER: You'll break it. You are always breaking things.

NATHANIEL: No, I won't.

Just then the cup fell on the floor and broke.

MOTHER: For crying out loud, you are so stupid. You break everything in the house.

NATHANIEL: You are stupid, too. You broke father's electric razor.

MOTHER: You called mother stupid! You are so rude.

52

NATHANIEL: You are rude. You called me stupid
first.

MOTHER: Not another word from you! Go up to
your room immediately!

NATHANIEL: Go ahead, make me!

At this direct challenge to her authority,
mother became enraged. She grabbed her son
and started spanking him in fury. While attempting to escape, Nathaniel pushed his mother into a glass door. The glass broke and cut
mother's hand. The sight of blood threw Nathaniel into a panic. He ran out of the house
and was not found until late in the evening.
Needless to say, the whole household was upset. No one in the house slept well that night.

Whether or not Nathaniel learned to avoid
empty teacups was less important than the negative lesson that he learned about himself and
his mother. The question is: Was this battle
necessary? Was the fighting inevitable? Or is it
possible to handle such incidents more wisely?

Upon seeing her son rolling the cup, mother
could have removed it and directed him to a
more suitable substitute, such as a ball. Or
when the cup broke, she could have helped her
son dispose of the pieces, with comments to the
effect that cups break easily and who would
have thought that such a small cup could make
such a big mess. The surprise of such a low-
toned sentence might have sent Nathaniel into
atonement and apology for the mishap. In the
absence of screams and spankings, he may even

53

have had the presence of mind to conclude for himself that cups are not for rolling.

Minor mishaps and major values.—From minor mishaps children can learn major lessons in values. A child needs to learn from his parents to distinguish between events that are merely unpleasant and annoying and those that are tragic or catastrophic. Many parents react to a broken egg as to a broken leg, to a shattered window as to a shattered heart. Minor misfortunes should be pointed out as such to children:

"So you lost your glove again. That is annoying, because gloves cost money. It's regrettable, but it is not a catastrophe."

A lost glove need not lead to a lost temper, a torn shirt need not serve as a prop for a do-it-yourself Greek tragedy.

ABUSIVE ADJECTIVES: WHAT'S IN A NAME?

Abusive adjectives, like poisonous arrows, are to be used only against enemies, not against little children. When a person says, "This is an ugly chair," nothing happens to the chair. It is neither insulted nor embarrassed. It stays just as it is regardless of the adjective attached to it. However, when a child is called ugly or stupid or clumsy, something does happen to the child. There are reactions in his body and in his soul. There are resentment and anger and hate.

54

There are fantasies of revenge. There is guilt about the fantasies, and anxiety stemming from the guilt. And there may be undesirable behavior and symptoms. (See Chapter 7, page 150) In short, there is a chain of reactions that makes the child and his parents miserable.

When a child is called clumsy, he may at first retort with, "No, I am not clumsy." But, more often than not, he believes his parents, and he comes to think of himself as a clumsy person. When he happens to stumble or to fall, he may say aloud to himself, "You are so clumsy." He may, from then on, avoid situations in which agility is required because he is convinced that he is too clumsy to succeed.

When a child is repeatedly told by his parents or teachers that he is stupid, he comes to believe it. He starts thinking of himself as such. He then gives up intellectual efforts, feeling that his escape from ridicule lies in avoiding contest and competition. His safety hinges on not trying. His motto in life becomes: "If I don't try, I can't fail."

HANDLING OUR OWN ANGER

In our own childhood, we were not taught how to deal with anger as a fact of life. We were made to feel guilty for experiencing anger and sinful for expressing it. We were led to

55

believe that to be angry is to be bad. Anger was not merely a misdemeanor: it was a felony.

With our own children, we try to be patient; in fact, so patient that sooner or later we must explode. We are afraid that our anger may be harmful to children, so we hold it in, as a skin diver holds his breath. In both instances, however, the capacity for holding in is rather limited.

Anger, like the common cold, is a recurrent problem. We may not like it, but we cannot ignore it. We may know it intimately, but we cannot prevent its appearance. Anger arises in predictable sequences and situations, yet it always seems sudden and unexpected. And, though it may not last long, anger seems eternal for the moment.

When we lose our temper, we act as though we have lost our sanity. We say and do things to our children that we would hesitate to inflict on an enemy. We yell, insult, and hit below the belt. When the fanfare is over, we feel guilty and we solemnly resolve never to render a repeat performance. But anger soon strikes again, undoing our good intentions. Once more we lash out at those to whose welfare we have dedicated our life and fortune.

Resolutions about not becoming angry are worse than futile. They only add fuel to fire. Anger, like a hurricane, is a fact of life to be acknowledged and prepared for. The peaceful home, like the hoped-for warless world, does not depend on a sudden benevolent change in human nature. It does depend on deliberate procedures that methodically reduce tensions before they lead to explosions.

There is a place for parental anger in child education. In fact, failure to get angry at certain moments would only convey to the child indifference, not goodness. Those who care cannot altogether shun anger. This does not mean that children can withstand floods of fury and violence; it only means that they can stand and understand anger which says: "There are limits to my tolerance."

For parents, anger is a costly emotion: to be worth its price it should not be employed without profit. Anger should not be used so that it increases with expression. The medication must not be worse than the disease. Anger should so come out that it brings some relief to the parent, some insight to the child, and no harmful side effects to either of them. Thus we should not bawl out a child in front of his friends; it only makes him act up more, which in turn makes us angrier. We are not interested in creating or perpetuating waves of anger, defiance, retaliation, and revenge. On the contrary, we want to get our point across and let the stormy clouds evaporate.

Three steps to survival.—To prepare ourselves in times of peace to deal with times of stress, we should acknowledge the following truths:

1. We accept the fact that children will make us angry.

2. We are entitled to our anger without guilt or shame.

3. Except for one safeguard, we are entitled to express what we feel. We can express our angry feelings *provided* we do not attack the child's personality or character.

These assumptions should be implemented in concrete procedures for dealing with anger. The first step in handling turbulent feelings is to identify them loudly by name. This gives a warning to whomever it may concern to make amends or to take precautions.

"I feel annoyed."

"I feel irritated."

If our short statements and long faces have not brought relief, we proceed to the second step. We express our anger with increasing intensity:

"I feel angry."

"I feel very angry."

"I feel very, very angry."

"I feel furious."

Sometimes the mere statement of our feelings (without explanations) stops the child from acting up. At other times it may be necessary to proceed to the third step, which is to give the reason for our anger, to state our inner reactions, and *wishful* actions.

"When I see the shoes and the socks and the shirts and the sweaters spread all over the floor, I get angry, I get furious. I feel like opening the window and throwing the whole mess into the middle of the street."

58

"It makes me angry to see you hit your brother. I get so mad inside myself that I see red. I start boiling. I can never allow you to hurt him."

"When I see all of you rush away from dinner to watch TV, and leave me with the dirty dishes and greasy pans, I feel murderous! I get so mad I fume inside! I feel like taking every dish and breaking it on the TV set!"

"When I call you for dinner and you don't come, I get angry. I get very angry. I say to myself, 'I cooked a good meal and I want some appreciation, not frustration!' "

This approach allows parents to give vent to their anger without causing damage. On the contrary, it may even illustrate an important lesson in how to express anger safely. The child may learn that his own anger is not catastrophic, that it can be discharged without destroying anyone. This lesson will require more than just expression of anger by parents. It will require that parents point out to their children acceptable channels of emotional expression and demonstrate to them safe and respectable ways of liquidating anger. The problem of finding suitable substitutes for destructive feelings will be dealt with at length in Chapter 5.

CHAPTER 3

Avoiding self-defeating patterns

Certain patterns of relating to children are almost always self-defeating; not only do they fail to attain our long-term goals, but they often create havoc at home here and now. The self-defeating patterns include threats, bribes, promises, sarcasm, sermons on lying and stealing, and rude teaching of politeness.

THREATS

Invitations to misbehavior.—To children threats are invitations to repeat a forbidden act. When a child is told, "If you do it once more . . ." he does not hear the words "if you." He hears only "do it once more." Sometimes he interprets it as "Mother expects me to do it once more, or she'll be disappointed."

Such warnings—fair as they may seem to adults—are worse than useless. They make sure that an obnoxious act will be repeated. A warning serves as a challenge to the child's autonomy. If he has any self-respect he must transgress again, to show to himself and to others that he is not a sissy.

Oliver, age five, kept on throwing a ball at the window in spite of many warnings. Finally mother said, "If the ball hits the window once more, I'll beat the living daylights out of you. I promise." A minute later, the crash of breaking glass told mother that her warning had had an effect: the ball had hit the glass for the last time. The scene that followed this sequence of threats, promises, and misbehavior can easily be imagined. In contrast, the following incident is an illustration of effective handling of misbehavior without resort to threats.

Peter, age seven, shot the popgun at his baby brother. Mother said, "Not at the baby. Shoot at the target." Peter shot at the baby again. Mother took the gun away. To Peter she said, "People are not for shooting."

Mother did what she felt had to be done to protect the baby and at the same time uphold her standards of acceptable behavior. Peter learned the consequences of his actions without any damage to his ego. The implied alternatives were obvious: to shoot at the target or to lose the privilege of having the gun.

In this incident, mother avoided the usual pitfalls. She did not embark on the predictable trail to failure: "Stop it. Peter! Don't you know better than to shoot at your brother? Don't you have a better target? If you do it once more, you hear, once more, you'll never see the gun again!" Unless the child is very meek, his response to such an admonition will be a repetition of the forbidden. The scene that would then follow need not be described—it can easily be reconstructed by every parent.

BRIBES

The "if-then" fallacy.—Similarly self-defeating is the approach that explicitly tells a child that *if* he will (or will not) do something, *then* he will get a reward:

"*If* you are nice to baby brother, *then* I'll take you to the movies."

"*If* you stop wetting your bed, *then* I'll get you a bicycle for Christmas."

"*If* you learn the poem, *then* I'll take you sailing."

This "if-then" approach may occasionally spur the child toward an immediate goal. But it seldom, if ever, inspires him toward continual efforts. Our very words convey to him that we doubt his ability to change for the better. "If you learn the poem" means "We are not sure you can." "If you stop wetting" means "We don't think you can do it."

There are also some moral objections to re-

wards that are used to bribe. Dorothy Baruch*
tells of a boy who said, "I get what I want by
keeping mother thinking I'll be bad. Of course,
I have to be bad often enough to convince her
she is not paying me for nothing."

Such reasoning may soon lead to bargaining
and blackmail, and to ever increasing demands
for prizes and fringe benefits in exchange for
"good" behavior. Some parents have been so
conditioned by their children that they do not
dare come home from a shopping trip without a
present. They are greeted by the children, not
with a "hello," but with a "what-did-you-bring-
me?"

Rewards are most helpful and more enjoy-
able when they are unannounced in advance,
when they come as a surprise, when they represent recognition and appreciation.

PROMISES

Unrealistic expectations and practices.—
Promises should neither be made to, nor demanded of, children. Why such a taboo on
promises? Relations with our children should
be built on trust. When a parent must make
promises to emphasize that he means what he
says, then he is as much as admitting that his
"unpromised" word is not trustworthy. Prom-

* See bibliography.

ises build up unrealistic expectations in children. When a child is promised a visit to the zoo, he considers it a commitment that the day will not be rainy, that the car will not be out of order, and that he will not be sick. Since life is not without mishaps, children come to feel betrayed and convinced that parents cannot be trusted. The relentless complaint "but you promised!" is painfully familiar to parents who belatedly wish they had not.

Promises about the future good behavior or the cessation of past misbehavior should not be requested or extracted from children. When a child makes a promise that is not his own, he draws a check on a bank in which he has no account. We should not encourage such fraudulent practices.

SARCASM

A sound barrier to learning.—A serious mental health hazard is a parent with a gift for sarcasm. A wizard with words, he erects his own sound barrier to effective communication:

"How many times must I repeat the same thing? Are you deaf? Then why don't you listen?"

"You are so rude. Were you brought up in a jungle? That's where you belong, you know."

"What's the matter with you anyhow? Are

67

you crazy or just stupid? I know where you'll end up!"

Such a parent may not even be aware that his remarks are attacks that invite counterattacks, that his comments block communication by stirring children to preoccupation with revenge fantasies.

Bitter sarcasm and cutting clichés have no place in child upbringing. It is best to avoid statements such as, "You have grown too big for your breeches"; "You have a swelled head"; "Who do you think you are anyway?" Wittingly or unwittingly, we should not deflate the child's status in his own eyes and in the eyes of his peers.

A POLICY ON LYING

Parents are enraged when children lie, especially when the lie is obvious and the liar is clumsy. It is infuriating to hear a child insist that he did not touch the paint or eat the chocolate when the evidence is all over his shirt and face.

Why do children lie?—Sometimes they lie because they are not allowed to tell the truth. When a child tells his mother that he hates his brother, she may spank him for telling the truth. If he turns around then and there and declares the obvious lie that he now loves his brother, mother may reward him with a hug and a kiss. What is the child to conclude from such an experience? He may conclude that truth hurts, that dishonesty rewards, and that mother loves little liars.

If we want to teach honesty, then we must be prepared to listen to bitter truths as well as to pleasant truths. If a child is to grow up honest, he must not be encouraged to lie about his feelings, be they positive, negative, or ambivalent. It is from our reactions to his expressed feelings that the child learns whether or not honesty is the best policy.

Lies that tell truths.—When punished for truth, children lie in self-defense. They also lie to give themselves in fantasy what they lack in reality. Lies tell truths about fears and hopes. They reveal what one would like to be or to do. To a discerning ear, lies reveal what they intend to conceal. A mature reaction to a lie should reflect understanding of its meaning, rather than denial of its content or condemnation of its author. The information gained from the lie can be used to help the child to distinguish between reality and wishful thinking.

When a little boy informs us that he received a live elephant for Christmas, it is more helpful to reply, "You *wish* you did," than to prove that he is a liar.

"You *wish* you had an elephant!"

"You *wish* you had your own zoo!"

"You *wish* you had a jungle full of animals!"

"And what did you get for Christmas?"

Provoked lies.—Parents should not ask questions that are likely to cause defensive lying. Children resent being interrogated by a parent, especially when they suspect that the answers are already known. They hate questions that are traps, questions that force them to choose between an awkward lie or an embarrassing confession.

Quentin, age seven, broke a new gun given to him by his father. He became frightened and hid the broken pieces in the basement. When father found the remains of the gun, he fired off a few questions that led to an explosion.

FATHER: Where is your new gun?

QUENTIN: It's somewhere.

FATHER: I didn't see you playing with it.

QUENTIN: I don't know where it is.

FATHER: Find it. I want to see it.

QUENTIN: Maybe someone stole the gun.

FATHER: You are a damned liar! You broke the gun! Don't think you can get away with it. If there's one thing I hate, it's a liar!

And father gave him a spanking he would long remember.

This was an unnecessary battle. Instead of sneakingly playing detective and prosecutor, father would have been more helpful to his son by saying:

"I see your new gun is broken."

"It did not last long."

"It's a pity. It's expensive."

The child might have learned some valuable lessons: "Father understands. I can tell him my troubles. I must take better care of his gifts."

DEALING WITH DISHONESTY

Our policy towards lying is clear: on the one hand, we should not play D.A. or ask for confessions or make a federal case out of a tall story. On the other hand, we should not hesitate to call a spade a spade. When we find that the child's library book is overdue, we should not ask, "Have you returned the book to the library? Are you sure? How come it's still on your desk?"

Instead, we state, "I see your library book is overdue."

When the school informs us that our child has failed his arithmetic test, we should not ask him. "Did you pass your arithmetic exam? Are you sure? Well, lying won't help you this time! We talked with your teacher and we know that you failed miserably."

Instead, we tell our child directly, "The arithmetic teacher told us that you have failed the test. We are worried and wonder how to be of help."

In short, we do not provoke the child into defensive lying, nor do we intentionally set up opportunities for lying. When a child does lie, our reaction should be not hysterical and moralistic, but factual and realistic. We want our child to learn that there is no need to lie to us.

71

STEALING

It is not uncommon for young children to bring home things that do not belong to them. When the "theft" is discovered, it is important to avoid sermons and dramatics. The young child can be guided into the path of righteousness with dignity. He is told calmly and firmly:

"The truck belongs to someone else, give it back to him."

"The gun does not belong to you. Take it back."

When a child "steals" candy and puts it in his pocket, it is best to confront him unemotionally: "The lollypop in your left pocket has to stay in the store." If the child denies having the candy, we point and repeat the statement: "The lollypop in this pocket belongs to the store. Put it on the shelf." If he refuses, we take it out of his pocket, saying, "It belongs to the store. It has to stay here."

The wrong question and the right statement— When you are *sure* that your child stole money from your pocketbook, it is best not to ask him, but to tell him, about it: "You took a dollar from my pocketbook. Give it back." When the money is retrieved, he is told sternly, "When you need money, ask me, and we will talk it over." If the child denies the act, we do not argue with him or beg him for a confession; we tell him: "You took the money, return it." If the money has already been spent, the discussion should focus on ways of reimbursement, in chores or by reduction in allowance.

It is important to avoid calling the child a thief and a liar or prophesying that he will end up in Sing Sing. It is not helpful to ask the child, "Why did you do it?" He, himself, may not know his motivation, and pressure to tell "why" can only result in another lie.

It is more helpful to point out that you expect him to discuss with you his need for money:

"I am disappointed that you did not tell me that you needed a dollar."

"When you need money, come and tell me. We'll talk it over."

If your child has eaten cookies from the forbidden jar, and there is a mustache of sugar on his face, do not ask him questions such as:

"Did anybody take cookies from the jar?"

"Did you by any chance see who took them? Did you eat one? Are you sure?"

Such questions usually push the child into making up lies, which adds insult to our injury. The rule is that *when we know the answer, we do not ask the question*. It is better to state openly:

"Son, you ate the cookies. I told you not to. I am angry and I am disappointed."

The last statement constitutes adequate and desirable punishment. It leaves the child with

73

discomfort, and the responsibility to do something about his misbehavior.

TEACHING POLITENESS: RUDELY OR POLITELY?

Private models and public manners.— Politeness is both a character trait and a social skill; it is acquired through identification with, and imitation of, parents who are themselves polite. Under all conditions, politeness must be taught politely. Yet parents frequently teach it rudely. When a child forgets to say "thank you," parents point it out to him in front of other people, which is impolite, to say the least. Parents hasten to remind their child to say "good-bye" even before they themselves bid farewell.

Six-year-old Robert has just been handed a wrapped gift. Full of curiosity, he squeezes the box to find out what is in it.

MOTHER: Robert, stop it! You are spoiling the gift! What do you say when you get a present?

ROBERT: (*angrily*): Thank you!

MOTHER: That's a good boy.

Mother could have taught this bit of politeness less rudely and more effectively. She could have said, "Thank you, Aunt Patricia, for this lovely gift." It is conceivable that Robert might have followed with his own thank you. If he had failed to do so, mother could have dealt

74

with social amenities later when they were by themselves. She could have said, "It was considerate of Aunt Patricia to think of you and get you a gift. Let us write her a thank-you note. She will be glad that we thought of her."

While more complicated than a direct reprimand, this approach is more efficient. The niceties of the art of living cannot be conveyed with a sledgehammer.

When children interrupt adult conversation, adults usually react angrily: "Don't be rude! It is impolite to interrupt!" However, interrupting the interrupter is also impolite. Parents should not be rude in the process of enforcing child politeness. Perhaps it would be better to state, "I would like to finish telling my story. Then you will have your turn."

No good purpose is served by telling a child that he is rude. Contrary to hope, it does not steer him into politeness. The danger is that he will accept our evaluation and make it a part of his self-image. Once he thinks of himself as a rude boy, he will continue to live up to this image. It is only natural for rude boys to behave rudely.

Visits to homes of friends or relatives provide opportunities for demonstrating politeness to children. Visiting should be fun for the parent and the child. This can best be achieved when the burden of responsibility for the child's *behavior* is left to the child and the host. (Our help will be confined to voicing understanding of the child's wishes and feelings.)

Children learn that we are loath to reprimand them in the homes of others. Trusting geography, they choose these locations to act up. This strategy can be counteracted best by letting the host set the rules of his own house and carry out their enforcement. When a child jumps on the sofa in Aunt Mary's house, let Aunt Mary decide whether or not the sofa is for jumping, and let her invoke the limit. A child is more likely to obey when restrictions are invoked by outsiders. Mother, relieved of disciplinary obligation, can help the child by restating the limit privately: "These are the rules here."

This policy can be implemented only when there is agreement between host and guest as to their respective areas of responsibility. It is the right, and the responsibility, of the host to demand compliance with the rules of his home. It is the responsibility of the visiting mother to relinquish temporarily her role of disciplinarian. By appropriate nonintervention, mother helps the child perceive the reality of the situation.

CHAPTER 4

Responsibility and independence

RESPONSIBILITY: CHORES AND VALUES

Parents everywhere are looking for ways of teaching responsibility to children. In many homes, daily chores are expected to provide the solution to this problem. Emptying trash baskets and mowing lawns are believed to be especially effective in making boys responsible; dishwashing and bedmaking are alleged to lay a foundation of responsibility in girls. In actuality, such chores, though important for home management, may have no positive effect on creating a sense of responsibility. On the contrary, in some homes the daily tasks result in daily battles that bring anguish and anger to both children and parents. Forceful insistence on the performance of chores may result in obedience and in cleaner kitchens and yards, but it may have an undesirable influence on the molding of character.

The plain fact is that responsibility cannot be imposed. It can only grow from within, fed and directed by values absorbed at home and in the community. Responsibility that is not anchored in positive values can be antisocial and destructive. Hoodlums often show great loyalty and high responsibility in relation to one another and to their gang. Members of the Mafia, for instance, take their duties in dead earnest; they carry out commands, give legal aid to needy associates, and take care of prisoners' families.

The wellspring of responsibility. -While we wish our children to be responsible persons, we want their responsibility to spring from ultimate values, among which are reverence for life and concern for human welfare. In more familiar words, responsibility must be based on respect for life, liberty, and the pursuit of happiness. We do not usually consider the problem of responsibility in its larger framework. We see responsibility, or the lack of it, in much more concrete terms: in our child's messy room, tardy school attendance, sloppy homework, reluctant piano practice, sulky disobediance, or bad manners.

Yet a child may be polite, keep himself and his room clean, do his assignments with precision, and still make irresponsible decisions. This is especially true of children who are always told what to do and who therefore have little opportunity to exercise judgment, to make choices, and to develop inner standards.

The child's inner emotional reaction to our

instruction is a decisive element in how much he learns of what we want him to know. Values cannot be taught directly. They are absorbed, and become part of the child, only through his identification with, and emulation of, persons who gain his love and respect.

Thus, the problem of responsibility in children is referred back to the parent, or more precisely to the parent's values as expressed in his child-rearing practices. The question to consider now is: Are there any definite attitudes and practices that are likely to create a desired sense of responsibility in our children? The rest of the chapter is an attempt to answer this question from a psychological point of view.

DESIRABLE GOALS AND DAILY PRACTICES

Responsibility in children starts with the parent's attitude and skills. The attitudes include a willingness to allow children to feel *all* their feelings; the skills include an ability to demonstrate to children acceptable ways of coping with feelings.

The difficulties entailed in meeting these two requirements are most formidable. Our own parents and teachers have not adequately prepared us for dealing with emotions. They themselves did not know how to cope with strong feelings. When confronted with turbulent emotions in children, they tried to deny, disown, suppress, or prettify them. They used pat phrases that were not too helpful:

Denial: You don't really mean what you say; you know you love your little brother.

Disowning: It's not you, it's the devil in you that is acting up.

Suppression: If you mention the word "hate" once more, you'll get the spanking of your life. A nice child does not feel like that.

Prettifying: You don't really hate your brother. Maybe you dislike him. You should rise above such feelings.

Such statements ignore the fact that emotions, like rivers, cannot be stopped, only diverted. Strong feelings, like the rising waters of the Mississippi, cannot be denied, reasoned with, or talked out of, existence. To attempt to ignore them is to invite disaster. They must be recognized and their power acknowledged. They must be treated with respect and diverted with ingenuity. Thus channeled, they may electrify our existence and bring light and joy into our lives.

These are lofty goals. The question still remains: What steps can we take to bridge the gulf between desirable goals and daily practices? Where do we start?

LONG-TERM AND SHORT-TERM PROGRAMS

The answer seems to lie in making a program that is a combination of long-term and short-term efforts. Immediately, we need clear recognition that character education depends on our *relationship* with our children and that character traits cannot be transmitted by words but must be demonstrated.

The first step in the long-term program is a determination to become interested in what children are thinking and feeling inwardly, and not just in their outward compliance or rebellion.

How can we become aware of what children think and feel inside?

Children give us clues. Their feelings come through in word and in tone, in gesture and in posture. All we need is an ear to listen, an eye to behold, a heart to feel.

Our inner motto is: Let me understand. Let me show that I understand. Let me show in words that do not automatically criticize or condemn.

When a child comes home from school silent, slow, and dragging, we can tell by his steps that something unpleasant happened to him. Following our motto, we shall *not* start our conversation with a critical comment, such as:

"What's the sour puss for?"

"What kind of face is that?"

"What did you do, lose your best friend?"

"What did you do this time?"

"What trouble are you in today?"

Since we are interested in the child's inner reaction, we shall avoid comments that only create resentment and hate inside him, comments that make him wish that the whole world would drop dead.

Instead, the parent can show understanding by saying any of the following:

"Something unpleasant happened to you."

"It was not a good day for you."

"It was a hard day."

"Someone gave you a hard time."

These statements are preferable to such questions as, "What's the matter with you? What happened?" The questions convey curiosity, the statements convey sympathy.

There is no escape from the fact that a child learns what he lives. If he lives with criticism, he does not learn responsibility. He learns to condemn himself and to find fault with others. He learns to doubt his own judgment, to disparage his own ability, and to distrust the intentions of others. And above all, he learns to live with continual expectation of impending doom.

FROM WAR TO PEACE

Parents who are in the midst of a declared or undeclared war with their children over chores and responsibilities should recognize the fact that this war cannot be won. Children have more time and energy to resist us than we have to coerce them. Even if we win a battle and succeed in enforcing our will, they may retaliate by becoming spiritless and neurotic, or rebellious and delinquent.

There is only one way in which we can win: by winning the children over. This task may seem impossible: it is merely difficult, and we have the capacity to accomplish it. Even if we do not presently have friendly relations with a child, such relations can be built in the near future.

Parents can initiate favorable changes in their child by:

1. *Listening with sensitivity.* Children experience frustration and resentment when parents seem uninterested in their feelings and thoughts. As a result, they conclude that their own ideas are stupid and unworthy of attention and that they themselves are neither lovable nor loved.

A parent who listens with attentiveness conveys to his child that his ideas are valued and that he is respected. Such respect gives the child a sense of self-worth. The feeling of personal worth enables the child to deal more effectively with the world of events and people.

2. *Preventing "grapes of wrath."* Parents should consciously avoid words and comments that create hate and resentment.

Insults: You are a disgrace to your school and no credit to your family.

Name Calling: Bum, big shot, shrimp, idiot.

Prophesying: You will end up in a federal penitentiary, that's where you'll end up.

Threats: If you don't settle down you can forget about your allowance.

Accusations: You are *always* the first to start trouble.

Bossing: Shut up, and let me tell you a thing or two.

3. *Stating feelings and thoughts without attacking.* In troublesome situations, parents are more effective when they state their own feelings and thoughts without attacking their child's personality and dignity. (See Chapter 2, page 54.)

When parents listen with sensitivity, suspend cutting comments, and state their feelings and requirements without insult, a process of change is initiated in the child. The sympathetic atmosphere draws the child nearer to the parents; their attitudes and fairness, consideration, and civility are noticed and emulated. These changes will not occur overnight, but the efforts will ultimately be rewarded.

In adopting these new attitudes and practices, a parent will accomplish a large part of educating his child for responsibility. And yet, example alone is not enough. A sense of responsibility is attained by each child through his own efforts and experience. While the parent's example creates the favorable attitude and climate for learning, specific experiences consolidate the learning to make it part of the child's character. Therefore, it is important to determine what specific responsibilities to give to children at different levels of maturity.

RESPONSIBILITY: VOICE AND CHOICE

Children are not born with a built-in sense of responsibility. Neither do they acquire it automatically at a certain prescribed age. Responsibility, like piano playing, is attained slowly and over many long years. It requires daily practice in exercising judgment and in making choices about matters appropriate to one's age and comprehension.

Conflict areas and realms of responsibility.— Education for responsibility can start very early in the child's life. Responsibility is fostered by allowing children a voice, and wherever indicated, a choice, in matters that affect them. A deliberate distinction is made here between a voice and a choice. There are matters that fall entirely within the child's realm of responsibility. In such matters he should have his choice. There are matters affecting the child's welfare that are exclusively within our realm of responsibility. In such matters he may have a voice, but not a choice. We make the choice for him—while helping him to accept the inevitable.

What is needed now is a clear distinction between these two realms of responsibility. Let us examine several areas in which conflicts between parents and children are not uncommon.

87

FOOD

Even a two-year-old can be asked whether he wants half a glass of milk or a full glass of milk. A four-year-old can be given a choice between half an apple or a whole apple. And a six-year-old can decide for himself whether he wants his boiled eggs hard or soft.

Children should be deliberately presented with many situations in which they have to make choices. The parents *select* the situations; the children make the choices.

A young child is not asked, "What do you want for breakfast?" He is asked, "Do you want your eggs scrambled or fried? Do you want the bread toasted or not? Do you want your cereal hot or cold? Do you want orange juice or milk?"

What is conveyed to the child is that he has some responsibility for his own affairs. He is not just a recipient of orders, but a participant in decisions that shape his life. From the parent's attitudes, the child should get a clear message: We provide tea and sympathy as well as milk and cookies—choosing is your responsibility.

Eating problems in children are often created by mothers who take too great a personal interest in their children's taste buds. They nag children into eating particular vegetables, and tell them (quite unscientifically) which vegetable is most healthful for each organ of the body. It is best for the child that mother not have strong feelings about food; that she offer food of quality and taste and trust her children to eat as much or as little as their own appetite demands, provided this does not conflict with medical advice. Clearly, eating falls within the child's realm of responsibility.

CLOTHES

In buying clothes for children, it is *our* responsibility to decide what attire they need and what to budget for it. In the store, we select several samples—all acceptable to us in terms of price and style. The child will choose the one he prefers to wear. Thus even a six-year-old can have a choice in buying his socks and shirts—from among those we have selected. There are many homes in which children get no experience, and develop no skill, in buying clothes for themselves. In fact, there are adults who cannot buy a suit for themselves without having along a wife or a mother to do the choosing.

Older children, particularly, should be allowed to have clothes that are not too different from the standards acceptable to their friends. A boy with brown shoes in a class where blue suede is the standard for that year is being exposed (perhaps unnecessarily) to attack and

89

ridicule. Parents should be aware of what is considered "cool" and "square" among children. The realms of responsibility in relation to clothes can be stated as follows: We do the selecting; they do the choosing.

HOMEWORK

From the first grade on, parents' attitudes should convey that homework is *strictly* the responsibility of the child and his teacher. Parents should not nag children about homework. They should not supervise or check the homework,* except at the invitation of the children. When a parent takes over the responsibility for homework, the child lets him, and the parent is never again free of this bondage. Homework may become a weapon in the child's hands to punish, blackmail, and exploit the parents. Much misery could be avoided, and much joy added to home life, if parents would show less interest in the minute details of the child's assignments and instead convey in no uncertain terms: "Homework is your responsibility. Homework is for you what work is for us."

The value of homework in the early grades should not be overestimated. There are many fine schools that assign no homework to young

---

* The writer is well aware that this policy may be contrary to teacher's demands.

children. The pupils seem to gain just as much wisdom as those who struggle with assignments at the ages of six and seven. The main value of homework is that it gives children the experience of working on their own. To have this value, however, homework must be graded to the child's capacity, so that he may work independently with little aid from others. Direct help may only convey to the child that on his own he is helpless. Indirect help, however, may be useful. For instance, we might make sure that the child has privacy, a suitable desk, and reference books. We might also help him figure out the right time for homework, in accordance with the seasons. In the mild afternoons of spring and fall, a child's fancy will surely turn first to playing and (hopefully) then to homework. In the cold days of winter, homework must come first if there is to be TV later.

Some children like to be near an adult while working at an assignment. Perhaps it is possible to allow the use of the table in the kitchen or dining room. However, few comments should be made at this time about manners of sitting, neatness of appearance, or the care of furniture.

Some children work better when they may chew a pencil, scratch their heads, or rock a chair. Our comments and restrictions increase frustration and interfere with their mental work.

The child's homework should not be interrupted by questions and errands that can wait.

We should remain in the background giving comfort and support rather than instruction and assistance. Occasionally, we may clarify a point or explain a sentence. However, we should avoid comments such as:

"If you weren't such a scatterbrain, you would remember your assignment."

"If you only listened to the teacher you would know your homework."

Our help should be given sparingly but sympathetically. We listen rather than lecture. We show the road but expect the traveler to reach his destination on his own power.

A parent's attitude towards the school and the teacher may influence a child's attitude toward homework. If a parent habitually berates the school and belittles the teacher, the child will draw obvious conclusions.

Parents should bolster the teacher's position and support his policies regarding responsible homework.

When the teacher is strict, the parent has a wonderful opportunity to be sympathetic:

"It's not an easy year—so much work!"

"It's really tough this year."

"He sure is a strict teacher."

"I hear he demands a lot."

"I hear he is especially tough about homework. I guess there will be lots of work this year."

It is important to avoid daily flareups over homework:

"Look here, Reggie, from now on you are

going to work on your spelling every afternoon of every day—including Saturdays and Sundays. No more playing for you and no TV either."

"Roger! I am sick and tired of reminding you about homework. Daddy is going to see to it that you get down to business. We don't want illiterates in our family."

Threats and nagging are common because they make one believe that something is being done about the situation. In reality such admonitions are worse than useless. They only result in a charged atmosphere, an irritated parent, and an angry child.

Many capable children lag in their homework and underachieve in school as an unconscious rebellion against their parents' ambitions. In order to grow up and mature, each child needs to attain a sense of individuality and separateness from his mother and father. When parents are too emotionally involved with the scholastic record of the child, he experiences interference with his autonomy. If homework and high grades become diamonds in his parents' crown, the child may unconsciously prefer to bring home a crown of weeds that is at least his own. By not attaining his parents' goals, the young rebel achieves a sense of independence. Thus the need for individuality and uniqueness may push a child into failure, regardless of parental pressure and punishment. As one child said, "They can take away the TV and the allowance, but they cannot take away my failing grades."

It is apparent that resistance to studying is not a simple problem that can be solved by getting either tough or lenient with children. Increased pressure may increase a child's resistance while a laissez faire attitude may convey acceptance of immaturity and irresponsibility. The solution is neither easy nor quick. Some children may need psychotherapy to resolve their struggle against their parents and to gain satisfaction in achievement, instead of underachievement.

Others may need tutoring with a psychologically oriented person. *It is imperative that the parent not do the tutoring.* Our goal is to convey to the child that he is an individual in his own right—apart from us—and responsible for his successes and failures. When the child is allowed to experience himself as an individual with self-originating needs and goals, he begins to assume responsibility for his own life and its demands.

MUSIC LESSONS

When a child plays a musical instrument, his parents will, sooner or later, hear a familiar tune: "I don't want to practice any more." To face this music with objectivity is not an easy task.

Some parents, remembering their own enforced music lessons, decide to spare their children such agony. To play or not to play is not their question: it is the child's. In this home the child decides whether or not to practice. He plays when he feels like it, and keeps or cancels lessons according to his desire. Except for tuition, which is still the parent's prerogative, instrument practice is seen as the child's responsibility.

Other parents, remembering with regret their own overpermissive musical experience, decide that come what may, their child will play. Even before the child is born, his musical medium has already been chosen for him. As soon as he can hold a fiddle, blow a horn, or bang a piano, he will begin to practice his predestined instrument. The child's tears and tantrums will be disregarded and his resistance overcome. The parents' message is loud and clear: "We pay—you play." Under these conditions a child may or may not achieve musical proficiency. However, the whole enterprise may be too costly. The price is too high if the results include prolonged disturbed relations between parents and child.

The main purpose of music education in childhood is to provide an effective outlet for feelings. A child's life is so full of restrictions, regulations, and frustrations that media of release become essential. Music is one of the best avenues of release: it gives sound to fury, shape to joy, and relief to tension.

Parents and teachers do not usually look

95

upon music education from this point of view: for the most part they look for skill in reproducing melodies. This approach inevitably involves evaluation and criticism of the child's performance and personality. Too often the results are sadly familiar: the child attempts to give up his lessons, avoid the teacher, and terminate his musical "career." In many a home a deserted fiddle, a locked piano, or a mute flute serve only as painful reminders of frustrated efforts and unfulfilled hopes.

What can parents do? The parents' job is to find a teacher who is kind and considerate—one who knows his pupils, not only his music. It is the teacher who holds the key to the child's continuous interest in music and it is he who can open or lock the doors of opportunity. The teacher's vital task is to gain a child's respect and confidence. If he fails in that, he cannot succeed in his instruction: a child does not learn to love music from a teacher whom he hates. The teacher's emotional tone has a stronger echo than his musical instrument.

To prevent avoidable trouble, teacher, parents, and child should discuss—and agree on—several basic rules. The following are examples:

1. No cancellation without notification, at least one day prior to appointment time.

2. If an appointment must be canceled, the child, not the parent, is the one to call the teacher.

3. Realistic leeway is provided in choosing the time and pace of music practice.

These rules discourage last minute "mood" cancellations, and encourage the child's sense of independence and responsibility. They also convey to the child that, while we have regard for music, we have even greater regard for his feelings and ideas.

A child should not be nagged about practicing. He should not be reminded how much the instrument cost and how hard father worked for the money. Such statements engender guilt and resentment. They do not create either musical sensitivity or interest.

Parents should refrain from prognosticating about their child's "great" musical talents. Statements such as the following are very discouraging:

"You have marvelous talents if you only used them."

"You can be another Leonard Bernstein, if you would only apply yourself."

The child may conclude that his parents' illusions can be best maintained by not putting them to the test. His motto may become: "If I don't try, I won't fail my parents."

A child is encouraged most when he knows that his difficulties are understood and appreciated.

During her third piano lesson, Roslyn, age six, had to try a new skill: to play the eight notes of an octave with both hands. The teacher demonstrated the exercise with great proficiency, saying, "See, it's easy. Now you try it." Reluctantly and clumsily, Roslyn extended her fingers in a not too successful attempt to imitate her teacher. She returned home from this lesson discouraged.

At practice time mother said, "It's not easy to play eight notes with one hand. With two hands it is even more difficult." Roslyn agreed readily. At the piano she slowly picked out the right notes with the proper fingers. Mother said, "I can hear the right notes and I can see the right fingers." With obvious satisfaction, Roslyn replied, "It is pretty hard." That day she continued her practicing beyond the agreed time. During the week, she set for herself more difficult tasks and was not satisfied until she learned to play the octave blindfolded.

A child feels more encouraged by sympathetic understanding of his difficulties than by advice, praise, or ready-made instant solutions.

ALLOWANCE

In the modern home, spending money—like food and clothes—is given to a child as a matter of course, because he is a member of the family. An allowance is not a reward for good behavior nor a payment for chores. It is an educational device that has a distinct purpose: to provide experience in the use of money by exercising choices and assuming responsibilities. Therefore, oversupervision of an allowance would defeat its purpose. What is required is a general policy which stipulates the expenditures the allowance is expected to cover: carfare, lunches, school supplies, etc. As the child grows older the allowance is increased to include additional expenses and responsibilities: membership dues, the cost of entertainment and clothing accessories, etc.

Abuses of an allowance can be expected. Some children will mismananage the budget and spend too much too soon. The abuses should be discussed with the child in a businesslike manner in order to arrive at mutually agreed solutions. In repeated cases of instant spending, it may be necessary to divide the allowance and give it to the child twice or thrice a week. The allowance itself should not be used as a club over the child's head to exert pressure for achievement or obedience. It should not be withheld in times of anger, or increased arbitrarily in times of good mood.

What is a fair allowance? There is no universal answer to this question. The allowance should fit our budget. Regardless of neighborhood standards, we should not be pushed into allowing more than we can afford comfortably. If the child protests, we can tell him sincerely and sympathetically, "We wish we could give you a larger allowance but our budget is limited." This is a better approach than trying to convince the child that he does not really need more money.

Money, like power, can be easily mishandled by the inexperienced. An allowance should not be greater than the child's capacity to manage it. It is better to start with a small allowance, which can be adjusted from time to time, than to overburden the child with too much money. The allowance might be started when the child begins attending school and has learned to count money and make change. One condition is essential to an allowance: the small sum of money left after the fixed expenditures should be the child's own to save or to splurge.

FRIENDS AND PLAYMATES

Theoretically, we want our children to choose their own friends. We believe in freedom, we oppose coercion, and we know that free association is a basic right in a democracy. However, not infrequently a child brings home "friends" whom we find repugnant. We may dislike bullies and braggarts, or have difficulty tolerating runny-nosed crybabies, but unless their behavior really gnaws us, it is best to study our child's preferences and attractions before attempting to interfere with his choices.

What yardstick can we use to evaluate our child's choice of friends?

Friends should exert a beneficial and corrective influence upon each other. A child needs opportunities to associate with personalities different from, and complementary to, his own. Thus a withdrawn child needs the company of more outgoing friends, an overprotected child needs more autonomous playmates, a fearful child should be in the company of more courageous youngsters, an infantile child can benefit from the friendship of a more mature playmate. A child who relies too heavily on fantasy needs the influence of more prosaic children. An aggressive child can be checked by playmates who are strong but not belligerent. Our aim is to encourage corrective relations by exposing the child to friends with personalities different from his own.

Some associations need to be discouraged. Infantile children only feed on each other's immaturity. Belligerent children only reinforce each other's aggression. Very withdrawn children do not engage in enough social give and take. Delinquent children may reinforce each other's antisocial tendencies.

Special care must be taken to prevent children who glamorize criminal behavior from becoming dominant "friends." Because of their greater "experience" they may attain hero status in school or in the neighborhood and serve as undesirable models of identification.

It takes a delicate system of checks and balances to allow a child the responsibility of choosing his own friends while we keep the responsibility of insuring that the choice is a beneficial one.

THE CARE OF PETS

When a child promises to take care of a pet, he is merely showing good intentions, not proof of ability. A child may need, want, and love a pet, but rarely is he able to take care of it properly. The responsibility for the life of an animal cannot be the child's alone. To avoid frustration and recriminations, it is best to assume that a pet for the child means work for the parent. The child may benefit greatly from having a pet to play with and to love. He may also benefit from sharing in the care of the pet—but the responsibility for the pet's survival and welfare must remain with the adult.

FREEDOM PHRASES

A good parent, like a good teacher, is one who makes himself increasingly *dispensable* to children. He finds satisfaction in relationships that lead children to make their own choices and to use their own powers. In conversations with children, we can consciously use phrases that indicate our belief in their capacity to make wise decisions for themselves. Thus, when our inner response to a child's request is "yes," we can express it in statements designed to foster the child's independence. Here are a few ways of saying yes:

"If you want to."

"If that is really what you like."

"You decide about that."

"It is really up to you."

"It is entirely your choice."

"Whatever you decide is fine with me."

Our "yes" may be gratifying to the child, but the other statements give him the additional satisfaction of making his own decisions, and of enjoying our faith in him.

CHAPTER 5

Discipline:
permissiveness and limits

MODERN UNCERTAINTY AND ITS RESULTS

What is the difference between the approach of our grandparents and of ourselves in disciplining children? Whatever grandfather did was done with authority; whatever we do is done with hesitation. Even when in error, grandfather acted with certainty. Even when in the right, we act with doubt. Where does our uncertainty in relation to children come from? By now we have all heard about Freud, psychoanalysis, and the costly consequences of an unhappy childhood, and we are deeply concerned lest we damage our children for life. The following letter from a mother will serve as an illustration:

It is often very difficult for me to express myself verbally concerning things which affect me deeply. Perhaps I can do better in writing. If I leave anything unsaid I know that you will be able to read between the lines. You were very kind to come to our church to conduct a discussion group for parents. While it was not completely satisfactory to me because I never learn enough on the subject of raising children, one thing that appealed to me was your statement that you knew that no parent deliberately did things to injure their children emotionally. Rather, they did so unwittingly.

Not one of us willingly would do anything to cripple our children spiritually, morally, or emotionally and yet we do just that. I cry often inside for things I have done and said thoughtlessly and I pray not to repeat these transgressions. Maybe they aren't repeated but something else just as bad is substituted, until I am frantic for fear that I have injured my child for life.

No one could question the sincerity and devotion of this mother. Yet she would be more helpful if she had less guilt and more skill. To use an analogy, we would not feel secure with a physician who cried at the sight of a broken arm or fainted at the sight of blood. From a physician we expect professional competence and some sympathy, but not emotionality and laments. Likewise, parents can learn to deal with children's immaturity in a semiprofessional manner. When handled without excessive emotion, many discipline situations dissolve. When handled hysterically, they may become serious problems to plague the parent and the child for years to come.

PARENTAL NEEDS AND CHILD TYRANNY

A parent must like his children, but he must not have an urgent need to be liked by them every minute of the day. Those who need children in order to derive justification for their marriage or significance for their lives are at a disadvantage. Afraid of losing his love, they dare not deny anything to the child, including control of the home. Sensing their parents' hunger for love, children exploit it mercilessly. They become tyrants ruling over anxious servants.

Many children have learned how to threaten their mothers with the withdrawal of love. They use blackmail quite bluntly. They say, "I won't love you if. ..." The tragedy is not in the child's threat, but in the fact that the parents feel threatened. Some parents are really affected by the child's words: they cry and beg the child to continue to love them, and they try to placate him by being overpermissive.

PERMISSIVENESS AND OVERPERMISSIVENESS

What is permissiveness and what is overpermissiveness? Permissiveness is an attitude of accepting the childishness of children. It means accepting that "boys will be boys," that a clean shirt on a normal child will not stay clean for long, that running rather than walking is the child's normal means of locomotion, that a tree is for climbing and a mirror is for making faces.

The essence of permissiveness is the acceptance of children as persons who have a constitutional right to have all kinds of feelings and wishes. The freedom to wish is absolute and unrestricted; all feelings and fantasies, all thoughts and wishes, all dreams and desires, regardless of content, are accepted, respected, and may be permitted expression through appropriate symbolic means. Destructive behavior is not permitted; when it occurs, the parents intervene and redirect it into verbal outlets and other symbolic channels. Permitted symbolic outlets are painting "mean" pictures, throwing darts at a target, sawing wood, boxing life-size Bobo, recording ill wishes on tape, composing caustic poems, writing murder mysteries, etc. In short, permissiveness is the acceptance of imaginary and symbolic behavior. Overpermissiveness is the allowing of undesirable acts. Permissiveness brings confidence and an increasing

110

capacity to express feelings and thoughts. Overpermissiveness brings anxiety and increasing demands for priveleges that cannot be granted.

THE NEW APPROACH: DIFFERENT HANDLING OF FEELINGS AND OF ACTS

The cornerstone of the new approach to discipline is the distinction between wishes and acts. We set limits on acts; we do not restrict wishes.

Most discipline problems consist of two parts: angry feelings and angry acts. Each part has to be handled differently. Feelings have to be identified and expressed; acts may have to be limited and redirected. At times, identification of the child's feelings may in itself be sufficient to clear the air:

MOTHER: It looks as if you are angry today.

SON: I sure am!

MOTHER: You feel kind of mean inside.

SON: You said it!

MOTHER: You are angry at someone.

SON: Yes. You.

MOTHER: Tell me about it.

SON: You didn't take me to the Little League game, but you took Steve.

MOTHER: That made you angry. I bet you said to yourself, "She loves him more than she loves me."

SON: Yes.

111

MOTHER: Sometimes you really feel that way.

SON: I sure do.

MOTHER: You know, dear, when you feel that way, come and tell me.

At other times, limits must be set. When Sam, age four, wanted to cut off his cat's tail "to see what's inside," mother accepted his scientific curiosity, but limited his action in no uncertain terms:

"I know you want to see how it looks inside. But the tail has to stay where it is. Let's see if we can find a picture to show you how it looks inside."

When mother found Ted, age five, doodling on her living-room wall, her first reaction was to pummel him. But he looked so scared that she could not bring herself to hit him. Instead she said, "No, Ted, walls are not for drawing. Paper is. Here are three sheets of paper." And mother started cleaning up the wall. Ted was so overwhelmed that he said, "I love you, mommy."

Contrast this to the handling of a similar smearing in another house: "What are you doing? What's the matter with you? Don't you know that you aren't supposed to dirty walls? Nasty child, I just don't know what to do with you. Wait, when daddy comes home I'm going to tell him about you. You'll get it."

DISCIPLINE: PAST AND PRESENT

There is a vast difference between the old and the new approach to discipline. In disciplining a child, parents used to stop undesirable acts, but ignored the urges that brought about the acts. The restrictions were set in the midst of angry argument and were often incoherent, inconsistent, and insulting. Furthermore, discipline was administered at a time when the child was least able to listen, and in words that were most likely to arouse his resistance. More often than not, the child was left with the dooming impression that not just his specific act had been criticized, but that as a person he was no good.

The modern approach helps the child both with his feelings and conduct. The parents allow the child (under conditions to be discussed later) to speak out about what he feels, but limit and direct undesirable acts. The limits are set in a manner that preserves the self-respect of the parent as well as of the child. The limits are neither arbitrary nor capricious, but educational and character-building.

The restrictions are applied without violence or excessive anger. The child's resentment of the restrictions is anticipated and understood; he is not punished additionally for not liking prohibitions.

113

Discipline, thus employed, may lead to voluntary acceptance by the child of the need to inhibit and change some of his behavior. In this sense, parental discipline may eventually lead to self-discipline. By identifying with the parents and the values they personify, the child attains inner standards for self-regulation.

THREE ZONES OF DISCIPLINE

Children need a clear definition of acceptable and unacceptable conduct. They feel more secure when they know the borders of permissible action. To use an analogy suggested by Dr. Fritz Redl, we might say that children's behavior falls into three color zones—green, yellow, and red. The green area consists of behavior that is wanted and sanctioned, the area where our "yes" is given freely and graciously. The yellow zone includes behavior that is not sanctioned but is tolerated for specific reasons. Such reasons may include:

1. *Leeway for learners.* A driver with a learner's permit is not given a ticket when he signals right and turns left. Such mistakes are tolerated for the sake of expected future improvements.

2. *Leeway for hard times.* Special stress situations—accidents, illness, moving into a new neighborhood, separation from friends, death or divorce in the family—call for additional lee-

way. We grant it because of our appreciation of hard times and new adjustments. We do not pretend that we like this behavior; in fact, our attitudes tell that this conduct is tolerated only because of exceptional circumstances.

The red zone covers conduct that cannot be tolerated at all and must be stopped. It includes behavior that endangers the health and welfare of the family or its physical and financial well-being. It also includes behavior forbidden for reason of law, ethics, or social acceptability.

It is as important to be prohibitive in the red zone as it is to be permissive in the green. When a child is allowed behavior that he knows should not be tolerated, his anxiety mounts. An eight-year-old boy who had been allowed to hang on the back of a moving bus accused his mother of not loving him: "If you really cared about me, you wouldn't have let me take that chance on getting killed."

Another child thought that his father did not have the right standards because he allowed the boy to carry a switchblade knife. Another boy lost respect for his parents because they did not stop the wild play of his friends who almost demolished his scientific laboratory. Young children have genuine difficulty in coping with their socially unacceptable impulses. The parents must be an ally in the child's struggle for control of such impulses. By setting limits, the parent offers help to the child. Besides stopping dangerous conduct, the limit also con-

115

veys a silent message: "You don't have to be afraid of your impulses. I won't let you go too far. It is safe."

TECHNIQUES OF SETTING LIMITS

In the setting of limits—as in all education—the product depends on the process. A limit should be so stated that it tells the child clearly (*a*) what constitutes unacceptable conduct; (*b*) what substitute will be accepted.

You may not throw dishes; you may throw pillows. Or in less grammatical, but more effective English: Dishes are not for throwing; pillows are for throwing. Brother is not for boxing; Bobo is for boxing.

It is preferable that a limit be total rather than partial. There is a clear distinction, for example, between splashing water and not splashing water on sister. A limit that states, "You may splash her a little, as long as you don't wet her too much," is inviting a deluge of trouble. Such a vague statement leaves the child without a clear criterion for making decisions.

A limit must be stated firmly, so that it carries only one message to the child: "This prohibition is for real. I mean business." When a parent is not sure of what to do, it is best that he do nothing but think and clarify his own attitudes. In setting limits, he who hesitates is lost in endless arguments. Restrictions, invoked haltingly and clumsily, become a challenge to children and evoke a battle of wills, which no one can win. A limit must be stated in a manner that is deliberately calculated to minimize resentment, and to save self-esteem. The very process of limit-setting should convey authority, not insult. It should deal with a specific event, not with a developmental history. The temptation to clean away all problems with one big sweep should be resisted. The following is an illustration of an undesirable practice:

Eight-year-old Annie went with mother to the department store. While mother made her purchase, Annie roamed around the toy counter and selected three toys she would save in case a fire broke out. When mother came back, Annie asked confidently, "Which toys can I take home?" Mother, who just spent too much money on a dress she was not sure she really wanted, blurted out, "More toys? You have more toys than you know what to do with. Everything you see, you want. It's time you learned to curb your appetite."

A minute later, mother, realizing the source of her sudden anger, tried to placate her daughter and to bribe her with ice cream. But the sorrowful look remained on Annie's face.

When a child requests something that we must deny, we can at least grant him the satisfaction of having the wish for it. Thus Annie's mother might have said:

"You *wish* you could take some toys home."

117

"I bet you *wish* you could take home the whole toy counter. But there is no budget for toys today. You can have a penny for a balloon or a piece of gum, though. Which do you choose, the balloon or the gum?"

Perhaps Annie would choose the latter, and the whole incident might be concluded with mother saying, "Annie, get your gum." Or perhaps Annie would cry. In either case, mother would stick to her decision, and to the offered choices. She may again show her understanding by mirroring her daughter's desire for toys— but the limit would be upheld. "You wish you could have the toys. You want them very much. You are showing me by crying. I know, darling, but no toys today."

There are different ways of phrasing specific limits. At times the following four-step sequence may prove effective:

1. The parent recognizes the child's wish and puts it in simple words: "You wish you could go to the movies tonight."

2. He states clearly the limits on a specific act: "But the rule in our house is 'no movies on school nights.' "

3. He points out ways in which the wish can be at least partially fulfilled: "You may go to the movies on Friday or Saturday night."

4. He helps the child to express some of the resentment that is likely to arise when restrictions are imposed:

"It is obvious that you don't like the rule."

"You wish there weren't such a rule."

118

"You wish the rule said: 'Every night is movie night.' "

"When you grow up and have your own home, you are sure going to change this rule."

It is not always necessary or feasible to phrase the limit in this pattern. At times, it is necessary to state the limit first and mirror feelings later. When a child is about to throw a stone at sister, mother should say, "Not at her, at the tree!" She will do well to deflect the child by pointing in the direction of the tree. She can then get at the feelings and suggest some harmless ways of expressing them:

"You may be as angry as you want at Sis."

"You may be furious. Inside yourself, you may hate her, but there will be no hurting."

"If you want to, you can throw stones at the tree and pretend it's your sister."

"If you want to, you can even draw her face on paper, stick it on the tree, and then throw stones; but she is not to be hurt."

Limits should be phrased in a language that does not challenge the child's self-respect. Limits are heeded better when stated succinctly and impersonally.

"No movies on school nights" arouses less resentment than "You know you can't go to the movie on school nights."

"It's bedtime" is more readily accepted than "You are too young to stay up that late. Go to bed."

"Time is up for TV today" is better than

119

"You have watched enough TV today, turn off the set."

"No shouting at each other" is obeyed more willingly than "You better stop shouting at him."

Limits are accepted more willingly when they point out the function of an object: "The chair is for sitting, not for standing" is better than "Don't stand on the chair." "The blocks are for playing, not for throwing" is better than either "Don't throw blocks," or, "I am sorry I can't let you throw blocks, it is too dangerous."

DISCIPLINE PROBLEMS AND PHYSICAL ACTIVITY

Many discipline problems with young children arise over restraint of physical activities. "Don't run—can't you walk like a normal boy?" "Don't jump all over." "Sit straight." "Why must you stand on one foot when you know you have two feet?" "You'll fall and break a leg."

Children's motor activities should not be overrestrained. For the sake of both mental and physical health, children need to run, jump, climb, skip, etc. Concern for the health of the furniture is understandable, but it must not supersede concern for the health of the children. Inhibition of physical activity in young children results in emotional tension which is expressed in hyperactivity and aggression.

Arranging a suitable environment for direct

discharge of energy in muscular activities is a prime—but frequently overlooked—condition for good discipline in children and for an easier life for parents.

ENFORCEMENT OF DISCIPLINE

When a parent's feelings about a restriction are crystal clear and the restriction is phrased in inoffensive language, a child will usually conform. Yet, from time to time, a child will break a rule. The question is: What is to be done when a child transgresses a stated restriction? The educational process requires that the parent adhere to his role as a kindly but firm adult. In reacting to a child who violates a limit, the parent must not become argumentative and verbose. He must not be drawn into a discussion about the fairness or unfairness of the limit. Neither should he give a long explanation for it. It is unnecessary to explain to a child why he must not hit his sister, beyond saying that "people are not for hurting," or why he must not break the window, beyond saying that "windows are not for breaking."

When a child exceeds a limit, his anxiety mounts because he expects retaliation and punishment. The parent need not increase the child's anxiety at this time. If the parent talks too much, he conveys weakness—at a time when he must convey strength. It is at times like this that the child needs an adult ally to help him control his impulses without loss of face. The following example illustrates an undesirable approach to limits:

Mother: I see that you won't be satisfied until you hear me yelling. O.K. [*Loud and shrilly*] *stop it*—or I'll beat the living daylights out of you! If you throw one more thing, I'll do something drastic!

Instead of using threats and promises, mother could have expressed her very real anger more effectively:

"It makes me mad to see that!"

"It makes me angry!"

"It makes me furious!"

"These things are not for throwing! The ball is for throwing!"

In enforcing a limit, a parent must be careful not to initiate a battle of wills.

Ursula (*at the playground*): I like it here. I am not going home now. I am going to stay another hour.

Father: You say you are, but I say you are not.

Such a statement may lead to one of two results, both of them undesirable: defeat for the child or defeat for the father. A better approach is to focus on the child's desire to stay in the playground, rather than on her threat to defy authority. For instance, father could have said, "I see that you like it here. I suppose you wish you could stay much longer, even ten hours. But time is up for today. Now we must go."

If after a minute or two Ursula is still persistent, father may take her by the hand and lead her out of the playground. With young children, action frequently speaks louder than words.

PARENTS ARE NOT FOR KICKING

A child should never be allowed to hit his parents. Such physical attacks are harmful for both child and parent. It makes the child feel anxious and afraid of retaliation. It makes the parent feel angry and hateful. The prohibition against hitting is necessary to spare the child guilt and anxiety and to enable the parent to remain emotionally hospitable to the child.

From time to time, one witnesses degrading scenes in which a mother, to escape, say, from being kicked in the shin, suggest to her child that he hit her on the hand instead. "You may hit me a little, but you mustn't really hurt me," begged a thirty-year-old mother of a four-year-old child, stretching her arm out in his direction.

One is tempted to intervene and say, "Don't do it, lady. It is less harmful if you hit him than if he hits you."

Mother should have stopped the child's attack immediately:

"No hitting. I can never let you do that."
"If you are angry, tell it to me in words."

The limit against hitting a parent should not be modified under any circumstances. Effective upbringing is based on mutual respect between parent and child *without* the parent's abdicating the adult role. In telling the child that he may "hit but not hurt," the mother is asking him to make too fine a distinction. The child is irresistably challenged to test out the prohibition and to find out the difference between hitting playfully and hurting seriously.

SPANKING

Spanking, though in bad repute, is a popular method of influencing children. It is usually applied to child-rearing as a last resort after the more conventional weapons of threats and reasoning have failed to hit the mark. Frequently, it is not planned, but occurs in a burst of anger when we have reached the end of our endurance. For the moment, spanking seems to work: it relieves pent-up tension in the parent and makes the child obey at least for a while. And as some parents say, "It clears the air."

If spanking is so effective, why do we have such uneasy feelings about it? Somehow we cannot silence our inner doubts about the long-term effects of physical punishment. We are a little embarrassed by the use of force and we keep saying to ourselves, "There ought to be a better way of solving problems."

What is wrong with spanking is the lesson it demonstrates. It teaches children undesirable methods of dealing with frustration. It dramatically tells them: "When you are angry—hit!" Instead of displaying our ingenuity by finding civilized outlets for savage feelings, we give our children a taste of the jungle.

One of the worst side effects of physical punishment is that it may interfere with the development of a child's conscience. Spanking relieves guilt too easily: the child, having paid for his misbehavior, feels free to repeat it. Children develop what Selma Fraiberg* calls a "bookkeeping approach" to misconduct: it permits them to misbehave, and thus go into debt on one side of the ledger, and pay off in weekly or monthly spanking installments. Periodically, they provoke a spanking by egging on their parents. "Sometimes they just ask for punishment," parents say.

A child who asks for punishment needs help with managing his guilt and anger, not compliance with his request. This is not an easy task: in some situations, guilt and anger can be reduced by discussing the misdeeds openly. In other situations, the child's urges need to be accepted without criticism, but limits set on his acts. The child's urges can then be directed into acceptable symbolic outlets. When the child

* See bibliography.

is given better ways of expressing guilt and anger, and when parents learn better ways of setting and enforcing limits, the need for physical punishment is diminished.

CHAPTER 6

A day in a child's life

Civilization has cast parents in the role of "killjoys" who must say no to many of the small child's greatest pleasures: no sucking of the thumb, no touching of the penis, no picking of the nose, no playing with feces, and no making of noise. To infants, civilization is cold and cruel: instead of a soft breast, it offers a hard cup; instead of instant relief and warm diapers, it offers a cold pot and the demand for self-restraint.

Some restrictions are inevitable if the child is to become a social being. However, parents should not overplay their role of policemen for civilization, lest they invite avoidable resentment and hostility.

THE "GOOD MORNING"

Mother should not be the one to wake up her school-age child every morning. The child resents a mother who disturbs his sleep and disrupts his dreams. He dreads her coming into his room and pulling off his blanket and her voice that says, "Get up. It's late." It is better for all concerned if the child is awakened by an alarm clock, rather than by what must look to him like an "alarm mother."

Yvonne, age eight, had difficulty getting out of bed in the morning. Every day she tried to stay in bed for a few endless minutes more. Mother was sweet, mother was sour, but Yvonne was persistent: slow to rise, unpleasant at breakfast, and late to school. The daily arguments left her mother tired and resentful.

The situation improved dramatically when mother gave to her daughter an unexpected gift—an electric alarm clock. In the gift box Yvonne found a note: "To Yvonne, who does not like other people to wake her too early in the morning. Now you can be your own boss. Love, Mother." Yvonne was surprised and delighted. She said, "How did you know that I don't like anyone to wake me up?" Mother smiled and said, "I figured it out."

When the alarm clock rang the next morning, mother said to Yvonne, "It is so early, honey. Why don't you sleep another few minutes?" Yvonne jumped out of bed saying, "No. I'll be late for school."

A child who cannot wake up easily should not be called lazy; and he who does not rise and shine instantly should not be labeled "sour puss." Children who find it hard to be alert and zestful in the morning do not need ridicule. Rather than engage with them in a battle, it is best to let them enjoy another ten golden minutes of sleep or daydreams. This can be accomplished by setting the alarm clock to ring earlier. Our statements should convey empathy rather than anger or scorn or alarm over health:

"It is hard to get up this morning."

"It is such a pleasure to lie in bed and dream."

"Take another five minutes."

Such statements make the morning bright; they create a climate of warmth and intimacy. In contrast, the following statements invite cold and stormy weather:

"Get up, you lazy thing!"

"You get out of that bed this minute."

"My God, you are another Rip Van Winkle."

Such statements as:

"Why are you still in bed? Are you sick? Does anything hurt? Do you have a tummy ache? A headache? Let me see your tongue" suggest to the child that the way to receive tender care is to be sick. He may also think that mother will be disappointed if he denies having any of the maladies she so graciously lists. To please mother, the child may feel obliged to admit that he feels sick.

THE RUSH HOUR

When a child is hurried, he takes his time. Most often he resists the adult's "Hurry up!" by engaging in a slowdown. What appears as inefficiency is in reality a child's very efficient weapon against the tyranny of a timetable that is not his.

Rarely should a child be told to rush. Instead, he should be given realistic time limits, and left with the challenge to be ready on time:

"The school bus will be here in ten minutes."

"The movies start at one o'clock. It is twelve-thirty now."

"Dinner will be served at seven o'clock: it is six-thirty now."

"Your guest will be here in fifteen minutes."

The intent of our brief statement is to convey to the child that we expect, and take it for granted, that he will be on time.

BREAKFAST: MEALS WITHOUT MORALS

Breakfast is not a good time for teaching children universal philosophies, moral principles, or polite manners. It is an appropriate time for conveying to children that their home has a kitchen and dining room with a pleasant atmosphere and good food.

In general, breakfast is not a good time for long conversations. Often the parent or the children are sleepy and grouchy, and arguments may easily degenerate into tantrums.

For a more detailed discussion about food, see Chapter 4, page 88.

GETTING DRESSED: THE BATTLE OF THE SHOESTRING

In some homes parents and child are entangled in a daily battle of the shoestring. Says one father, "When I see my son with shoes unlaced, I am fit to be tied. I want to know if we should force him to tie the laces, or just let him walk around sloppy. Happy as he may be, should we not teach him responsibility?"

It is best not to tie up the teaching of responsibility with the tying of shoes; it is better to avoid arguments by buying the child a pair of loafers or by tying the laces without comment. One can rest assured that sooner or later the child himself will learn to keep his shoes tied.

Children should not go to school dressed like Little Lord Fauntleroy. They should not have to worry about keeping clothes clean. The child's freedom to run, to jump, or to play ball should take precedence over neatness of

133

clothes. When the child returns from school with a dirty shirt, mother might say, "You look like you had a busy day. If you want to change, there is another shirt in the closet." It is not helpful to tell the child how sloppy he is, how dirty he looks, and how sick and tired we are of washing and ironing his shirts. A realistic approach does not rely on a child's capacity to put cleanliness ahead of playfulness. Instead, it takes for granted that children's clothes will not stay clean for long. A dozen inexpensive and wash-and-wear shirts contribute more to mental health than do twelve sermons on cleanliness.

For further discussion about clothes, see Chapter 4, page 89.

GOING TO SCHOOL

It can be expected that in the morning rush, a child may forget to pick up his books, his glasses, his lunch box, or lunch money. It is best to hand him the missing item without adding any sermons about his forgetfulness and irresponsibility.

"Here are your glasses" is more helpful to the child than "I want to live to see the day when you remember to wear your glasses." "Here is your lunch box" is a more helpful statement than "You are so absentminded. You would forget your own head if it were not fastened on your shoulders." "Here is your lunch money" is more appreciated by the child than the sarcastic question, "And what will you buy your lunch with?"

The child should not be given a list of admonitions and warnings before leaving school. "Have a pleasant day" is a better parting phrase than the general warning, "Don't get into trouble." "I'll see you at two o'clock is more instructive to the child than "Don't go wandering off in the streets after school."

THE RETURN FROM SCHOOL

It is desirable that the mother be home to greet her child upon his return from school. Rather than asking him questions that bring worn-out answers—"How was school?" "O.K." "What did you do today?" "Nothing."—mother can make statements that convey her understanding of the trials and tribulations at school:

"You look as though you had a hard day."

"I bet you could not wait for school to end."

"You seem glad to be home."

When mother cannot be home personally to greet her returning child, a message as to her whereabouts is most helpful. Some parents of school-age children use the written message to deepen the relationship with their children. It is easier for them to express appreciation and love in writing. Some parents leave messages on a little tape recorder. The child can listen to mother's words over and over again. At any rate, such messages encourage meaningful communication between parent and child.

FATHER'S HOMECOMING

When father returns home in the evening, he needs a quiet transition period between the demands of the world and the demands of his family. Father should not be met at the door with a bombardment of complaints and requests. A ready drink, a hot shower, the daily mail, the weekly magazine, and the "no questions" period help create an oasis of tranquillity that adds greatly to the quality of family life. From early childhood, children learn that when daddy comes home, he needs a short period of calm and comfort. Dinner, on the other hand, should be conversation time. The stress should be less on food and more on food for thought. There should be few remarks on how and what the child eats, few disciplinary actions, and many examples of the old-fashioned art of conversation.

BEDTIME

In many homes bedtime is bedlam time, with the children and mother forming a mutual frustration society. Children try to stay up as late as possible, while mother wants them bedded down as soon as possible. The evenings become prime nagging time for mothers and tactical-evasion time for children.

Preschool children need mother or father to tuck them in. Bedtime can be utilized for intimate conversation with each child. Children then begin to look forward to bedtime. They like having "time alone together" with mother or father. If the parent takes pains to listen, the child will learn to share his fears, hopes, and wishes. These intimate contacts relieve the child of anxiety and lull him into pleasant sleep.

Some older children also like to be tucked in. Their wish should be respected and fulfilled. They should not be ridiculed or criticized for wanting what looks to parents like "baby stuff." Bedtime for older children should be flexible: "Bedtime is between eight and nine [or nine and ten]. You decide exactly when you want to be in bed."

It is best not to get involved in a fight when a child claims that he "forgot" to go to the bathroom or that he wants a glass of water. However, a child who keeps calling mother back to his room should be told, "I know you wish I could be with you longer. But now is my time for father." Children need to know that there are relationships and situations from which they are exluded.

NO ENTERTAINMENT LICENSE REQUIRED

In some homes, children have the power of veto over their parents' comings and goings. Parents have to get permission from several children for an evening away from home. Some mothers shun going to the movies or to the theater because of the expected curtain raiser at home.

Parents do not need permission or agreement from children on how to live their lives. If a child cries because his mother and father are going out in the evening, his fears need not be condemned, but his wishes need not be complied with. We can understand and sympathize with his desire not to be left with a baby-sitter, but it is not necessary to buy an entertainment license from him. To the weepy child we say with empathy, "I know you wish we were not going out tonight. Sometimes when we are not here, you get scared. You wish we would stay with you, but your father and I are going to enjoy a movie [or friends, or dinner, or a dance] tonight."

The content of the child's objections, pleadings or threats should be ignored. Our reply should be firm and friendly: "You wish we could stay with you, but we made arrangements to go out and enjoy an evening with each other."

138

TELEVISION: THE NAKED AND THE DEAD

No discussion of a child's day would be complete without estimating the influence of television on his values and conduct. Children like to watch TV. They prefer it to reading books, listening to music, or engaging in conversation.

For the sponsors, children are a perfect audience: they are suggestible and believe the commercials. They learn idiotic jingles with amazing facility and are only too happy to oblige the announcer by pestering their parents with silly slogans. And they ask so little of the programs: no originality is required and no art is necessary. Horses and gunmen hold their interest. So, for hours on end, day after day, children are confronted with violence and murder intermingled with jingles and advertisements.

Parents feel two ways about television. They like the fact that it keeps the children occupied and out of trouble, but they are concerned about possible harm to the children's eyes and minds. As for the effect on vision, experts assure us that there is no harm even in prolonged viewing.* However, there is less certainty about the impact of TV on personality. The experts give contradictory opinions:

* A less reassuring report, entitled "Those Tired Children," appeared in *Time* magazine (November 6, 1964,

A day in a child's life

1. Television is bad for children. It engenders a lust for violence and makes children insensitive to human suffering.

2. Television is good for children: violence acted out dramatically helps children get rid of hostile urges.

3. Television has little effect on children: personality and values are shaped by parents and peers, not by images on a screen.

On one fact all agree. Television consumes a significant part of a child's day. More of his time is spent with the TV set than with his father or mother. Even if spectacles of sex and brutality were nothing more than innocent fun, they do keep children from more constructive activities. In some homes children are allowed to view TV only on weekends. In other homes they are allowed certain times and programs, selected with the parents' approval. These parents believe that television, like medication, must be taken at prescribed times and in the right doses.

---

p. 76). Pediatricians, at two Air Force bases, were puzzled by a large group of children, ages three to twelve, who suffered from chronic fatigue, headaches, loss of sleep, upset stomachs, and vomiting. No medical reasons could be found for the symptoms. After persistent prodding of the parents it was discovered that these children were TV addicts: they watched television from three to six hours on weekdays and from six to nine hours on Saturdays and Sundays.

Treatment was radical and effective: No TV at all for a while. Where the rule was observed, symptoms disappeared; where it was ignored, symptoms remained.

140

An increasing number of parents feel that the choice of programs cannot be left entirely to the child. They are not willing to let murderers and thugs influence their children in their own living rooms.

Parents have a right to protect their children from exposure to daily doses of sordid sex and vivid violence. While children need not be sheltered from all tragedy, they should be protected from entertainment in which man's brutality to man is not a tragedy, but a formula.

❀ CHAPTER 7

Jealousy

THE TRAGIC TRADITION

Jealousy between brothers has an ancient and tragic tradition. The first murder, recorded in the Old Testament, was Cain's slaying of his brother, Abel. The motive was sibling rivalry. Jacob escaped death at the hands of his brother, Esau, only by leaving home and hiding in a foreign land. And Jacob's sons were so envious of their younger brother, Joseph, that they threw him into a snake pit before changing his death sentence to life slavery and selling him to a passing caravan in the desert.

What does the Bible tell about the nature and origin of jealousy? In each of these cases, jealousy was sparked by a parental figure who showed favoritism to one of the children. Cain slew his brother after God favored Abel's gift, but not his. Esau became jealous because his mother showed preferential treatment for Jacob by helping him receive his father's blessings. And Joseph was envied by his brothers because their father loved him best; he gave him a "coat of many colors" and did not discipline him when he indulged in impudent boasting.

Children like to hear and read case histories of envy and revenge. The motif fascinates them and the motives speak to their hearts. Interestingly, their sympathy is not always with the victims.

THE NOT-SO-BLESSED EVENT

In contrast to their parents, children do not question the existence of jealousy in the family. They have long known its meaning and impact. Regardless of how thoroughly they were prepared, the arrival of a new baby brought jealousy and hurt. No explanation can gracefully prepare a wife for sharing the home with a young mistress, or a primadonna for sharing the spotlight with a rising newcomer. Jealousy, envy, and rivalry will inevitably be there. To fail to anticipate them, or to be shocked at their appearance, is an ignorance that is far from bliss.

The coming of a second baby is a first-rate crisis in the life of a young child. His space orbit has suddenly changed, and he needs help in orientation and navigation. To be of help rather than to be merely sentimental, we need to know our "star" and his true sentiments.

In announcing the blessed event to a young child, it is best to avoid long explanations and false expectations, such as:

"We love you so much and you are so very wonderful that daddy and I decided to have another baby, just like you. You'll love the new baby. It will be your baby, too. You'll be proud of him. And you'll always have someone to play with."

This explanation sounds neither honest nor convincing. It is more logical for the child to conclude, "If they really loved me, they would not look for another child. I am not good enough, so they want to exchange me for a newer model."

It hurts to share mother's love. In a child's experience, sharing means getting less, like sharing an apple or a piece of gum. The prospect of sharing mother is worrisome enough, but our expectation that the child should delight in it is beyond his logic. As pregnancy proceeds, his suspicions seem more valid. He notices that even though the baby has not yet arrived, it has already occupied mother. Mother is less available to him. She may be sick in bed, or tired and resting. He cannot even sit in her lap, because it is taken by a hidden, yet ever present, intruder.

Introducing the intruder.—The coming of a baby can be announced without pomp and fanfare to a young child. It is sufficient to state,

147

"We are going to have a new baby in our family." Regardless of the child's immediate reaction, we will know that there are many unasked questions on his mind, and many unexpressed worries in his heart. Fortunately, as parents, we are in a good position to help our children live through these times of crisis.

Nothing can change the fact that a new baby is a threat to a child's security. However, whether his character will be enhanced or warped by the stress and strain of the crisis depends on our wisdom and skill. The following is an extreme example of a devastating introduction to a new baby:

> When John was born ... my father took me up to see him, [and] to this *day* I can remember seeing that red-faced baby in my mother's arms and hearing my father say to me: 'Now you're going to have to be extra good because we have another baby now. You are not the *only one* any more. From now on it's going to be *you and your baby brother*. Two of you, where there was only one before.' ... I think my whole life from then on was devoted to seeing if I could not outshine my brother ... and make life hell for him.*

* Virginia M. Axline, "And Hast Thou Slain the Jabberwock?" (Unpublished Ed.D. thesis, Teachers College, Columbia University, 1950), pp. 178-79.

In contrast, the following example illustrates a helpful introduction to a future sibling.

When Virginia, age five, found out that mother was pregnant, she reacted with great joy. She painted a picture of sunshine and roses about life with brother. Mother did not encourage this one-sided view of life. Instead she said:

"Sometimes he will be fun, but sometimes he will be trouble. Sometimes he will cry and be a nuisance to all of us. He'll wet the crib, make in his diapers, and he will stink. Mother will have to wash him, feed him, and take care of him. You may feel left out. You may feel jealous. You may even say to yourself, 'She does not love me any more—she loves the baby.' When you feel that way, *be sure* to come and tell me, and I'll give you extra loving, so you won't have to worry. You'll know that I love you."

Some parents would hesitate to use such an approach. They would fear putting "dangerous" ideas into a child's head. These parents can be assured that such ideas are not new to the child. Our statement cannot but do good: it reflects understanding of feelings. It immunizes against guilt and it invites intimacy and communication. A child is bound to feel anger and resentment for the new baby. It is best that he feel free to voice his anguish to us loudly, rather than languish by himself silently.

EXPRESSING JEALOUSY: WORDS OR SYMPTOMS?

When children repress their jealousy, it comes out in disguised ways in symptoms and misbehavior. Thus when a child resents his brother, but is forbidden to voice his feelings, he may dream that he pushed him out of a tenth-floor window. The dreamer may become so frightened that he may wake up screaming. He may even run to his brother's bed to check if he is still there. He may be so delighted to find him in one piece that the parents may mistake his relief for love.

A nightmare is the child's way of telling in pictures what he fears to tell in words. It is better for children to express jealousy and anger in words rather than in nightmares.

Soon after the birth of a sister, Warren, age five, had a sudden series of wheezing attacks. His parents thought that Warren was very protective of his sister and that "he loved her to death" (perhaps "to death" was an apt description). The physician could find no physical basis for Warren's asthma and he referred him to a mental health clinic, where he might learn to express jealousy and anger in words rather than in wheezes.

Some children express their jealousy in coughing and skin rashes, not in words. Others wet the bed, thus expressing with one organ

150

what they should be able to express with another. Some children become destructive: they break plates instead of voicing their hates. Some children bite their nails or pluck their hair as a cover-up for wanting to bite and hurt their brothers and sisters. All these children need to express their feelings in words rather than in symptoms. Parents are in a key position to help children unlock their feelings.

The many faces of jealousy.—To be on the safe side, parents need to assume that jealousy exists in their own children, even though it is not visible to the naked eye. Jealousy has many faces and many disguises: it can manifest itself in constant competitiveness or in avoidance of all contests, in pushy popularity or in wallflower meekness, in reckless generosity or in ruthless greed. The bitter fruits of unresolved childhood rivalries are all around us in adult life. They can be seen in the irrational rivalry of the man who is in a perpetual race with every car on the road, or who cannot gracefully lose a ping-pong game, or who is always ready to bet his life and fortune in order to prove a point, or who needs to contribute more than others even when it is more than he can afford. They can also be seen in the man who shuns all competition, who feels defeated before a struggle begins, who is always ready to take a back seat, who does not stand up even for his legitimate rights. Thus sibling rivalry affects a child's life more than is realized. It may indelibly stamp his personality and distort his character.

151

The origins of jealousy.— Jealousy originates in an infant's desire to be his mother's only "dearly beloved." This desire is so possessive that it tolerates no rivals. When brothers and sisters arrive, the child competes with them for the *exclusive* love of both parents. The competition may be open or hidden, depending on the parents' attitudes toward jealousy. Some parents are so angered by sibling rivalry that they punish any overt sign of it. Other parents bend backward almost acrobatically to avoid giving cause for jealousy. They try to convince their children that all of them are loved equally and therefore have no reason to be jealous. Gifts, praise, vacations, favors, clothes, and food are measured and doled out with equality and justice for all.

Yet neither of these approaches brings relief from envy. Neither equal punishment nor equal praise can quench the desire for exclusive love. Since such a desire is unfulfillable, jealousy can never be totally prevented. However, whether the fire of jealousy will flicker safely or flare up dangerously depends on our attitudes and acts.

ATTITUDES THAT FOSTER JEALOUSY

Under normal conditions, age and sex differences may cause jealousy among siblings. The older brother is envied because he has more privileges and greater independence. The baby is envied because he is more protected. A girl envies her brother because he has a penis and seems to have greater freedom. A boy envies his sister because she seems to receive special attention.

Danger develops when parents, out of their own needs, give the age and sex differences preferential emphasis. When the helplessness of a baby is preferred to the independence of a six-year-old, or vice versa, jealousy will be intensified. The same is true if a child is overvalued because of his gender, looks, intelligence, musical abilities, or social skills. Superior natural endowment may cause envy, but it is the overprizing of a trait or a talent that leads to relentless rivalry among children.

It is not suggested that older and younger children should be treated alike. On the contrary, age should bring new privileges and new responsibilities. An older child will have, as a matter of course, a larger allowance, later bedtime hours, and more freedom to stay outside the home than a younger child. These privileges are granted openly and graciously so that all children will look forward to growing up.

The younger child may envy the privilege of the older one. We can help him deal with his feelings, not by explaining facts, but by understanding emotions:

"You wish you too could stay up late."

"You wish you were older."

"You wish you were not six years old, but nine years old."

153

"I know, but your bedtime is now."

Parents may unwittingly foster jealousy by demanding that one child make sacrifices for another:

"The baby needs your crib. You can sleep on the sofa."

"Sorry. We cannot get your new skates this year. We need the money to buy winter clothes for the baby."

The danger is that the child may feel deprived not merely of possession but also of affection. Therefore, such demands should be cushioned with affection and appreciation.

DEALING WITH JEALOUSY

The very young express their jealousy undiplomatically: they inquire whether babies ever die, suggest that "it" be sent back to the hospital or put in the garbage disposal unit. The more enterprising youngsters may even engage in military operations against the invader. They may harass him mercilessly: they may hug him boa-constrictor style and may push, punch, or pummel him whenever possible. In extreme cases, a jealous sibling can cause irreversible harm.

As parents, we cannot allow a child to bully his brother or sister. Sadistic attacks, whether physical or verbal, must be stopped because they harm both the victim and the bully. And both children need our strength and care. Fortunately, to protect the physical safety of the young child, we do not need to attack the emotional security of the older child.

When a three-year-old child is caught harassing the baby, he should be stopped promptly and his motives stated to him openly:

"You don't like the baby."

"You are angry at him."

"Show me how angry you are. I'll *watch*."

The child should be handed a large doll, upon which he is allowed to vent his anger. He may spank the doll, stick a finger in the eye, throw it on the floor and step on it.

We do not suggest to the child what to do.

Our role is to observe with a neutral eye and to respond with a sympathetic tongue: we will not be shocked by the ferocity of his feelings or at the cruelty of his attacks. The feelings are honest and the attack is harmless. It is better that his anger be vented symbolically against an inanimate object than directly against a living baby or symptomatically against himself.

Our comments should be brief and easy:

"You are showing me how angry you are!"

"Now mommy knows."

"When you get angry come and tell me."

This approach is more helpful in reducing jealousy than either punishment or insult. In contrast, the following approach is unhelpful:

When mother caught Walter, aged four, dragging his baby brother by his feet, she exploded: "What is the matter with you? You want to kill him? You want to kill your own

155

brother? Don't you know that you can maim him for life? You want him to be a cripple? How many times have I told you not to take him out of his crib. Don't touch him, just don't touch him, ever!"

Older children, too, should be faced with their feelings of jealousy. With them it is possible to converse more openly:

"It is easy to see that you don't like the baby."

"You wish he were not here."

"You wish you were the only one."

"You wish you had me all for yourself."

"You get angry when you see me fuss with him."

"You want me to be with you."

"You were so angry that you punched the baby. I cannot ever allow you to hurt him, but you can tell me when you feel left out."

"When you feel all alone, I will make more time for you, so that you won't feel lonely inside."

Love—uniform or unique? quality or equality?—Those who want to be superfair to each child often end up being furious with all their children. Nothing is so self-defeating as measured fairness. When a mother cannot give a bigger apple or stronger hug to one child for fear of antagonizing the other, life becomes unbearable. The effort entailed in measuring either emotional or material giving can make any person tired and angry. Children do not yearn for equal shares of love: they need to be loved

156

uniquely, not uniformly. The emphasis is on quality, not equality.

We do not love all our children the same way, and there is no need to pretend that we do. We love each child uniquely, and we do not have to labor so hard to cover it up. The more vigilant we are to prevent apparent discrimination, the more alert each child becomes, in detecting instances of seeming inequality. Unwittingly and unwillingly, we find ourselves on the defensive against the child's universal battle cry, *"No fair."*

Let us not be taken in by the children's propaganda. Let us neither claim extenuating circumstances, nor proclaim our innocence, nor disprove their charge. Let us resist the temptation to explain the situation or to defend our position. Let us not be drawn into endless arguments about the fairness or unfairness of our decisions. And above all, let us not be pushed into rationing or portioning our love for the sake of fairness.

To each child, let us convey the uniqueness of our relationship, not its fairness or sameness.

When we spend a few moments or a few hours with one of our children, let us be with him fully. For that period, let the boy feel that he is our only son and let the girl feel that she is our only daughter. When we are out with one child, let us not be preoccupied with the others; let us not talk about them or buy them presents. For the moment to be memorable, our attention must be undivided.

CHAPTER 8

Some sources of anxiety in children

Parents are aware that every child has his share of fear and anxiety. They are not aware, however, of the sources of such anxiety. Parents frequently ask, "Why is my child so fearful? He has no reason to be afraid." One father went so far as to say to his anxious child, "Stop this utter nonsense. You know you are perfectly happy."

It may be helpful to describe some of the sources of anxiety in children and to offer some ways of coping with anxiety.

ANXIETY DUE TO FEAR OF ABANDONMENT

A child's greatest fear is of being unloved and abandoned by his parents. As John Steinbeck put it so dramatically in *East of Eden:* "The greatest terror a child can have is that he is not loved, and rejection is the hell he fears. ... And with rejection comes anger, and with anger some kind of crime in revenge. . . . One child, refused the love he craves, kicks the cat and hides his secret guilt: and another steals so that money will make him loved; and a third conquers the world—and always the guilt and revenge and more guilt."

A child should never be threatened with abandonment. Neither in jest nor in anger should a child be warned that he will be deserted. One frequently overhears an exasperated mother in the street or supermarket scream at her dawdling child, "If you don't come right away, I shall leave you here." Such a statement will arouse the ever lurking fear of abandonment. It fans the flames of the fantasy of being left alone in the world. When a child dawdles beyond toleration, it is better to drag him by the hand than to threaten him with words.

Some children feel frightened if mother is not home when they return from school. Their dormant anxiety of being abandoned is momentarily awakened. As already suggested, it is helpful to leave a message as to mother's whereabouts on the bulletin board or by means of an inexpensive tape recorder. The taped messages are especially helpful for young children. The parents' calm voice and loving words enable them to bear temporary partings without excessive anxiety.

When the tides of life force us to be separated from our young children, separation must be preceded by preparation. Some parents find it hard to convey that they will be away for an operation, a vacation, or a social obligation. Fearing their child's reaction, they sneak out at night or when he is in school and leave a relative or a sitter to explain the situation.

A mother of three-year-old twins had to undergo surgery. The atmosphere at home was tense and troubled, but the children were told nothing. On the morning of hospitalization, mother, with a shopping bag in hand, pretended that she was going to the supermarket. She left the house and did not return for three weeks.

The children seemed to wilt during this time. Father's explanations were no consolation. They cried themselves to sleep every night. During the day, they spent much time at the window, waiting for mother.

Children take the stress of separation more easily if they have been prepared for the experience beforehand. Meaningful preparation requires much more than ordinary verbal explanation. It requires communication in the child's native language of toys and play.

Two weeks before entering the hospital, mother told Yvette, age three, about the pending event. Yvette showed little interest, but mother was not fooled by the lack of curiosity.

She said, "Let's play 'mother is going to the hospital.'" She produced a set of dolls (bought for this occasion) which depicted the family figures, a doctor, and a nurse. While manipulating the appropriate toys and speaking for them, mother said:

"Mommy is going to the hospital to get well. Mommy will not be home. Yvette wonders, Where is mommy? Where is mommy? But mommy is not home. She is not in the kitchen, not in the bedroom, not in the living room. Mommy is in the hospital, to see a doctor, to get well. Yvette cries, I want my mommy. I want my mommy. But mommy is in the hospital to get well. Mommy loves Yvette, and misses her. She misses her every day. She thinks about Yvette and loves her. Yvette misses mommy, too. Then mommy comes home and Yvette is glad."

The drama of separation and reunion was played out by mother and daughter over and over again. At first mother did most of the talking, but soon Yvette took over. Using the appropriate dolls, she told the doctor and nurse to take good care of mommy, to make her well, and to send her home soon.

Before mother left, Yvette asked her to repeat the play once more. Yvette supplied most of the lines and ended her performance reassuringly, "Don't worry, Mommy, I'll be here when you come back."

Before leaving, mother made several other helpful arrangements. She acquainted Yvette with the new housekeeper; she put a large photograph of herself and Yvette on the dresser, and she left a loving message on a small tape recorder. During moments of inevitable loneliness, mother's picture and spoken words reassured Yvette of the nearness of mother's love.

ANXIETY DUE TO GUILT

Wittingly and unwittingly parents arouse guilt in children. Guilt, like salt, is a useful ingredient in flavoring life, but it must never become the main course. When a child has transgressed a rule of social or moral behavior, there is a place for disapproval and guilt. However, when a child is forbidden to have negative feelings or "nasty" thoughts, he will inevitably have too much guilt and anxiety.

To prevent unnecessary guilt, parents should deal with children's transgressions the way a good mechanic deals with a car that breaks down. He does not shame the owner; he points out what has to be repaired. He doesn't blame the car's sounds or rattles or squeaks; he uses them for diagnostic purposes. He asks himself, "What is the probable source of the trouble?"

It is a great comfort for children to know inwardly that they are really free to think as they please without being in danger of losing their parents' love and approval. Statements such as the following are helpful:

165

"You feel one way, but I feel another way. We feel differently on the subject."

"Your opinion seems true to you. My opinion is different. I respect your view, but I have another view."

Unwittingly, parents may create guilt in children by being wordy and giving unnecessary explanations. This is expecially true of "modern" parents, who believe they must govern by consent even when the subject is intricate and the subjects immature.

Five-year-old Zachary was angry with his nursery school teacher because she had been out sick for two weeks. On the day of her return, he grabbed her hat and ran out into the yard. Both mother and teacher followed him.

The teacher said, "The hat is mine. Give it to me."

The mother said, "Zachary, you know perfectly well that the hat is not yours. If you keep the hat, Miss Marta may catch a cold and be sick again. She was sick, you know, for two weeks. Weren't you now, Miss Marta? Now, Zachary, you don't want your teacher to be sick again? Do you?"

The danger is that such an explanation may make Zachary feel responsible for, and guilty about, the teacher's sickness. The long explanation was irrelevant and harmful. All that was necessary at that moment was to retrieve the hat. A hat in the hand is better than two explanations in the yard.

Perhaps later the teacher will discuss with

Zachary his anger about her absence, and point out better ways of coping with it.

ANXIETY DUE TO DENIAL OF AUTONOMY AND STATUS

When a child is prevented from engaging in activities and assuming responsibilities for which he is ready, his inner reaction is that of resentment and anger. Anger, in turn, may lead to revenge fantasies, which bring either guilt or fear of retaliation. In either case, the result is anxiety.

Little children do not master skills with polished proficiency. They take a long time to tie their shoes, to button their coats, to put on their galoshes, to unscrew the lid of a jar, or to turn a doorknob. The best help that can be offered to them is tolerant waiting and a light comment about the difficulty of the task. "It is not easy to put on these galoshes." "The lid of this jar is hard to unscrew."

Such comments are of help to the child whether he fails or succeeds in his efforts. If he succeeds, he has the satisfaction of knowing that he managed a difficult chore. If he fails, he has the consolation that his parents knew the task was hard. In either case, the child experiences sympathy and support, which leads to greater intimacy between him and his parents. The child does not consider himself inadequate because he did not succeed in a task.

It is essential that a child's life not be ruled by the adult's need for efficiency. Efficiency is the enemy of infancy. It is too costly in terms of the child's emotional economy. It drains the child's resources, prevents growth, stifles interests, and may lead to emotional bankruptcy.

ANXIETY DUE TO FRICTION BETWEEN PARENTS

When parents fight, children feel anxious and guilty—anxious because their home is threatened, guilty because of their actual or imagined role in the family friction. Justifiably or not, children assume that they are the cause of domestic strife.

Children do not remain neutral in the civil war between the states of mind. They side either with father or with mother. The consequences are harmful to both their psychosexual and character development. When a boy rejects his father or a girl her mother, the children remain without a proper model of identification. Rejection is expressed by an aversion for identifying with traits, for emulating values, and for imitating conduct. In extreme cases, such rejection may result in a confused sexual identification, and an inability to live out one's biological destiny. When a boy rejects his mother or a girl her father, the child may grow up suspicious of, and hostile to, all persons of the opposite sex.

When parents are forced to compete for their children's affection, they frequently use unpedagogic means, such as bribery, flattery, and lies. The children grow up with divided loyalties and abiding ambivalence. Furthermore, the need to protect one parent from the other and the opportunity to play one parent against the other leave a permanent mark on children's character. From early childhood, they become aware of their inflated worth to the bidding rivals, and they put an ever increasing price on themselves. They learn to manipulate and exploit, to plot and blackmail, to spy and gossip. They learn to live in a world where integrity is a liability and honesty a hindrance; a world which fosters and rewards psychopathic behavior.

ANXIETY DUE TO INTERFERENCE WITH PHYSICAL ACTIVITY

In many modern homes, young children are frustrated by a lack of space for motor activity. Cramped apartments and costly furniture result in strict inhibition of climbing, running, and jumping. The restrictions usually start very early in the child's life. The infant may not be allowed to stand in his carriage, the toddler to climb stairs, or the baby to run around the living room.

Children, so frustrated, store up tension that creates anxiety. The solution is indicated in the description of the problem. Young children need to release their tension in physical activity. They need space to run and adequate materials for play. They need a room or a yard that permits assertive activity within a setting of psychological security.

ANXIETY DUE TO LIFE'S END

To adults, the tragedy of death lies in its irreversibility. Death, so final and eternal, is the end of all hope. Therefore death is personally inconceivable; no one can imagine his own cessation, the dissolution of his own self. The self consists of memories and hopes, of a past and a future, and a person cannot see himself without a future. The consolation that faith brings is precisely in this realm. It offers man a future, so he may live and die in peace.

If death is a riddle to adults, to children it is an enigma veiled in mystery. The young child cannot comprehend that death is permanent; that neither his parents nor his prayers can bring back the departed. The futility of his magic wishes in the face of death is a severe blow to the child. It shakes his belief in his power to influence events by wishful thinking, and it makes him feel weak and anxious. What the child sees is that in spite of his tears and protests, a beloved pet or person is no longer with him. Consequently he feels abandoned and unloved. His fear is reflected in the question often asked of a parent: "After you die, will you still love me?"

Some parents try to protect their child from the experience of pain and grief inherent in the loss of someone he loved. If his goldfish or turtle dies, they hurry to replace it with a new one, hoping that the child will not notice the difference. If his cat or dog dies, they rush to offer the grieving child a prettier and costlier substitute.

What lessons does the child learn from these early experiences of sudden loss and quick replacement? He may conclude that the loss of loved ones is of no great importance; that love may easily be transferred and loyalty easily shifted.

A child should not be deprived of his right to grieve and to mourn. He should be free to feel sorrow in the loss of someone loved. The child's humanity is deepened, and his character ennobled, when he can lament the end of life and love.

The basic premise is that children should not be excluded from sharing the sorrows as well as the joys that inevitably arise in the course of family life. When a death occurs and the child is not told what happened, he may remain shrouded in nameless anxiety. Or he may fill the gap in his knowledge with fearful and confused explanations of his own. He may blame himself for the loss and feel separated not only from the dead, but also from the living.

171

The first step in helping children face their loss is to allow them to express fully their fears, fantasies, and feelings. Comfort and consolation come from sharing deep emotions with a listener who cares. The parents may also put into words some of the feelings that a child is bound to have, but may find difficult to express. For example, after the death of a grandmother to whom the child was attached, a parent might say:

"You miss grandma."

"You miss her a lot."

"You loved her so much."

"And she loved you."

"You wish she were with us."

"You wish she were still alive."

"It is hard to believe that she died."

"It is hard to believe that she is no longer with us."

"You remember her so well."

Such statements convey to the child his parent's interest in his feelings and thoughts, and encourage him to share his fears and fantasies. He may want to know whether dying hurts, whether the dead ever come back, whether he and his parents will ever die. The answers should be brief and truthful: when one dies the body feels no pain at all; a dead person never returns; it is natural to die when one is very old.

In talking to children about death, it is best to avoid euphemisms. When told that grandfather went to his eternal sleep, one four-year-old girl asked if he took his pajamas with him. She was also afraid that grandpa was angry at her because she had not said "good night" to him before he went to sleep.

When told that "grandmother went to heaven and became an angel," one five-year-old boy prayed that the rest of the family would die and become angels, too.

When a child is given the facts simply and honestly, accompanied by an affectionate hug and a loving look, he feels reassured. This approach is effective when the parents themselves have accepted the realities of life and death. In all matters of importance, attitudes speak louder than words.

❀ CHAPTER 9

Sex education

Many parents think that sex education is a conversation. "One of these days," the parent will take his preadolescent aside and tell him the "facts of life." Boys are warned of the dangers of V.D. and girls are told of the perils of pregnancy. But sex education begins before that.

Parents' own sensuality.—Sex education starts with the parents' attitudes toward their own sensuality. Do they like the sights and smells and feel of their bodies, or do they think that there is something uncouth and unesthetic about them? Do they delight in each other's naked presence, or do they close their eyes and clothe their bodies in shame? Do they have any special aversions to their own or the partner's sex, or do they appreciate it? Do they see each

177

other as inconsiderate and exploitive, or as exciting initiators of shared pleasures?

Whatever the parents' unspoken feelings are, they will be conveyed to the children, even if their spoken words tell about birds, bees, and daffodils. This is the reason why it is so difficult to tell parents precisely what to reply to a child's questions about sex. Their own bewilderment in this area must first be known and their worries and embarrassment modified.

BEGINNING OF SEXUAL FEELINGS

From birth on, infants are equipped to feel body pleasures, and from birth on, sex attitudes are in the process of forming. Though not in an adult way, the infant's enjoyment of his body and its functions is sexual in nature. As soon as he is physically able, a child explores his body. He handles his limbs and delights in being touched, tickled, and cuddled. These early touchings and strokings are part of his sex education. Through them he learns to receive love.

There was a time when mothers were warned against cuddling and playing with their babies, lest they be spoiled. Even then, this maxim did not make sense to most mothers. Mothers know instinctively that *not* playing with a baby may spoil him. Now we know that a baby needs a great deal of tender touching and of cuddly care.

When a child discovers that the mouth grants extra pleasure, anything he can move goes there: a thumb, a blanket, a toy. The sucking, chewing, and biting bring pleasant sensations even when applied to inedible objects. These mouth pleasures should not be stopped, only regulated. We must see to it that what goes into the mouth is hygienic. Some infants get all their oral pleasures in eating; others need supplemental sucking, which should be granted unstintingly. During the first year or so, the mouth is the main mirror by which the world is reflected to the child. Let it be a pleasant reflection.

When sucking needs are unfulfilled, they do not disappear. They come out in thinly or thickly disguised ways. A baby may continue sucking his thumb, a child his eraser, and an adult his cigarettes and cigars. Babies may bite all objects, children may bite their nails, and adults may make biting remarks.

SEX AND TOILET TRAINING

The organs of sex and of eliminating are so close to each other that attitudes acquired in toilet training are likely to have an effect on sexual development. During the second year of life a child becomes more focused on the pleasures of evacuation. For him there is nothing disgusting in the sight, smell, and touching of feces. While we guide him into civilized elimination habits, special care must be taken not to infect him with disgust toward his body and its products. Harsh and hasty measures may make the child feel that his body and *all* of its functions are something to dread, rather than to enjoy.

Impatient training is self-defeating. A child is not ready for bowel control before his second year or for urinary control before his third year. Accidents, of course, are expected and are tax-exempt until his fifth year of life.

In the course of early training, children must be led to give up the handling of body products. However, it is neither necessary nor wise to prohibit their *desire* to do so. We can allow children to enjoy forbidden pleasures in acceptable substitute ways. It is very helpful to children to be able to mess to their hearts' content with sand, mud, paint, clay (brown, of course), and water. In their subconscious, every messy substance represents the real stuff, which brings substitute satisfaction as well as consolation for the loss of the original pleasure.

Lack of training is also self-defeating. When a child is left completely to his own devices, he may continue wetting and soiling for a long time. It may be pleasurable to the child, but meantime he will miss the satisfactions that come with real accomplishments. When the child is ready, he should be told clearly and kindly what we expect of him: "It was fun to mess when you were a little baby. You like the warm feeling inside your diapers, but we don't want that any more. Now we want you to do it in the potty."

During the training years, especially tender care must be taken when using enemas or rectal thermometers. Harsh or even routine treatment may so frighten children that even in adulthood they may still fear penetration.

Frequent spankings, too, may have a negative impact on sex development. Because of the proximity of the organs, a child may get sexually aroused when spanked. Or he may so enjoy the making-up that follows the punishment that he will come to seek suffering as a necessary prelude to love. There are many adult couples who seem to need a good fight before a good night.

GENITAL PLEASURES

As physical and emotional development progresses, the child finds the most pleasant body sensations in the genital area. Here, too, our attitudes should allow him to have guilt-free, pleasant body feelings. In fact, now more than ever he needs our guiding love in order to be sure that his pleasurable sensations are not emotionally harmful.

When a little girl discovers her clitoris and confides to mother that it is her "best-feeling place," it takes both faith and diplomacy not to cry out "Don't touch!" Yet, in actuality, there is cause to rejoice that the child has progressed normally, so that her most pleasurable sensations now come from the genitals rather than from the anus or the mouth.

GENDER DIFFERENCES

Children do not take gender differences for granted. It is a momentous mystery to them, and they develop fantastic explanations and fears about the basic body differences. Regardless of how frank our explanations are, the child decides and sometimes even declares that everyone is entitled to a penis.

A girl may imagine that her penis was lost or was taken away as a punishment, or that it may still grow when she is better behaved or older. A boy may deduce with dread that if a girl can lose her penis, so can he. Parents must not treat such fears as funny or cute childish sayings to be repeated to others for a laugh. Such fears merit serious consideration and remedy. It is necessary to help children bring out in the open their imaginings about anatomical differences. We may say to our daughter, "Sometimes girls have scary thoughts when they see that they don't have a penis. Do you sometimes wonder about that?"

Or we may say to a son, "Sometimes boys get scared when they see that girls don't have a penis. Do you sometimes wonder about that? Sometimes a boy imagines, 'If something happened to her, it may happen to me.' But boys and girls are different from one another. They are born that way. And that is why boys become fathers and girls become mothers."

Some parents try to console little girls for their implied loss by mimimizing the basic difference between the sexes. They may say to the crying daughter, "Your brother is like you in every respect—except for his little weenie. So stop crying." One mother even suggested to her three-year-old that she make a clay penis for herself—a solution that is fraught with many future problems.

When a child discovers that there are anatomical differences between boys and girls, it is a good time to emphasize, rather than minimize, the differences:

"Yes, there is a great difference between a boy and a girl. You have a penis, you are a boy. When you grow up, you will be a father."

"You are a girl. You have a vagina. When you grow up, you will be a mother. I am glad you have noticed that girls are made one way and boys are made another way."

The message must be clear and definite, in order to prevent possible confusion in sexual identification.

ANSWERING QUESTIONS

A new preacher came to deliver his first sermon in a prairie parish, but no one showed up except one cowhand. The preacher wondered aloud whether or not to proceed with the services. The man replied, "I can't tell you what to do, I'm just a cowhand. But if I came to feed my cows and only one showed up, I'd be darned if I wouldn't feed her." The preacher thanked him and gave the prepared hour-long sermon. When he finished, he asked the man if he had liked it. The answer was: "I don't know much about sermons. I'm just a cowhand; but if I came to feed my cows and only one cow showed up, I'd be darned if I would give her the whole load."

In sex education, we must forego the temptation to dump the whole load and give too much too soon. While there is no reason why children's sex questions cannot be answered frankly, the answers need not be a course in obstetrics. They can be brief, phrased in a sentence or two, not in long paragraphs or chapters.

The right age to inform a child about sexual matters is when he asks questions. When a two- or three-year-old boy points to his genitals and wonders, "What is it?" it is the right moment to tell him. "It is your penis." Although children may refer to the penis as a peepee, weenie, or tinkler, the adult should call it by its rightful name.

When a child wonders where a baby comes from, we shall *not* tell him that it comes from the doctor's bag, the hospital, the supermarket, the mail-order store, or the stork. We tell him, "It grows inside a special place in mother's body." Depending on further questions, it may or may not be necessary at this time to identify the place as the uterus.

In general, from early childhood on, children should learn the names and functions of their organs and the anatomical differences between the sexes. The explanations should not involve plants and animals; we should avoid what Selma Fraiberg* calls the "agricultural fallacy." Alice Balint* tells of a boy who was taken to a farm at the time his mother was due to give birth to another child. Upon his return he said, "Look, Daddy, I know everything, but just tell me, did mommy go to the bull, or did the bull come to mommy?"

Two questions puzzle almost all preschool children: How does a baby get started and how does it get out. It is advisable to hear the child's version of creation and exile, before giving our own. His answers usually involve food and elimination. One bright child explained, "Good babies start from good food. They grow in mommy's stomach and pop out from her

* See bibliography.

belly button. Bad babies start from bad food. They come out from the B.M. place."

Our explanation should be factual but it does not need to give full account of sexual intercourse:

"When a father and a mother want to have a baby, a cell from the father's body joins a cell in the mother's body, and a baby starts to grow. When the baby is big enough it comes out through the vagina."

Sometimes a child demands to be shown the place he came from. It is best not to allow such invasion of privacy. Instead, we can draw a human figure or use a doll for demonstration.

Our answers may satisfy the child for a short while only. He may come back with the same, or with additional, questions. If a child asks again, "How is a baby born," we can give him a more detailed answer: "Father starts the baby growing in mother's body. A fluid called semen, with many tiny sperm cells, comes from father's body. One sperm cell joins one egg cell in mother's body. The joining of the two cells starts the baby."

The child's next question may be the one parents dread: "How does father's cell get into mother's." Again, we shall first ask the child for his version of the event. We shall probably hear theories of "seed planting" (daddy plants a seed into mommy), of "seed eating" (daddy tells mommy to swallow a fruit pit), of pollination (the wind makes the seeds fly into the mother), of operation (the doctor plants a seed in the mother through surgery).

The child's question can then be answered briefly: "The semen comes out from the father's penis. It fits into mother's vagina." This may be a good time to emphasize that semen is different from urine: "Urine is a body waste. Semen is a fluid that carries sperm cells."

The next question that may pop up is "When do you and daddy make babies?" This is not as snoopy a question as it sounds. And a simple answer will suffice: "Mothers and fathers choose a time when they are comfortable and alone. They love each other and want to have a baby to love." It may also be necessary to add that the getting together or mating is a personal and private event.

Some boys wish that fathers too were able to have babies. They ask, "Why doesn't the mother egg go into the father?" The explanation is offered that a woman's body has a place—the uterus—in which a baby can grow. A man's body does not. "Why?" "Because men's and women's bodies are built differently." It is desirable to assure the boys that babies also need a father to love them and protect them.

THE NAKED BODY

There are homes that resemble nudist colonies. The parents and children parade around naked, in a self-made paradise of Adams and Eves. Yet children reared in such freedom are not free of worry or guilt about the human body. The direct observations do not satisfy their curiosity, and may stir up some secret strivings that cannot be fulfilled.

Four-year-old Betsy was allowed to take showers with her father. She liked to watch him and to compliment him on his physique. But when she expressed a desire to touch his penis, father's liberalism faltered. In fact, it turned to shock.

In infancy, the sight or touch of mother's naked breast stimulates sucking responses which can easily be satisfied. In childhood, the sight of naked mom or dad may stimulate genital excitement and sexual desire that can never be fulfilled. Does it mean that we must go back to Victorian prudery? Not at all. But it does mean that we need privacy, not only for our own peace but also for the sake of the children's normal development. We may tolerate children's occasional intrusions and stares when we are showering and dressing, but we should not encourage such behavior. We shall especially be careful not to lead children to believe that we want them to explore us. When children are allowed to be present while we sunbathe or exercise in the nude, they may imagine that they are invited not only to be there, but to do something to please us. They become overstimulated, confused, and caught in hopeless fantasy.

We recognize that children are curious about

the human body. They have had a chance to observe the differences between little boys and girls, and they have also had occasional glimpses at us. And they would like to see more of us. It is best to recognize openly their curiosity, but insist on our privacy.

"You want to know how I look, but in the bathroom I like to be alone. I'll tell you how grownups are made. You ask, and I'll answer."

This approach does not attack or block the child's curiosity; it only diverts it into more socially acceptable channels. Instead of by looking and touching, curiosity will now be expressed by words.

BEDS AND BEDROOMS

It is definitely undesirable for children to share beds or bedrooms with their parents. Children see and hear more than we imagine. Even if they cannot understand what goes on, the sights and the sounds are retained in fantasy and may reappear incognito in fears and nightmares. The danger is clear: children are neither deaf nor blind, not even when they are, or seem to be, asleep.

Architecturally, our homes are antisex. Few modern houses or apartments have deliberate safeguards for sexual privacy. The walls are thin, and the children are near. It is a sad

189

comment on our civilization that the sounds of legitimate love must be so low.

THE HOPELESS ROMANCE

There comes a time in every boy's life (between three and five) when he wants mother all for himself. She is his first love, and he can stand for no one else to "date" her. The girl, too, declares her love for father—a love so possessive that it tolerates no rival. It is essential that this desperate love not be encouraged by words or deeds. Even in jest, a boy should not be called by mother, "My strong man," or "My little lover." Nor should the daughter be addressed in such fashion by the father.

These are the very roles that the children wish they could assume in life, roles which they must give up—and the sooner the better. We should not increase their frustration by letting them hope hopelessly. Indulgence by parents and nurses (kisses on the mouth, caressing of genitals) is pleasurable to the child, but it brings him guilt rather than contentment. Sensual indulgence, either tactual or verbal, ties the child erotically to his parents and blocks normal development of sex and love.

MASTURBATION: SELF-GRATIFICATION OR SELF-ABUSE?

Childhood masturbation may bring comfort to children, but it certainly causes conflicts to parents. Children may find in it self-love when lonely, self-employment when bored, and self-consolation when rejected. To parents, it brings vague anxiety and obvious concern. The sight of her five-year-old walking around holding his penis in public arouses embarrassment and anguish even in the most progressive mother. Of course, parents have heard, read, or even experienced that masturbation is harmless; that it does not cause insanity, sterility, impotence, or any of a dozen other plagues. But the assurance itself produces anxiety. One would not readily buy food that lists poisons that it does *not* contain, or trust a person who lists offenses he does not commit.

Intellectually, parents recognize that masturbation may be a phase in the development of normal sexuality. Emotionally, it is hard to accept. And perhaps parents are not altogether wrong in not sanctioning masturbation.

Self-gratification may make the child less accessible to the influence of parents and peers. When he takes this short cut to satisfaction, he does not have to depend on pleasing anyone but himself. Without much effort, and without help from others, he has the whole world at his

191

command and its pleasures in his hand. There is more than a grain of truth in the saying, "What's wrong with masturbation is that one does not meet interesting people this way."

Persistent masturbation may become a too ready consolation for mishaps and failures and a too easy substitute for efforts and accomplishments.

Children's entry into civilization hinges on their willingness to delay or give up immediate gratification for the more lasting satisfaction of parental and (later) social approval. Parental love and care not only fulfill but also create needs in children, needs for affection and acceptance. Therefore children who have known love are more willing to modify behavior in exchange for, and in anticipation of, the familiar feelings and favors.

Parents may exert a mild pressure against self-indulgence, not because it is pathological, but because it is not progressive; it does not result in social relationships or personal growth. The pressure must be mild or it will backfire in wild explosions. The solution lies in so involving the infant with our love, and the child with our affection and interest in the outside world, that self-gratification will not remain his only means of satisfaction. The child's main satisfactions should come from personal relationships and achievements. When this is so, occasional self-gratification is not a problem. It is just an additional solution.

FORBIDDEN GAMES: DEALING WITH SEX PLAY

Infants like to investigate their bodies and children to explore each other. This thirst for knowledge is not easily quenched. The difference in anatomy baffles children and challenges them to find out again and again that nothing is wrong with their own equipment.

Even when the facts are explained and the feelings understood, children may go on with mutual exploration and excitation. They invent games, such as playing doctor or house, that give legitimacy to their quest. They may also negotiate and arrange peeping games. The more daring may take on more advanced experiments. By mutual consent, they may engage in genital manipulation and may even attempt intercourse.

Parents are at a loss in dealing with these embarrassing events. They exaggerate the future consequences of the present acts and fear the possibility of sex maniacs growing up right in their own backyards.

Even sexually enlightened parents find it difficult to cope unemotionally with such situations. They may refrain from spanking or shaming the child, but they are not sure how to set a positive limit on such activities. In our day and age some parents even wonder if they should interfere in such intimate affairs, for fear of harming their offspring's future sex life.

What is wrong with secret sex play? It burdens the child with guilt, but it does not satisfy his needs. When a two- or three-year-old girl watches with wonder how a little boy urinates, it is considered par for the course in anatomy. In nursery school, where children share the same toilets, curiosity can be satisfied by direct observation. However, by the first grade, a child is presumed to have seen enough. A lingering need to peep and inspect can no longer be attributed to sheer curiosity about gender differences. The urgency of the need and the persistence of the practice indicate that the child is anxious and needs help, rather than permission to indulge. Furthermore, his true needs can never be satisfied by looking and touching, just as the alcoholic's needs cannot be fulfilled by drinking. A peeping Tom, Dick, or Harriet needs, first and foremost, limits on such behavior—limits set and enforced with kindness and justice.

When a parent finds a boy and a girl with pants down and dress up, he should not ask them, "What are you doing?" (It may be too embarrassing if the child replies with the whole truth.) The children should not be shamed or berated. On the other hand, they should not be provided with an easy excuse or a false alibi, such as: "Don't you think it is too cold to walk around naked in the wind?"

The children should be told to get dressed

and find something else to play with. When the guest has left, the incident should be discussed frankly. Without threats and sermons, the child should be told in plain English: "You and Penny were undressing each other. This is not allowed. You were also touching her vagina. This is not allowed. Little children do it because they wonder why a boy has a penis and a girl doesn't. If you wonder about it, ask us and we'll help you figure things out. But no undressing."

Our calm unblaming attitude makes it possible to limit sexual experimentation without harming the child's interest in sex and love.

DIRTY WORDS

No parent really wants his child to be naive about dirty words used by his peers. These words are so vigorous, expressive, and forbidden that they make the children feel big and important. When children use a string of dirty words in a secret council, they feel as though they have just composed their declaration of independence.

Four-letter words have a place that must be delineated and defined for the child. Parents should express their feelings on the subject frankly:

Father can say, "Not around ladies, George. That's man to man talk."

Mother can say, "I don't like them at all, but I know boys use them. I prefer not to hear them. Spare them for the locker room. In our home they are forbidden."

Again, we recognize and respect the child's wishes and feelings, but set limits and redirect his actions.

CHAPTER 10

Sexual role and social function

IDENTIFICATION AND BIOLOGICAL DESTINY

To fulfill their biological destiny, boys must identify with their fathers and girls with their mothers. Identification is the crucial process whereby boys become men and girls women. Identification is facilitated when relationships with children are based on respect and love. By winning our children's affection, we also win their wish to emulate our respective sexual roles. Yet parents themselves are not entirely clear as to what their roles entail.

Patterns of mothering and fathering.—In many societies the function of the mother is more clearly defined than that of the father. To be mothered means to be nursed, diapered, cuddled, loved, played with, smiled at, talked to, and cared for. The need for maternal care is biologically determined. Lack of mothering endangers the infant's mental health and

199

threatens his very survival. In contrast, fathering involves less nature and more culture. Biologically speaking, father's contribution begins
and ends before the child is born. All other
fathering activities are socially determined.
Thus, in some societies, fathers take an interest
only in sons. Daughters are not even acknowledged. In other societies, the father maintains
the role of a tolerant teacher, and child-rearing
is left entirely to the mother. In still other
societies, the father rules his children like an
absolute monarch.

In our society, the titular head of the family
is the father, but his role and status are often
uncertain and ill-defined. Some authorities
maintain that the American father is mainly an
absentee provider; he rushes out in the morning, disappears for the day, and returns tired at
night. On weekends, if he does not play golf, he
watches television or mows the lawn. Children
have little opportunity to participate with their
fathers in meaningful activities and conversations.

As a result, mother is the dominant figure in
the family, and the chief, if not sole, disciplinarian. Such a position jeopardizes mother's
age-old role. In former times, mother represented love and sympathy, while father per-
sonified discipline and morality. The children,
especially the boys, derived their conscience
mainly from him. It was the internalized image
of the father that warned them against tempta-
tions and scolded them for transgressions.

Thus, father served as a link between the family and the world.

In the modern family, the roles of mother and father are no longer distinct. Many women work outside the home in the "man's world," and many men find themselves involved in mothering activities, such as feeding, diapering, and bathing the baby.

Though some men welcome these new opportunities for closer contact with their infants, there is the danger that the baby may end up with two mothers, rather than with a mother and a father.

THE ROLE OF THE FATHER

A child needs a father who accepts his role. Masculinity cannot be acquired by a formal course of study. It may be learned in the course of daily life from a father who serves as a model. Freud stated, "There is not any need in childhood as strong as that for a father's protection." From his infancy, the child needs to be aware that he has a father who can protect him from danger.

Three danger areas in particular require a father's guiding presence. The child needs protection against threats from the outer world, against fears from the inner world, and against overprotection by mother. The outside world is a dangerous place for a young child. Simply to survive, he needs protection against the hazards of modern gadgets in the home and the old-fashioned bullies in the neighborhood. He has to learn, among other things, to cross a street without being struck by a car and to use electrical appliances without being electrocuted.

The child also needs father's help in dealing with his angry wishes and fearful fantasies. Every young boy wants his mother all for himself. Tolerating no rivals, he gets rid of his father and siblings in fantasies and dreams. The fantasies may be violent and the dreams may turn to nightmares. Since he cannot yet separate wishes from deeds, the child becomes desperately frightened. He has no way of knowing that his thoughts will not become reality. Here father's role is twofold: to view sympathetically the child's frustration, fury, and fear, and at the same time, in silent strength, convey the reassuring message, "Don't worry son, I shall not let you carry out your fearful wishes."

Some parents are not aware of the need to protect a child from his incestuous and destructive fantasies. In some homes, the parental bedroom can be invaded by the children at any time of day or night. In other homes, children abuse mother verbally or even physically in the presence of an overpermissive father. It is best that such practices not be tolerated. They cannot but bring anxiety to the child and anguish to the parent.

Just as he must defend the mother against an

abusive child, so must the father defend the child against an overprotective mother. It is not implied here that all mothers are overprotective. But some mothers enjoy babying their children far beyond infancy. It is the father's function to provide the child with love that is more than merely sheltering, but is liberating as well. While mother's love conveys to the infant that he is lovable, father's confidence tells the child that he is competent. Because of their own less inhibited upbringing, it is easier for fathers than for mothers to allow children to experiment with independence. Father's willingness to witness and sanction a child's new ventures encourages the child to grow up without undue guilt.

The context in which father imparts trust and confidence is not crucial. These attitudes can be displayed at any time and in many places. Their display does not necessarily require special skills in athletics or participation in hobbies. It does require the ability to sense children's needs and the willingness to serve as a firm guide and friendly guardian.

STANDARDS FOR BOYS AND FOR GIRLS

Both boys and girls need help in their progress toward their different biological destinies. Parents can help by not demanding the same standard of conduct from both sexes. Boys should be allowed to be more boisterous both because of their greater energy and because society requires them to be more assertive.

Mothers and teachers must refrain from fostering feminine behavior in boys. Boys should not have to bear female names, or to wear restrictive clothes, or to grow girls' curls. They should not be expected to be as neat and as compliant as girls, or to have ladylike manners. The dictum that "boys will be boys" is a valid one, and it demands leeway for the discharge of energy in strenuous masculine activities.

Parents must take special care not to feminize a son because of their disappointment in not having a daughter. A nice curly-haired boy may look cute to relatives, but he is sure to be a sissy to his playmates—if he has any. Such a stigma stings deep into personality. It damages the child's image of himself and his status in the group.

Girls, too, should not be made to pay for the parent's unfulfilled longings for a child of the opposite sex. Although a girl loses less prestige by being a tomboy than a boy by being a sissy, it is important to help her find pleasure and pride in femininity. Girls need to feel that they are enjoyed and valued for being girls. Such feelings are best conveyed by a mother who likes being a woman. Both parents, however, should be aware of the need to cultivate their children's maleness or femaleness. It is appropriate for a father to compliment his daughter on her looks, dress, and feminine pursuits. It is inappropriate for him to engage her in shadow boxing and rough play, lest she conclude that father would have loved her more if she were a boy.

Family life provides ample opportunity to demonstrate to children the fundamental fact that men and women in their different roles need each other and need to take care of each other.

EDUCATION FOR MANHOOD AND WOMANHOOD

Education in maleness or femaleness starts early in life. Yet, children should not be forced to assume gender-appropriate roles too early. During preschool age, both boys and girls like to play with dolls and to engage in "mothering" activities. This is as it should be, although some fathers and mothers seem horrified at the sight of a five-year-old boy feeding a doll.

Preschool boys and girls should be allowed to use the same toys and games if they so desire. At this age no sharp line need be drawn between the play of boys and girls. Fathers should not try to make boxing champions out of four- or five-year-old boys who would rather play with a doll house. Preschool children of either sex should be able to play both feminine and masculine games without fear of disapproval.

During school years, sexual differences are

emphasized. Boys and girls are expected to develop different interests and aspirations. Boys need to achieve prestige in masculine activities and girls in feminine pursuits. Sexual identification is reinforced by provision of interests and activities that are culturally differentiated as masculine and feminine.

School years are a good period for intensifying a son's relationship with father and a girl's with mother. This is the time for introducing girls to the culinary and other homemaking arts. Girls can learn to cook, bake, and prepare simple meals as well as to sew, knit and take care of the house. Miles of leeway should be granted for messiness and clumsiness. The emphasis is on the joys of homemaking, not on the sorrows of perfection. This is mother's golden hour to convey to her daughter the satisfactions of being a woman, a wife, and a mother.

Father, too, should welcome his son's readiness to relate to him, and his willingness to walk, talk, and dress like him. These imitations should not be ridiculed—they should be encouraged. Imitations of language and manner may lead to the emulation of interests and values. In their intimate contacts, father exemplifies to his son what it means to be a man in the family as well as in the community. Children derive much pride at witnessing father's skills, efforts, and dedication in situations outside the home. Spending time with father at his place of work and at civic and political activities makes them aware of the interest and pride that a man takes in his work and his community.

DIFFERENT FAMILY PATTERNS

The best models of identification are parents who respect their own and each other's sexual roles. In many subtle ways, their daily behavior conveys to their children that masculinity and femininity are valued.

In some families, children will get the message that a man's destiny is to make his mark in the world and to leave traces in time and eternity. Such an atmosphere nourishes great dreams of exploration, discovery, and accomplishment in the arts and sciences. Women, too, are expected to contribute to society in addition to raising a family. Such a view is successful if father and mother accept their different roles with satisfaction, show appreciation for each other's position, and share interest in each other's achievements.

In some homes, children will get a different message. Where the woman is bored with child-rearing and housekeeping, or where the husband does not appreciate the complexity and ingenuity entailed in being a wife and mother, the children will look down on the traditional roles of women. The girls in such homes may become competitive and feel compelled to out-

207

do the boys, and later the men, at their own game.

Still a different message comes from a home where the sex roles are reversed. The woman is boss in word and deed. She may or may not be the main provider, but she is the last court of appeal in all matters of importance. As one husband said, "I decide the big things, whether China should be accepted into the U.N., or whether TVA should be sold to private industry. My wife decides the smaller things: what car to buy, what house to live in, what college to send the children to." The husband in such a home seems to avoid being the head of the house. He openly refers to his wife as "the boss." When his children ask him for a decision, his response usually is "Ask mother."

In such homes, children grow up with little respect or admiration for men. Both boys and girls see father through mother's eyes: a sweet, but "half-baked" boy, a good-natured blunderer, a caricature of a man.

Both sons and daughters are affected by the example of a weak father and dominant mother. The boys may try to overcompensate and to prove their masculinity by drinking, promiscuity, delinquency, or cruelty to women. Girls often duplicate in their own choice of partners the patterns of their original home and thereby continue the reversal of roles for another generation.

Sexual role and social function.—The importance of rearing sons and daughters who are individuals should not obscure the need to bring up sons who are male and daughters who are female.

In our desire for sex equality, we must not forget that some biological functions are immutable and have both social and psychological consequences. While social roles need not be narrowly patterned on the basis of sexual function, they cannot be totally divorced from it. Since the majority of women are destined to be wives and mothers, their public education and private expectations should enable them to derive deep satisfaction from these roles. Of course, individual women may decide to choose different roles: they may want to be mechanics or sailors or astronauts, or to run a business, or to run for Congress. While there should be sufficient flexibility for a person of either sex to find fulfillment in any occupational or political role, life is easier when most men and women are not engaged in mutual competition and rivalry.

CHAPTER 11

Children in need of professional help

Many children who are not seriously disturbed react with emotional upset to stressful situations or inner conflicts. They may have fears and nightmares, bite their nails, bait brothers and sisters, suffer from tics and tantrums, and act in many other symptomatic ways. Typically, they are wanted children from unbroken homes, reared by parents of good will, who may have been overprotective, overindulging, or overpowering. Such children and their parents can benefit from professional help.

Some children suffer from more serious disturbances. They are murderous in their jealousy, violent in their hostility, and relentless in their sexual preoccupation. These children need and must receive psychological help if they are to grow up to become normal and productive people.

Children in need of professional help.

What follows are brief descriptions of (*a*) children who are in dire need of psychotherapy; (*b*) children who can benefit readily from psychotherapy.

CHILDREN IN URGENT NEED OF PSYCHOTHERAPY

Too intense sibling rivalry.—Children with intense hatred toward brothers and sisters need help. These are children whose jealousy pervades their whole personality and colors their whole life. They seek exclusive attention and seem intent on destroying anyone seen as a competitor. They abuse their brothers and sisters both physically and verbally and seem totally unable to share the affection of an adult, be it a parent, a teacher, or a scout leader. Neither are they able to share "worldly goods." At parties or at home, they do not hesitate to appropriate for themselves most of the ice cream, candy, cake, or toys. They would rather hide what they cannot use than share it.

Extremely competitive, they have a compelling need to excel. If they cannot win honestly, they will win dishonestly, for win they must. Competition becomes their way of life, and being ahead of others the goal of life. If the jealousy of such youngsters is not diminished in childhood, they may go through life treating people as though they were substitute siblings. They become embroiled in a competition for life and death even in trifles, and they take every loss in sport or business as a crushing blow to their status. When they drive, they have to overtake other cars; when they play chess, they must win or they experience stress and failure. They may also continue consciously to hate their brothers and sisters, and seek to humiliate them throughout life. (See Chapter 7, page 150.)

Normal children, too, feel jealous of brothers and sisters, but their jealousy is neither a pervasive pattern nor a predominant trait. They may feel that their siblings receive more love and they may vie with them for affection. But when love is given, they are readily reassured. They, too, may like competition and excelling, but they can also enjoy games for the fun of playing. Moreover, they can accept defeat without much pain or strain.

Too intense interest in sex.—Some children evidence premature and persistent preoccupation with sexual matters. They dream, think and talk sex. They masturbate habitually in private or in public, and try to engage in sexual explorations with other children, including brothers and sisters. They peek and peep, and attempt to "catch" their parents in sexual relations.

These are children who have been exposed to sexual overstimulation. They may have slept in their parents' bedroom, shared a bed with brother or sister, or been fondled erotically by a deviant adult. At any rate, sex is on their mind too much and too soon. Their preoccupation

215

indicates impairment in psychosexual development. They definitely need treatment, and need it without delay.

Normal children, too, show interest in sexual matters. They may tease the opposite sex, giggle about boy friends or girl friends, or talk about getting married and having babies. They may also be pleasurably conscious of their sensuality: they may touch themselves and masturbate occasionally. However, sex activity remains only a part of their life.

Extremely modest children may also need professional help. These are children who get panicky when they are observed undressed. They are painfully self-conscious about their bodies; they are uncomfortable in classes of physical education and are mortified during a medical examination, even when the doctor is of the same sex.

Normal children may also dislike undressing for a physical examination or the gym. They may fuss and protest, but they do not panic.

Extremely aggressive children.—Very hostile children need professional help. The meaning of the hostility must be thoroughly evaluated and understood. Since hostility may stem from a variety of sources, it is necessary to find the cause of aggression in each specific case, so that treatment may be fitted to the cause and the case.

Occasionally we meet children whose aggression does not diminish with expression and whose destructiveness is not accompanied by visible guilt. Some of these children are capable of extreme cruelty without apparent anxiety or repentance. They seem to lack capacity for sympathy, and show no concern for the welfare of others. Nothing seems to impress these children. Censure and criticism have little effect on them, as though they were indifferent to what others think of them. Not even penalties and pains impel them to make amends. Such children need expert professional help.

Some children engage in aggression only on a part-time basis. The aggressive behavior occurs at home but not outside of it, or vice versa, at school but not at home. This is known as reactive hostility. The fighting, cruelty, truancy, or general destructiveness is a reaction against real or imagined mistreatment by parents. Because they feel that their parents have failed them, these children are suspicious of all grownups. They fear adults, distrust their kindliness and reject their favors. Establishing a relationship with such children is not a simple matter. Children with such a history benefit from treatment when the therapist is able to win their trust and to establish a relationship based on mutual respect.

Normal children, too, occasionally engage in destructive behavior. Much of it is due to curiosity and high energy. Some of it is due to frustration and resentment. They may destroy their own toys, from curiosity or from anger, but they are more cautious with property of other children. The normal child is not too fussy about his possessions. He may or may not put them away after playing, and he lets other children play with his toys and materials without fear of breakage. When he breaks a toy, he does not become upset. He shrugs off the incident and looks for another toy. He does not even feel compelled to tidy up the room. In fact, at the end of his play he may walk out of the room without even a backward glance at the mess he is leaving behind.

Habitual stealing.— Children with long histories of stealing need professional help. Persistent stealing is a serious symptom which often represents intense resentment against authority. Some of these children show total disregard and defiance of property rights. They engage in petty, and not so petty, pilfering whenever an opportunity presents itself. They may steal at home, school, camp, the supermarket, or from neighbors. Therapy for them may be a prolonged process; such deep hostility is not easily uprooted.

Children who steal only at home do not belong to this category. Pilfering from mother's purse may represent a bid for affection or for revenge for real or fancied mistreatment. Normal children may also be involved in occasional episodes of mild pilfering outside the home. They may take fruits and candy, or fail to return "borrowed" or "found" property. Gesell's*

* Francis L. Ilg and Louise B. Ames, *Child Behavior* (New York: Harper & Row, 1955), p. 286.

co-workers, Frances L. Ilg and Louise B. Ames, state:

> At five [a child] prefers pennies to half dollars. ... At six he responds to the beauty of some trinket and he takes it before your very eyes even though he denies it when accused. At seven his passion for pencils and erasers is so strong that he wants more and more and more within hand's reach. And by eight the loose money in the kitchen drawer is indeed a temptation, for he is beginning to know about money ... and what things it can buy. When the theft is discovered, he is punished and admonished. He probably excuses himself that he "did not mean to" and he certainly promises that he will never do it again. Another day—another theft.

However this mode of behavior is transitory and lasts only briefly. As they grow older, the children come to recognize property rights and to respect them.

Recent trauma.—Children exposed to a sudden catastrophe may develop severe symptoms, even in the absence of underlying personality disturbances. A child may react with overwhelming anxiety to a fire, a car accident, or the death of a beloved person, and he may develop dramatic symptoms.

Prompt treatment is necessary. Anxiety generated by a recent disaster is diminished when in the presence of an understanding adult, the child is able to re-enact with toys, and to tell in words, the fearful events and memories.

In her book *Children in Wartime*, Anna Freud describes the difference in reaction, between young children and adults, to the bombing of London. After a night of bombing, adults felt compelled to tell and retell their experience of fright and horror. Children who lived through the same experience seldom talked about it. Their fears and tensions came out in their play. They built houses out of blocks and dropped bombs on them. Sirens screamed, fires raged, and ambulances removed the injured and dead. For weeks on end they played out their feelings of shock and horror. Only after such prolonged symbolic re-enactment of the events were the children able to talk about their feelings and memories without fear and anxiety.

Psychotherapy provides an appropriate setting, suitable materials, and a sympathetic adult to help the child in his hour of great need. The therapist enables the child to relive, through play and words, the fearful events so that he may assimilate and master his panic and anxiety.

The atypical child.—When a young child shows many signs of bizarre behavior, a professional consultation is indicated to determine if there is severe mental disturbance. The extremely disturbed child is strikingly different from other children. He is withdrawn and insulated. He is like a stranger in his own home. He does not approach anyone and does not respond when he is approached. He is indifferent to friendliness as well as to anger. There is no change in his responses: no look of interest, no smile of pleasure, no sigh of sadness.

When separated from mother he may show apathy, impassively following anyone who takes his hand. Or he may cling to mother in extreme panic, as though separation were annihilation. Other children may cry on separation; however, their crying is diminished with cuddling and reassurance. The atypical child's crying is unmodulated and unaffected by variations in approach.

The atypical child seems oblivious to the world around him. He may remain fixed in one position or rock to and fro for long periods. His main concern is with his own body. Showing no veneer of civilization, he may masturbate openly, urinate in public, or soil himself without embarrassment. He may eat nasal mucus or smear saliva on himself and others. He makes no distinction between edible and nonedible objects, but indiscriminately mouths anything. He may swallow sand, eat clay, or fill his mouth with trash. Other children, too, experiment with eating chalk or mud, but they do not persist in it.

The atypical child may engage in repetitious activity for hours on end. He may twiddle a piece of string, open or close drawers, twist his hair, pull his ear, or stick his finger into a wall crack. With monotonous fascination he will spin a wheel, click a switch on and off, or turn a door knob back and forth. He prefers to play with blocks and beads and insists on arranging them in precisely the same patterns and sequences. He has an unusual memory for the kind, number, and location of the toys in his room, and he gets extremely upset when they are misplaced or broken. His tears and tantrums may stop abruptly when things are restored to their former condition.

An atypical child may display strange reactions to physical pain. He may indulge in serious self-injury without a word of complaint; he may bang his head against the wall, squeeze his finger in a door, sit on a hot radiator, or cut his hand until it bleeds. His only reaction to his pain may be queer grinning or hollow laughter. Any attempt to offer sympathy will go unacknowledged.

Even when he has learned to speak, the atypical child shows no interest in communication. When he talks, he uses phrases that are irrelevant to the situation. When directly questioned, he may respond with parrot-like repetition of the question. Or he may never use speech, remaining totally indifferent to all urging.

CHILDREN WHO CAN BENEFIT READILY FROM PROFESSIONAL HELP

The too-good-to-be-true's.—Some children seem too good to be real. They are obedient, orderly, and neat. They worry about mother's health, are concerned about father's business, and are eager to take care of little sister. Their whole life seems to be oriented toward pleasing their parents. They have little energy left for playing with children their own age.

In school and in the neighborhood, such children may continue with their goody-goody behavior. They will be meek and gentle and spend their time and energy in placating the teacher whom they fear. They may bring her the proverbial apple, draw pictures for her, or volunteer to clean up the board. From the first day on, they may tell the teacher how nice a person she is and how much they love her. The compliments and declarations of love cannot be taken at face value. These children may use the same words to a stranger or to the class bully. The sweet talk may be their way of revealing how afraid they are of their own hostile impulses and of consequent retaliation from others.

A frequently noticed symptom in such children is chronic fatigue. Under the goody-goody mask, many a "bad-bad" impulse is hidden. The effort of transforming hostile impulses into

223

angelic behavior, and the eternal vigilance required to maintain a façade, consume the life energy of these children. No wonder they are exhausted and weary.

Therapy provides an effective setting to modify over-good behavior. The setting encourages children to give up slavish compliance and to assume normal assertiveness. By observation and experience they learn that there is no need to be ingratiating and self-effacing. They slowly begin to allow their impulses to gain some expression. They come to discover their own wants, know their own feelings, and establish their own identity.

Immature children.—Under this heading are included children who are wanted and loved as babies, but not as growing individuals who have ideas and needs of their own. These overindulged, overprotected children are unprepared for the realities of life outside the family shelter. They have little opportunity to develop appreciation for the needs and feelings of others, and they find it difficult to share possessions or to delay gratification. They are spoiled and want what they want when they want it. They show excessive dependence upon parents, siblings, and playmates, and they annoy everyone with their constant demand for attention, assistance, and approval. Instead of exerting their own efforts, they want to be served. They may demand to be dressed, waited on, and fed. Children who remain infants are constantly involved in conflicts. They create tension at home, turmoil in school, and quarrels in the neighborhood.

Psychotherapy in carefully selected groups is of particular value to immature children. The group offers motivation and support for growing up, as well as a safe arena for the trying out of new patterns of behavior. In the group they learn what aspects of their behavior are socially unacceptable, and what behavior is expected. As a result, they make an effort to adjust to the standards of their peers. In the group they learn a variety of essential social techniques, such as sharing materials and activities and the attention of a friendly adult. They learn to compete and to cooperate, to fight and to settle fights, to bargain and to compromise. These techniques prepare such children to deal with their contemporaries on an equal footing.

Withdrawn children.—These children can be described as shy, timid, submissive, isolated, inhibited, silent, and meek. They have difficulty expressing ordinary feelings of affection and aggression, have few friends, and avoid social games and play. They are extremely ill at ease in all interpersonal situations, and they avoid meeting people and making friends. They always want others to make the first friendly overture and even then they may not respond in kind.

Withdrawn children find it difficult to relate to the teacher in school or to classmates in the yard. They are mortified when called upon to read aloud or to answer a question. They may respond with a yes or a no answer, or not at all. They spend many a day sitting silently and staring into space. On the playground, too, they are loners. They wander aimlessly around. When they do play, they choose a quiet and safe activity that does not demand social give and take. When social contact is forced on them their anxiety may mount to the point of panic.

Withdrawn children can be helped in psychotherapy. The friendly adult, the enchanting materials, and the selected group members make it difficult for them to stay within their shells. The setting accelerates emergence from isolation and encourages freedom in play and conversation with other children.

Fearful children.—Like ham and eggs, little children and fears, go together. In one study, it was found that for more than 90 per cent of the children, specific fears were reported at least once. Dogs were the main fear of three-year-olds; darkness, of four-year-olds. These fears declined with age, disappearing almost completely by the age of eight. Other fears reported by normal children were of fire engines, sirens, earthquakes, kidnaping, fast driving, snakes, and high places. Some of the children showed slight apprehension, but did not withdraw from the situation if a parent was around. Others felt greater discomfort; they wanted a light left on at night or showed tension when a fire engine passed by or a burglary was mentioned.

Some fearful children require professional

help. These are children with persistent and intense fears. The intensity of their reaction is the telling clue. They are paralyzed and incapacitated by their anxiety even if the fear is obviously irrational; the sky may fall down, lightning may strike the house, the whole family may be swept away by a flood. There is no end to their kaleidoscope of feared objects and people.

Some of the children are compulsively clean; their whole world seems dirty to them, and they are careful not to become contaminated. They fear any speck of dust on their hands or clothes and become distressed if they cannot wash it off immediately. Other children are afraid of loud noises, high places, new people, running water, dark corners, small insects, and large animals. They try to escape anxiety by avoiding places and activities that seem threatening to them. Thus they may not go near the water, avoid climbing a ladder, or refuse to stay in a dark room.

In therapy, some of the children are likely to engage in activities that will require the fearful child to deal with his fears. They may shoot noisy cap guns, use finger paints, cover themselves with mud, or turn out the lights. The group makes it impossible for the fearful child to escape facing his problem. The therapist can then deal with the fearful reactions as they occur. He helps the child to play out and talk out his frantic fears and to lessen and master his vague anxiety.

Children in need of professional help

Effeminate boys.—Professional help is at times indicated for boys who come from fatherless homes or from households where there is only one boy in a family of many females. Since the identification models in such homes are almost all nonmasculine, the boys cannot help but assume some feminine roles. They may lack the characteristic aggressiveness expected of boys in our culture. They may shy away from rough games or be unable to mingle freely with other boys, and they feel more comfortable in the company of girls. Such boys usually receive rough treatment from other children. They are nicknamed, attacked, and abused. They are socially stigmatized and emotionally scarred, and they may grow up to be inadequate adults.

Such boys need professional help, which can offer to them a desirable model of identification, encourage assertiveness, and call forth the masculine components of their personalities.

Tics and mannerisms.—Some children exhibit persistent mannerisms that are annoying to parents. They squint, sniff, grimace, twitch, pick noses, rub eyes, clear throats, hunch shoulders, bite nails, suck thumbs, crack knuckles, or tap feet. The contortions and mannerisms may be so obvious and grotesque that they compel attention. The fingers may be disfigured, the skin water-logged, or the nails bitten down to the quick. And there is no escape from the discordant sounds of noses, throats, knuckles, and feet. These children need psychological consultation, as well as medical attention, to determine the necessary treatment.

Normal children may also exhibit a variety of mannerisms and tics. However, these manifestations are not persistent. They appear mostly when the child is over-fatigued, sleepy, preoccupied, or under some emotional strain.

Enuresis (wetting) and encropresis (soiling).— It is estimated that about 10 to 15 per cent of children still wet their beds after the age of four. Some of them wet also during the daytime. Most of these children never attained bladder control. Some went "dry" only to begin wetting again.

Enuresis (wetting) is usually considered an indication of emotional upset; only about 5 per cent of wetting is attributed to organic causes (to rule them out, children who wet should be seen by a physician).

By itself, enuresis does not tell the degree of emotional upset. It is found in mildly upset children and in more serious cases. Sometimes it disappears after brief psychotherapy and other times it proves hard to get rid of.

Encropresis (soiling) that persists beyond age three or four is considered a symptom of emotional difficulties when organic causes have been ruled out by a physician. Soiling is common among preschool children, but it is also found among school-age children and adolescents. The older the child, the more serious the problem. Soiling represents a form of rebellion against parental authority in general and against strict toilet training in particular. Therefore shaming and blaming a child may only bring additional conflicts and a stiffened resistance.

Enuresis and encropresis are such bothersome symptoms that even in mild cases it may be worthwhile to seek professional help. In any case, improved relations between parent and child will contribute considerably to the solution of these problems.

CHAPTER 12

Parents in need of professional help

PARENTS' CHARACTER AND CHILDREN'S BEHAVIOR

The personality of a child is colored by the emotional atmosphere of his home. This truth seems self-evident, yet it is only recently that we have come to recognize the relation between a parent's character and a child's conduct. Some parental practices are overt and obvious; they can be observed and their influence identified. Other practices are more covert and subtle: they can only be inferred and their impact hypothesized.

Any list of undesirable attitudes and characteristics will include those of parents who are overemotional, overprotective, childish, alcoholic, seductive, rejecting, or overconscientious.

OVEREMOTIONAL PARENTS

Private attitudes and public conduct.—
Children who have overemotional parents can
be recognized easily: they are always heard
and seen. Since early life, they have learned
that they must yell to be heard, and talk fast if
they are not to be interrupted. They mirror
faithfully the turbulence of their own parents.
Frequently both children and parents are unaware of their excessive emotionality and ever-
ready explosiveness. When it is brought to their
attention, they may attribute it, not without
pride, to some ethnic characteristic or stereo-
type: "I'm a redhead, you know," or "It's my
Irish temper."

As long as they stay within their own subcul-
ture, such people are not too troublesome. But
when they come in contact with the wider community, they become a nuisance. They are argumentative and time-consuming. They are
loud talkers, but poor listeners. They are melo-
dramatic, but unaware of their unpleasant impact.

Such parents may not be psychiatrically disturbed, but they are socially disturbing. They
need some professional help to alter their private attitudes and public conduct.

OVERPROTECTIVE PARENTS

Relentless concern with minutiae.—Overpro-
tectiveness essentially means a relentless concern
with the minute details of a child's functioning.
From birth on, such parents may worry endlessly about the child's survival. What is simple
routine to most parents becomes a life-and-
death decision to an overprotective mother. She
is like a person who would drive a car with the
hood open in order to watch the engine.

Several times a day she may check her child's
breathing, or measure his food intake, or examine his bowel movement, or worry about his
sleep. When he stands, she is afraid he may
fall; when he runs, she fears he may get hurt;
and when he has a fever, she is certain that he
is near death.

Such a parent really works hard for her living. She does not stop doing unnecessary things
for her child. What she can do for him, he must
not do for himself, even when he is willing and
able. This mother will overdress and overfeed
her child; if she could, she would digest the
food for him.

In short, the child's job of living and functioning is taken over by mother, and the results
are disastrous. The child grows, but does not
mature. Having lived, so to speak, on a borrowed ego, he has failed to develop his own. He

235

remains an infant dependent on mother. He does not know his own feelings and wishes, and lacks elementary social skills. And since mother always made up his mind for him, he has great difficulty thinking. He has little insight into himself or the world around him. He does not relate cause to effect, and is satisfied with magical explanations. Such children waste much energy in an ever-present conflict between dependence on mother and their dimly conscious wish for autonomy. Overprotective parents need professional help if their children are to become self-sufficient.

CHILDISH PARENTS

Children as playthings and as protectors.— Some women who become mothers find it hard to supply their children with a lasting, stable relationship. Though they may momentarily enjoy their infant and play with him as one plays with a toy, they cannot carry the burden of motherhood.

They themselves need motherly care and seek it from their children. In a reversal of roles, they demand service and security from their offspring. The children feel compelled to protect, entertain, and worry about mother. And since they are incapable of fulfilling such demands, they are left with perpetual feelings of failure and anxiety. They grow up deprived of childhood, guilty and self-blaming. These mothers need help in growing up.

ALCOHOLIC PARENTS

Sudden storms and periodic desertions.—The child of an alcoholic parent is exposed to incomprehensible sudden storms. He witnesses his parent change moods and behavior in an unpredictable and frightening manner. He knows that at such times nothing is as important to his parent as a bottle of scotch. He feels abandoned and helpless.

The scenes of the binges are indelible. A child sees his security symbol crumble before his eyes. He sees his father or mother dazed and disoriented, weak and wordy, tearful and tyrannical, in a world beyond his comprehension or reach. He may also be forced to cope with his parent's illness and nausea.

The alcoholic parent may love his children very much, but because of his own problems he cannot take care of them consistently. Such parents need professional help in order to cope with their difficulties.

SEDUCTIVE PARENTS

The need for mature modesty.—Some parents are not aware that their own child may look at them erotically and react to them sexually. Unwittingly, they may intensify a child's sexual urges toward them. A father who undresses in front of his daughter, or a mother who continues to bathe her school-age boys, stimulates sexual feelings and fantasies. Some parents allow their older children to sleep with them in the same bed, and indulge in excessive mutual fondling and caressing. Some parents see nothing wrong with kissing children on the mouth or in holding them in long tight embraces. Other parents use verbal equivalents of lovemaking. They address their children as though they were lovers and expect from them cavalier behavior. Some mothers love to dance with their sons. Even when dressed in a bathing suit, they do not hesitate to twist with them.

Such behavior has damaging effects on children's sexual development. Girls reared by seductive fathers have a tendency to get involved sexually with older men, while sons of seductive mothers may be flooded by erotic impulses and driven prematurely and immaturely into sexual affairs. Conversely, some may be so frightened by their parent's erotic approaches that in adult life they may shun sex altogether or seek satisfaction with members of their own sex. Seductive parents need psychotherapy.

REJECTING PARENTS

Physical abandonment and emotional desertion.—Many parents cannot even imagine a mother who really hates her baby. They are shocked at newspaper reports of children abused or abandoned by parents. The very idea of physical desertion of a child seems incredible.

In contrast, emotional desertion is more prevalent. A considerable number of parents do not provide children with the loving care essential for their growth. Emotional rejection stems from many sources, among them: immaturity, narcissism, inadequacy, and non-acceptance of sexual role.

Emotional rejection has many faces. It may appear in constant nagging and demands for perfection as well as in uninterest and detachment. It may even put on the disguise of over-concern and excessive sheltering.

Rejected children get a morbid message from their parents: "Don't bother me with your life. Grow up fast and get out." Such parents wish away their offspring's infancy and childhood so that they themselves will be rid of unpleasant chores and obligations. They feed their children with dispatch, toilet-train them in a hurry, and thrust on them responsibility for which they are not ready. Pushed into autonomy

239

prematurely, the children are dominated by fear of failure and criticism. They expect accusation and censure and are preoccupied with mustering arguments for defense. They live as though they were in a courtroom where they must justify their very existence. They are so obsessed with undoing past "sins" and evading future dangers that they do not perform well the tasks of the present.

The constant preoccupation with danger and defense is a heavy burden that leaves them emotionally exhausted and physically drained. If they are to achieve a measure of happiness, such children and their parents must receive professional help.

OVERCONSCIENTIOUS PARENTS

Happiness on a gold platter.—Many conscientious parents need guidance in bringing up children. The parents may be loving and devoted, but they are overly child-centered. They are determined *to make* their child happy even if it kills them. They strive to avoid all possible frustration in their child's life, even if in the process they themselves become frustrated and worn out.

Happiness, at best, is an illusory goal. It is not a destination; it is a manner of traveling. Happiness is not an end in itself. It is a by-product of working, playing, loving, and living.

Living, by necessity, involves delay between desire and fulfillment, between plan and realization. In other words, it involves frustration and the endurance of frustration.

We do not have to plan frustration, just as we do not have to premeditate illness. But when a child is frustrated, a parent need not go to pieces. When a child cries, it is not necessary for mother to perform somersaults to bring back his smile. Above all, children need wise management that is not based on guilt or martyrdom.

When mild demands and reasonable requests are met with tears and tantrums, it is best to insist on performance and to live through the storm. Placating a child will not clear the air. Some clouds will bring rain, regardless. All one can do is to wait for the storm to pass without getting cold feet. Children draw strength and security from our ability to remain imperturbable and sympathetic.

DIVORCED PARENTS

A semblance of cordiality.—Divorce, like amputation, is a soul-shaking experience to all involved. To parents it represents an end to many cherished dreams and aspirations. To children it may seem like the end of the world. Amidst the bitterness and confusion of a family breakup, parents must choose the course least damaging to their children.

The worst that parents can do is to use a child as a weapon of revenge against one another. The feelings are raw, the opportunity is there, and the temptation is tremendous. The other parent may be blamed and maligned, and the children may be forced or induced to take sides in virulent battles over loyalty, custody, money, education, and visits. The effect on children can be disastrous.

The best that divorced parents can do is to continue to be parents, although no longer husband and wife. It is not an easy arrangement, since it requires a semblance of cordiality amidst bitterness and enmity. Professional help may enable parents to handle their grievances more objectively and to do what is really best for their children. As Dr. J. Louise Despert states in her book *Children of Divorce:* "A man and woman may have been unable to make a success of their marriage. But they can yet make a success of divorce. With effort . . . wisdom and guidance . . . they can make of their divorce the maturing experience which their marriage has failed to be."

EPILOGUE

The new solutions offered in this book can lighten the task of parenthood only when applied selectively and appropriately. Children vary in their responses to demands. Some children are compliant; they easily accept change in routines and relationships. Others, more conservative, accept change only under protest and after prodding. Still others are more reactionary: they actively resist any "new deal" in their lives. A wise application of the new approach will not ignore the basic grain of the child's temperament and personality.

In human relations, ends depend on means, and outcome depends on process. Personality and character flourish only when methods of child-rearing are imbued with respect and sympathy. It is hoped that the new approach will create deeper sensitivity to feelings and greater responsiveness to needs in the challenging relationship between parent and child.

243

BIBLIOGRAPHY

Books you may find enjoyable and useful

ARNSTEIN, HELENE S. *What To Tell Your Child About Birth, Illness, Death, Divorce, and Other Family Crises.* New York: Pocket Books, 1964.

BALINT, ALICE. *The Early Years of Life: A Psychoanalytic Study.* New York: Basic Books, 1954.

BARUCH, DOROTHY W. *New Ways in Discipline.* New York: McGraw-Hill Book Co., 1949.

FRAIBERG, SELMA. *The Magic Years.* New York: Charles Scribner's Sons, 1959.

HALPERN, H. M. *A Parent's Guide to Child Psychotherapy.* New York: A. S. Barnes & Co., 1963.

SUEHSDORF, ADIE. (Ed.) *What To Tell Your Children About Sex.* New York: Pocket Books, 1959.

WOLF, ANNA, *The Parent's Manual.* New York: Popular Library, 1951.

Where to go for help

The helping agencies.—Mental health facilities vary from community to community. There are child guidance centers, mental health clinics, and family service agencies. Information about needed services (child guidance, family counseling, or adult treatment) can be obtained from local and state mental health associations, state departments of health, and the local council of social agencies.

Information about the location and qualifications of an agency can also be obtained by writing to:

The National Association for Mental Health
10 Columbus Circle, New York 19, N.Y.

The Family Service Association of America
44 East 23 Street, New York 10, N.Y.

The helping professions.—Psychologists, psychiatrists, and psychiatric social workers, function as a team in Mental Health agencies. The psychologist* (Ph.D. or Ed.D.) is a scientist with intensive training in understanding personality and its disorders. His specialties are psychotherapy, diagnostic testing,

* Some qualified psychologists do not have a doctorate but an M.A. A number of them are very competent "old-timers" who started practice long before the doctorate became an essential requirement.

and research. The psychiatrist is a physician (M.D.) with special training in diagnosis and treatment of mental disorders. In a clinic his specialties are psychotherapy, diagnosis, and prescription of drugs. The psychiatric social worker (MSW) has had his basic training in social work. His specialties are psychotherapy, initial interviewing (intake), and preparation of case histories.

The psychologist, psychiatrist, and social worker have one function in common: psychotherapy. In addition each has a function not shared by the others. The psychologist administers tests, the psychiatrist prescribes drugs, and the social worker prepares case histories.

Members of the three professions can also be found in the private practice of psychotherapy. To check on the qualifications of a particular practitioner, it is advisable to consult the directory of his main professional association. The directories are:

Directory of the American Psychological Association

Directory of the American Psychiatric Association

Directory of the National Association of Social Workers

Another member of the Mental Health professions is the psychoanalyst. He works mainly in private practice. The psychoanalyst is an expert in a special form of intensive psychotherapy called psychoanalysis. While most psychotherapists see their patients once a week, psychoanalysts see them three or four times a week. The psychoanalyst is either a psychologist or a psychiatrist. In some instances he may be a psychiatric social worker.

Index

Index

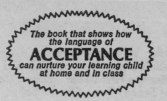

THE BIG BESTSELLERS
ARE AVON BOOKS

The
important and
acclaimed new
book on
child-raising

Liberated
Parents
Liberated
Children

by Adele Faber and Elaine Mazlish

How the teachings of famed child psychologist
Dr. Haim G. Ginott helped a group of
parents and children find new
understanding and fulfillment
in family relationships

"Not only bridges the gap between theory
and practice but also between generations."
Los Angeles Times

SELECTED BY THE BOOK-OF-THE-MONTH CLUB

LP 6-79